BOLD AS BRASS

BOLD AS BRASS
A Bandsman's Tales
George Clarke

UNITED WRITERS
Cornwall

UNITED WRITERS PUBLICATIONS LTD
Ailsa, Castle Gate, Penzance, Cornwall.

British Library Cataloguing in Publication Data:
A catalogue record for this book is
available from the British Library.

ISBN 1 85200 075 9

Printed in Great Britain by
United Writers Publications Ltd
Cornwall.

Dedicated to
the 'Dirty Dozen'
of Stacksteads Band, Bacup.

CONTENTS

BRASS RUBBINGS
George Clarke

Now gather round you merry folk
A story I shall tell,
Of brass bandsmen who now are old
And of their road to hell.

I'd met this crew with things to do
To make our brass band great,
We were eleven in forty-seven
With more in forty-eight.

We worked so hard to get things done
The first thing was succinct,
With throats all parched from practising
Our need was just one drink.

The deed was done and we were lost
The darts and cards were played,
The evil brew took over
We could not then be saved.

This is one story to be told
You'll see our downward trait,
The underworld of smoke and drink
A wonderful escape.

Once dragged back to reality
By women fair and good,
We argued it was not our fault
We were misunderstood.

That was the end of our affair
Though lasting for some years,
Withdrawn like guzzlers from the booze
Through gratefulness and tears.

Lost in the world of gambling men
Back in those years gone past,
The life we led was downward bent
We knew it couldn't last.

But though we knew our time was done
We'd travelled through this land,
Our days of wild oats was now gone
Left was the great brass band.

Goodbye my now departed friends
Your memories still remain,
Of friendliness and comradeship
We'll dream of them again.

1

The Early Years

The notable thing about Burston is that it is in the middle of a long valley. The Rowleydale Valley. The valley itself is about eight miles long and contains no less than four towns, one of which is Burston. Why single out Burston? Well, it is the Burston Band and some of its unsavoury characters that this story is about.

Rowleydale was noted in its yesteryear as a cotton manufacturer's paradise. More money was available here than anywhere else in England during the nineteenth century. Another thing it was noted for was its Brass Bands. Two of them brought fame into a hard-working population. One, the Burston Old Band said to be the best in Britain in its day, which was during the middle nineteenth century and the other The Irwell Head (Burston) Band which made its name in the early nineteen hundreds.

Today, if you happen to be sitting on the hillside above the valley and the wind is right, should you listen carefully it may seem that you can hear the faint strains of brass music drifting on the breeze. Maybe of the tune *Great Harmony* loved by so many people and played by the wonderful bands of the past who made this valley famous all over the world. Some of the older people say that when the time for the old September Belle Vue contest comes round, the evening previous to the contest the old bandsmen buried in the local cemetery arise in memory of old friends and comrades who they played with of old. They drift aimlessly around the village in search of their old bands until the midnight hour is struck when the wraiths of the past once more

9

return to their rest for another year.

The tales are probably untrue but who is to say? Tales are handed down and no one knows how they were started.

Just imagine for one moment all those once great bandsmen, heroes one and all, sending down that wondrous tone to remind us of those bygone days of triumphant returns from the National Championship of Great Britain at Crystal Palace with the great trophy, and the British Open Championship at Belle Vue.

It was around the eighteen seventies that Burston Band came into being. The exact date is unknown due to the records being lost or left to rot in someone's cellar. The only records we have uncovered are a reference in the *Burnley Herald* dated 1st May 1872 which gives a brief paragraph on the band's beginning.

It tells how four villagers, Burston only being a village in those days, met by chance in the Duke of Wellington public house and over a drink the talk turned to brass bands. It stemmed from a Brass Band Concert that one of their bosses had attended in Manchester while there on business the previous month. He had returned full of enthusiasm for the wonderful music that had delighted his ear. The enthusiasm of this man had sparked off the idea amongst the four villagers.

From the newspaper reports it seems that Harvey Sellers, one of the four men, had said that he could probably learn to play an instrument, him being an organist in the local church and being able to read the music. The main problem was to get an instrument and a book showing the fingering. The question puzzled them all that evening until at last Harvey had come up with a solution that would fit their requirements. He suggested that they should all join at the cost of the first instrument and when he had learned how to use the fingering he would then show the others. It was said that they had thought some about this but had then agreed. Before that Harvey had indicated that he wanted to see and hear for himself how a good band sounded before he put any of their hard earned cash into a venture of such magnitude.

It seems that about one month later Harvey received news that the great Yorkshire band Black Dyke Mills was to give a concert in a park in Bradford the following week.

Harvey could hardly wait and the day of the concert arrived to find him seated on the grass in Baldwin Park in Bradford ready for the concert that was about to start.

The effect of that concert must have fired Harvey's enthusiasm to an even greater height and on his return home he set about checking just where he could go to acquire an instrument. What particular instrument would depend on what was available when he inspected them.

He must have succeeded to learn to play a cornet and taught the others because in the following year it was again reported in the *Burnley Herald* that 'On Saturday last, 7th August 1873, during a church picnic Mr Harvey Sellers gave a demonstration of cornet playing. He played a number of tunes before calling on three other players to join him in playing a number of popular tunes of the day. He announced at the end of the playing that he would be willing to teach anyone willing to learn.' He must have been a remarkable man to learn to play with so much proficiency in so short a time.

There was nothing else could be found until later in that same year when it was reported that the St Martins Church had a coffee morning in the schoolrooms which was a great success and that the musical entertainment was provided by the Burston Amateur Brass Band now consisting of ten players. Harvey Sellers had not only taught himself to play an instrument in a very short time but had then taught nine others to play as well. The resources coming no doubt from money saved and donated to their cause. How or where this was done is not recorded but the band had now come into its own.

From then on only a few of the band's records have survived but, with various cuttings from newspapers we can trace the fact that the Burston Band, as it was now known, had entered and won many contests. Having won the same march or quickstep contest for three years running they were now entitled to put the word 'Prize' in front of their name. The Band would now be known as the Burston Prize Band, a title and honour well won.

It was mentioned again in cuttings from the newspaper that the band had played at various functions such as athletic meetings of which there were many at that time.

The prizes that had been won by the band were not from the top contests of the day. These contests were held in Leeds, Belle Vue, Manchester and the Crystal Palace in London. There are no records of the band having won at any of these great venues, although it is argued amongst the older bandsmen that they should have been in the prizes at Roundhill Park in Leeds just before the Second World War. There is a record of their playing at this contest but nothing to show that they won any prizes there.

2

In The Beginning

My name is Joe Clayton. At the beginning of the Second World War I was eight years old. At the time I am writing about we were only a fourth section band. That is, like in the football league, first section or first division then second, third and fourth. The top section or championship bands would be in the first division or section one and the rest would be graded accordingly, down to the fourth section with us.

The works' bands were, in most cases, subsidised by the works whose name they advertised and were considered by many of the amateur bandsmen to be the nearest thing to a professional that could be found in the brass band world.

The ordinary village band had to make a go of it by making street collections and by money made in the summertime, walking days and concerts etc. It can be done. Some of the great bands of the past are, or were, public subscription bands and they made it.

When we did turn out on these occasions we were expected to be dressed in the correct uniform, or as near as was possible. I recall on one occasion, Joe Sudders, our second euphonium player, turned up in brown shoes, someone else turned up in coloured socks. Jimmy Hogan once turned up without his mouthpiece, luckily for him Tom Bibby, our other E flat bass player had a spare one and loaned it to him. As Adam remarked to him at the time, 'dozy prat' or words to that effect.

As you may have surmised, the band was not the smartest

looking band around, at least not at the time I am writing about. One or two would have benefited from a bit of marching practice, including young Joe Bailey. He was the son of Adam Bailey, our musical director.

Adam Bailey was not a big man, standing about five foot ten in height. He had served in the army during the war (World War II that is) and when he was demobbed had reached the rank of sergeant. And very smart with it. I suppose that he hoped to pass on his smartness to any band that he played with. Well hope is a fine thing.

Before the war Adam had been a very good cornet player. He had played with a few top bands of the day and was considered to be a very good musician by the people who knew him. Now he was out of the army and had got a good job with an engineering firm, not far from Burston, he decided to apply for the vacant post of conductor with the Burston Band, as advertised in the brass band paper which he received every month. All that about Adam Bailey comes later, let me start with my beginnings.

Before the war, my father had played with the Burston Band on cornet. When he was practising at home in the bedroom I would sit and listen to some of the lovely sounds that he could produce from this small instrument. I decided then that one day I would play an instrument in the band.

I would be about eight years old when my father decided that the time had come for me to start my musical 'edification'. That was when the real trouble began.

My first lessons were of course very hard, not just for me but for my dad. He must have had the patience of Job. First the positioning of the mouthpiece on my lips, in order to produce the correct embouchure. That means to start the building of a muscle on the lips.

My first attempts at blowing were to say the least horrendous. Just one straight note played by me must have caused my father a great deal of distress, because one day after one of our sessions I saw him taking the cotton wool out of his ears.

I had often sat and listened to my dad play, watching his fingers move quickly from one valve to another and this had obviously helped me a great deal because I soon got the hang of it. At the time I think that he was pleased, possibly because he did not have to stand there tapping out the time on the music stand.

14

I am not quite sure why, but after a few weeks of my practising, my dad arranged for me to go to one of his friends who was a music teacher. This, of course, cost money. I knew that at the time we did not have any money to spare and, although no one ever said anything to me, I feel sure that the neighbours got so fed up with listening to my practising that they took up a collection to send me to a tutor, anywhere, even to the next town, if that were possible.

Then one day something happened which was to effect all our lives. My father arrived home dressed in a different uniform from the one I had been used to seeing him in when he was going out with the band. It was a browny colour called khaki. Dad said that it was an army uniform. He had been called up into the army. He was going away. War had been declared.

At the time it did not seem important but then it hit me. Who was going to show me how to play all the twiddly bits? I thought that as I had been practising on my cornet for a full month I should be about ready to play a solo any time now.

My dad gone! It did not seem much different. He had been gone before, out all day looking for work. This was the depression in the late thirties and although I did not know it then, I was not going to see a lot of him during the next seven years.

All I could think of was, my dad gone? Will he be away long? Oh lord, I hope he has not taken his cornet with him, I will be lost without it.

He had not taken it with him so my mother decided that what I had started I was going to finish, even though my music teacher had been called up as well.

My mother did not know much about music, but she did know enough about it to go to Dad's music case and get out the little red book that he always kept in there. It was called *The Brass Band Trainer* and it was from this little book that I was to learn the basics about playing a brass instrument.

After a few months and many hours of practising down in the cellar, because that was the only place where I was allowed to blow my cornet, where no one could hear me, my mother allowed me to apply to the local brass band for an audition for third cornet.

If it had not been for the war I do not think that I would have stood a chance of getting into the band. I think that the old maxim that 'beggars can't be choosers' came into it because the band had lost fourteen players into the forces leaving the band very short of players of any experience and the chances of the band being put into moth-balls until the end of the war was very real. So for once even a player of my limited experience was welcomed and it was not long before my mother admitted that even she had noticed a distinct improvement in my playing.

The band-room was only a large wooden hut, set back from the main road on land just on the outskirts of Burston. As there were no houses in the immediate area around the spare land, it was ideal for band practice.

Sometimes when only a few players turned up for practice we would have what can only be loosely described as a busking session. That is when someone is playing the melody while others try to harmonise. I do underline TRY. We knew that at first it was not going to be very good, but we hoped to get better as time went on. Also it did help us to keep our lips in good shape, and the girls really liked that, once they got hold of our embouchures they just would not let go. It is no fault of ours that the girls think it is sexy.

Another thing it did was to keep us out of trouble, something that we were very expert at getting into. Then again the committee allowed us to use the band-room at anytime so that they (being parents and local people) knew just where to find us if trouble occurred or when they needed someone to blame and if they could not find anyone else.

Once every year, if we could, we would give the band-room a coat of paint though we did not have a choice of colour. We just used whatever colour we could get. In the end the band-room was painted with a mixture of most colours of the rainbow and I am sure that we improved on what the War Office called camouflage. There were times when even we could not find it and we were sure that we knew just where we had left it. During those years we only missed painting it once. After the war was over when we had the band-room rebuilt, they said that it was only the paint that had kept it standing so long.

During the war the band carried on the best it could with practice nights, what with the older members having war duties to attend to. There were Fire-watching, Air-raid Wardens, Home Guards and many more. These duties were three or four times a week and some of them every night, so fitting a band-practice in on top of their duties was sometimes too much, although on

Sunday morning all available band members were expected to turn up for practice. Even then they might be called out for a sudden practice drill. Everyone was expected to attend these sudden drills which were meant to prepare everyone for air-raids and it was during these drills that we would be expected to put on our gas-masks.

When we heard the air-raid sirens, we had to hurry to the nearest air-raid shelter. No running, we were told, because this would cause panic, but if that air-raid siren sounded and I heard planes overhead you would not have seen me for dust. The shelter at our school was always kept locked and if any siren went a teacher would be there to let us in. What would happen if the teacher could not get there for any reason? You may well ask. Well as it happened we never found out. We never got bombed.

The reason that the air-raid shelters were kept locked was very simple. Many of the senior boys and girls had been caught in the shelters together. I still cannot see what all the fuss was about, just because some of the girls had no knickers on and the lads had their pants down! The teachers called it disgusting. Today they call it Biology. The only difference was that in my younger days we learnt about the human body by theory. These modern days you learn by practice and theory.

As it was, when we happened to be practising with the band and the siren went, we obviously took our instruments with us. Although we offered to give them a tune or two, just to pass the time away, they would not allow us to play in the shelters. I do not think that they appreciated good music. Then again, perhaps they did. That is why they would not allow us play.

As for practice nights, being as the older band members were usually out on duty, the only members at the practice were us youngsters.

Ernie Benson was the eldest of our young group. He conducted us and, as our regular solo cornet player he had to play as well. He did this by playing the cornet with his right hand and conducting us with his left hand. You might think that this method was very awkward. Well, it was, but this was something that Ernie got used to. It was not anything new for a conductor to play his instrument and conduct as well. In the early days of brass band training there were not always enough players capable of playing the solos so the conductor, who more often than not had taught

17

them all to play, would play with one hand and conduct with the other. Ernie showed us that it could still be done, just as it had been done in earlier days. You may have gathered by now that we were not quite championship standard yet.

Over the next four years the band was not used in any official capacity. Just a few of us got together once and sometimes twice a week. There was talk of putting the instruments into storage for safe-keeping, just until the end of the war but thank goodness they did not do this. We youngsters needed something to keep us occupied and out of mischief and I think that looking after the band-room and instruments was the best thing that could have happened to us.

To the half dozen youngsters, including myself, the band-room was a sort of refuge. When we were not practising in it all our games were centred around it. As far as we were concerned, we were the guardians.

In the early nineteen forties, when it was thought that the Germans were going to invade Britain, we took the duty of guardians very seriously, digging great big holes all round the band-room. Straight home from school, our jobs at home quickly done and then round to the band-room to make sure that everything was OK.

My job at home was to light the fire and then set the table. My sisters did the rest. My other job was to take a bucket down to the factory tip. The ashes from the factory boiler were tipped there and my job was to sort through the hot ashes for coke. Sometimes, if we were lucky, we got there just after the boilers had been emptied and before anyone else got there. What we had to do was to separate the coke from the clinkers. This was the only way to supplement our coal supply which was rationed like everything else.

The first one to get to the tip got the unenviable choice of picking the best spot to start raking. Unenviable because the ashes were still very hot and the only thing that we had to rake with was an iron bar, not unlike a poker, but with the end bent at right angles. Even then we had to pick up the hot coke with our fingers and put it into our bucket. Had anyone been watching us without knowing what we were doing, they would have been excused for thinking that we had Saint Vitus's Dance. They would hear 'ohs' and 'ahs' as we picked up the hot cinders as quickly as possible before anyone else got there. There were many fights on the tip as we defended our buckets of coke from being tipped into someone else's bucket and all over a bit of coke or in some cases clinkers.

When I think back to it all it seems so stupid but at the time it was very important. Lack of fuel in the winter meant that not only could we go without heating but that there would not be much baking of bread or muffins, something I was very partial to.

Clogs were the main footwear at that time. They were made like boots but with the sole made of wood. Fastened to the wooden sole were narrow shaped irons which were nailed on. When anyone had to have the irons replaced we would go to a specialist repairer called a 'clogger'. In his shop, which was never anything fancy, the 'clogger' would be sitting on a wooden stool in the centre of the room surrounded by shelves packed with tobacco tins in which were many different sized nails. Down by his side he would have a box filled with hundreds of used matchsticks, these were used to fill in the holes made by the clog nails. In between his knees was his 'last'. The rest of his furnishings would be a box for us to sit on while he mended our clogs. He had many different sizes of last and we would sit fascinated as we watched him fitting a new pair of irons.

The cloggers name was William Barstone but we always knew him as 'Johnny Clogger'. He collected his matches by calling at all the pubs in the district where the landlord would, in most cases, have saved them for him, as can be imagined as 'Johnny' came to the end of his collecting he would have a definite stagger on, but he was a kindly man and many's the time after setting my clogs alight on the tip I would have to go to Johnny's for new irons. He would take one look at them and then chide me for burning them and say, "I can only do so much and then tha will have to go and get new feet never mind new clogs." He would look at me with a toothy grin, "Reight you young bugger, there thy are. They'll be all reight as long as tha keeps away from the tip."

This was one thing that I knew I could not do and, although I got told off many times, I never got punished. My mother knew that the reason that they got burnt was because I had been working hard on the hot ashes scraping for coke.

Doing these jobs was not any sort of punishment. It was just that with Dad being away in the army and my mother working in the factory everyone had to help. Doing these small jobs at home always helped in some way and, whenever I asked to go to the band I was seldom refused her permission. First tea and then we were free to go out but only till nine o'clock, unless it was practice night.

On practice nights the first thing to do was to meet the lads and examine our defensive dug-outs. (We had heard them called this on the radio.) They were our defences against the invading hordes. Unfortunately we were licked before we had really started. When we got there we found them full of water and more like a harbour for our submarines.

Although we emptied the dug-outs time and again, they were never to be free of water. When Jim Hogan, who was the Air-Raid Warden at this time, saw what we had done, he blew his top. After he had finished ranting and raving he told us that the holes would have to be filled in, first with stones and then covered with soil. He said that it had been a miracle that no one had fallen down any of the holes, they could have broken their necks.

We decided that it had been a daft idea anyway but Jim's outburst had proved to us that our defences could have caused trouble to unwanted intruders. Although we did not know it at this time, it was not going to be the last daft thing that we did.

Imagination was rife at this time. There were posters plastering every vacant spot. 'Be like Dad, keep mum'; 'Loose talk costs lives'; 'Watch the skies for parachutists' or 'Walls have ears'. You could not walk more than a few yards without seeing one, even in the shops and pubs. These posters did not go unnoticed by our sometimes over-fertile minds. This to us was a very exciting time.

Most of our weekends were spent fantasising about what we would do if the Germans did invade Britain. The posters said, 'Watch the skies for parachutists' and no one watched the skies more fervently than our small group, not all of which were members of the band.

Saturday morning was what we always looked forward to. That was when we were allowed to go to the 'Pictures'. Subterfuge was what we practised. Two pence was what we were allowed for the pictures. That meant that there was no money left for the purchase of any off-ration sweets or anything else that might be available. While my two sisters paid at the kiosk, I ducked beneath the counter where they could not see me and went into the toilets where another door led into the 'cowboy' seats of the cinema. They were called this because when we sat in the cheap front seats we got covered in dust when a cowboy film was showing.

On certain occasions this trick failed and I would be grabbed by the collar and thrown out, missing a chapter of the great Flash Gordon serial, with perhaps a cartoon and a cowboy film as well. After waiting for my sisters to come out after the Matinée, (put on especially for children on Saturday mornings), we would spend my tuppence between us on anything we could. The condition being that my sisters told me everything that had happened in the serial.

Then it would be back to what we called the normal world. We would once again get to thinking about how to recognise any saboteurs or spies, not to mention looking for parachutists.

Sometimes, when the air-raid siren went during the day, we would hide and not go down to the shelters provided. We would go outside town into the woods and watch the German bombers going overhead. We could watch the vapour trails as our fighters attacked them. It was very exciting for us to watch but we never saw one shot down, much to our disgust. When the all-clear was sounded and we got back to our frantic parents, they let us know in no uncertain way just what they thought of our escapade. It was not really worth it because we were punished by being kept in for a few nights and we had not even seen a parachutist let alone caught one, or anything else for that matter.

Sunday morning at ten o'clock. That was the official starting time for our weekly band practice, or at least that is what it was supposed to be. We looked forward to it all week and you were never sure if this week we would have a decent attendance. We were always hopeful every Sunday, but that was the day when the Home Guard and the ARP wardens chose to practise as well.

This Sunday was no exception. Eight of us turned up. Luckily there were two cornets, one baritone, one tenor horn, a trombone and two basses. For once, although thinly spread, we were able to have a decent practice.

Monday morning, as usual, meant back to school and some sort of normality. We were not really interested in the lessons but with a little aid from the teacher (like a rap across the knuckles with a ruler) maths and geography were introduced into our somewhat infertile minds.

Geography was a subject which seemed to create much more interest for me. Names like Dunkirk, Normandy, Crete, Alamein, the Western Desert, had me looking with much more interest at the atlas in front of me.

Dunkirk, where was that? These were only names that I had heard over the radio. Now I could find them on a map. This was something that I could relate to the war. There were also other things which reminded us that the war was still on.

Occasionally one of our class mates would be called to the headmaster's study. He or she might not return to the class. It only happened once in our class thank goodness. No one wanted to be told that their father or some relation had been killed in action or even captured, though being a prisoner of war did at least leave some room to hope. We were lucky around Burston. Only a few bombs fell near us during the whole of the war but we were very much alive to the sound of planes flying overhead both day and night.

After dark, if we looked in the direction of Manchester, some thirty miles away, we would see the glow of the fires after the city had been bombed. We thought at the time that it must have been a nightmare living under that bombardment. Night after night the city and dockland were bombed but in the morning the people came out of their shelters and went back to work bringing the city to life once more.

These were things that to us as children were part and parcel of everyday life, like football and cricket but some things were harder to understand as we sometimes sat and talked.

"My dad's in the Desert. He drives a tank."

"Mine's in the RAF."

And so it would go on until someone would ask:

"What about your dad Alfie, why isn't he in the forces?"

"Well he's deferred," would come the reply.

"What's that mean?"

"It means that they want him to stay at home to do his own job because it's very important."

We would carry on like this for some time but could never understand why some dads had to go away and some did not. It did not seem fair, but in the end some of the deferred men had to join the army if they were found to be fit enough.

As days passed into weeks and weeks into months and years, there was happiness when fathers or brothers came home on leave and sadness when the bad news of their missing or death arrived. There did not seem one household that was not touched by the war.

I remember one time when my father came home on leave and brought me a brand new football, orange in colour. All the lads wanted to see it and they even helped me to blow it up all ready to play with. How slow could I have been? Once it was blown up and ready to play with it was suggested that we go on the school football pitch for a game. Oh ye of little brain. Once we got to the ground where there was plenty of grass they all put on their football boots or shoes and started a game. I was relegated to be goal-keeper and even then I was threatened with the direst consequences if I kicked the ball. The point was that I did not own any football boots. I only had clogs and if I kicked the ball with my clogs I could ruin it and it was the only real football in the village. I was allowed to play from time to time but only when I had my one and only pair of shoes on. When my mother found out that I had been playing football in my shoes she all but crowned me and I did hear her once declare that she would be glad when the damn football was worn out. We very carefully looked after that football but after a time it became so worn and patched that it resembled a rugby ball and playing football with a ball that bounced anyway but straight became much too frustrating, but it did last us a good year and a half before it was regarded as totally unplayable.

At last the great news came. The war in Europe was over. Britain and her allies had defeated Nazi Germany. The joy became complete when a few months later the Japanese also surrendered.

There were parties and dancing in every town and city. Flags flew from every conceivable place that anyone could find to fasten them to. In our town the streets were filled with men women and children all cheering and dancing with each other, not quite sure whether to laugh or cry. The scenes were incredible. Before the war the only excitement that I could remember was when a local road-sweeper got drunk and threw Jack Taylor into the horse trough. (Jack Taylor was the driver of the town 'muck-cart' and whether he was driving the 'muck-cart' or walking, you could always tell when he was coming long before he got there, just by his smell.) He not only threw him in the horse trough, he held his head under and there was a distinct chance that he would have drowned him. Normally they would not have cared but if anything happened to Jack who would have driven the 'muck-cart'? Jack had been the only applicant for the job when it had been advertised before the war and it was said that he had been deferred, not because he had been unfit but because no one would drive the evil smelling cart and empty all the tub toilets. I think that the real reason was because he had one leg shorter that the other.

When all the excitement had died down, which took quite a while, everyone's thoughts turned to getting their loved ones back into 'civvy street'. The waiting was terrible. When would Dad be home? The war was over now.

We waited. Sometimes patiently and sometimes damning the war office for sliding their feet. Men and women were coming home from the forces all around us and still no sign of Dad.

Although my mother explained to me over and over again that Dad had to come all the way from Burma, it didn't mean a thing. The war was over and he should be home, that Burma was on the other side of the world and it would take time for him to travel thousands of miles to get here I just could not accept.

At last the letter arrived. My father was back in England and would be home in a week's time, a full week. How the time passed slowly. Then here he was coming in the front door. He very nearly got killed in the rush and after the initial joy of seeing him home safe and sound we once again thanked God for his safe return.

After Dad had been home for a few days he applied for a job in the factory just up the road from where we lived.

Before the war a lot of men had joined up because there were no jobs to be had but now that the war was over they expected to be put to work. They were not disappointed and neither was my father. He got the job he had applied for.

Much to my surprise Dad had decided not to go back into the brass band. While in the army he had transferred his affections from the cornet to the trumpet, which was not all that different. He said that as soon as he could he would go and join a dance band.

24

The estimation I had for my father suddenly dropped. Not going back into the brass band? Joining a dance band? What had they done to him in the army? Thank God it was all over. They would not get me to give up brass banding, it was the only thing that I wanted to do and, with my dad home once again to teach and advise me, perhaps one day I could become a good player.

b

3

The New Conductor

Anyway, to get back to Adam Bailey. It was nineteen forty-seven and we still only had sixteen players in the band. Some of our old players from before the war had not yet rejoined us. Our secretary, David Green, was thinking of going to see them to try to persuade them to come back to the band but after them being away from home for seven years we could be disappointed. Old Jim Baxter, our librarian, said, "They'll be back soon, give 'em time. They'll soon get fed up with th'owd girl pattering about how she did the man's job while he were away fraternising with the fräuleins and such, an that'll have to be stopped. Them women're getting too big for their boots. If we aren't careful they'll be wanting to see us pay packets next."

On Sunday morning we had a chap called Adam Bailey coming to the band-room for an audition as band conductor. What were we going to ask him to conduct us on? It had to be something that we could play reasonably well, and at present those pieces of music were few and far between. After a lot of argy-bargying we settled on *Rule Britannia* for the main piece and *Southport* for the hymn tune. We felt that we were pretty safe on these two. We should be, we had been practising them both regularly for the last couple of months.

Sunday morning practice now started at ten-thirty. When I got there at twenty-five past ten, Adam Bailey was already there sorting out music with our secretary David. There were a few new faces with us this morning, David having invited one or two

26

players from another band to help us out, just for this audition. You might think that this was being a bit underhand, but what Adam did not know would not hurt him, anyway he was not our conductor yet.

When we were all settled David introduced Adam to the band and then handing him the baton said, "Right Adam, they're all yours."

After conducting us on our selection of music, Adam handed us his choice of music and what a choice! There were more dots that I had ever seen before. At first I thought there were flies on the paper but when they would not brush off I realised that I'd just have to play them. The music was called *Lorenzo!* I had heard of it from my dad, he said that it was an old Belle Vue test piece. Well, I could have saved Adam a lot of trouble, if he had only asked me. We had not a cat in hell's chance of playing it. I suppose that could be the reason he put it up in the first place. Well, now he knew just what he was up against. We made a right pig's ear of it. But he did not stop there, he kept us going at it over and over again, stopping now and again to explain to us exactly what he wanted. By the end of the rehearsal we were shattered, but I think that we learned something from it and felt that perhaps, just perhaps, someday we might be able to play it correctly. The rehearsal had been started about five minutes when one or two late-comers arrived. In the past no one had bothered too much. We were pleased if they arrived at all. Times were changing, as we were about to find out.

At a quarter to eleven Adam stopped the rehearsal and said, "Is everyone here now, or are we going to have more interruptions? When I conduct a band I start and finish on time. At ten-thirty I lock the door. If you decide to appoint me as your conductor that is how it is going to be. I will want everyone here on time."

Well that flabbered our gast! No one had ever spoken to us like that before and we were left to think on it.

After the rehearsal had finished, the committee sat down and had a talk to Adam. They told him that there were only sixteen regular players in the band at present, that we were hoping for more to come in the following weeks when more of our pre-war players returned from active service and would he be prepared to take on the position of conductor? (We did not tell him at this time that his had been the only answer to our advertisement.)

Adam agreed to think about it but after being plied with a few pints in our local leisure parlour he accepted. It was, after all, his first band and he had to start somewhere so why not here? There was also his son Joe to consider. He was learning to play the cornet.

It seemed that everyone who joined the band wanted to play the cornet but that was because it was the smallest instrument in the band. Easy to hold and carry and the valves were near together. Handy for small fingers. Once they had reached a good enough standard of playing ability they applied to join the band. At the time they applied to join there could be vacancies for various instruments, but on the whole we were always short of cornet players. Later, if they wished, they could transfer to any instrument that might be available.

During the next few months some of our old players did return to play with the band. We now had a 'soprano' cornet player, a 'repiano', one second and two third cornet players as well as four on the front row. These were three first and a solo cornet. Things were looking up. Our euphonium and baritone positions were filled as were all our four basses, still only two trombones and two horns but we were nearly made up. The addition of a bass trombone and a couple of good cornets would benefit us and a bass drum player for street jobs would come in handy, that is when we had any street jobs.

It was up to our committee to get moving and get these jobs in, the only jobs we had at present were two park concerts and a walking day in May. These were only given to us because another band had backed out at the last minute due to double booking a date. Oh, that someday we could be in that position - to be able to give jobs away.

First of all we had to become better known outside our small town of Burston. The town is situated near the Lancashire and Yorkshire borders, about thirty miles from Manchester. Although it is only a small town, I am sure that it has more pubs than shops, or at least that is how it seemed to me in my early teens.

Concerts in the park were OK but a bit long winded. We had to play all Sunday afternoon and then go back again for an evening concert, all for ten pounds plus a collection. If you were on the gate taking the collection, you had to watch the boy'oos, instead of putting some money in, they took it out!

After we had finished the concerts in the park and had packed everything away we were free to go to the nearest pub or club for a pint and maybe a sing-song.

If it was a club that was nearest we would usually have someone handy to sign us in being as we were not members. The officials of the club were used to having bandsmen arriving at the club in a rather breathless state and gasping for a drink after a park concert, it was real thirsty work. Usually the first pint would go down without touching the sides and, as the club officials quickly realised, they were on to a good thing.

Ale would be consumed in great quantities and there would always be the chance that the band would put on an impromtu concerts of sorts. It could be a cornet solo from one of the players, or even a song from one of the bandsmen. Every band had at least one or two good singers in it. In our case we were considered to have a very good choir, which somehow seemed to go better as the evening progressed. The more ale we drank and the better we seemed to sound, or so we imagined. Great quantities of beer have a definite bearing on the dulling of the senses.

4

The Toilet Jockeys

The following Sunday the band had been engaged to play for a church parade at the small town of Chetburn, about five miles away. The town was not very large but it was situated at the junction of the roads from quite a few villages. The church we were to walk to was St Michael's just on the outskirts of the town.

The parade was made up of the Scouts, Girl Guides, the Boys' Brigade, Army Cadets and a number of men from the fire service. The Mayor and a number of council officials would be there, the Mayor being required to take the salute, this being a church parade. The parade would of course be led by the Burston Band. The band would follow two mounted policemen, they being there to keep the crowds back from us, and they would lead us round the small town finishing up at the church of St Michael's. The procession would then file into church for a service.

One of the odd things about towns is that where there is a church you invariably find a public house. Why this is I could never understand but, as bandsmen we appreciate the thoughtfulness of the councils for doing this and for thinking about us.

So, as you may have guessed, the parade went into church and the band turned off towards the pub, The Globe Inn. We then sent the cheekiest member of the band round to the back door of the pub to enquire of the landlord that should he perchance give us a pint of ale now, we would return after the parade and spend a bit more time and money in his establishment.

Bert Fallows, being the more forward member of the band, was quickly moved into the advance position. As he rounded the corner of the pub he stopped suddenly spreading his arms wide to stop us from passing him. We peered past Bert to a sight that shook us all to the core, there in front of him, tied to the railings were the two police horses which had accompanied us all the way from the town centre.

It was enough to make your blood boil. These two horses had been directly in front of us all the way during the march, and we certainly knew about it! I don't know if you are aware of it but, when a horse needs a toilet, he does not worry about who or what is behind him (or her as the case may be), he just lets fly and no matter how disciplined the band is, there is a distinct lowering of morale in both playing and marching, as the band tries to sidestep the issue. It was not without good reason that we try to keep away from these two mobile water closets. Everyone, even back to the cornets had been splashed in one way or another and it really stank, making mixing with people totally out of the question. Now here they were again. Even our drinking places are not sacrosanct. Wait a minute! If the beasts are outside the pub, where are the jockeys? It did not take an 'Einstein' to work that one out.

We followed Bert round the side of the pub, passing the dreaded beasts at a reasonably safe distance. We did not trust them from any angle. Bert crept up to the window and looked into what turned out to be the bar. There they were large as life, the damned toilet jockeys, leaning on the bar with pints of what looked like pure nectar in front of them. That was enough for Bert. He quickly returned to the rest of us and said, "Come on lads, the bobbies are inside having a pint and what is good enough for them is good enough for us."

With that we all sidled round to the back door, which was open and into the bar. Now, as the rest of the parade would be in church for the next hour or so, we could get down to some necessary refreshment, in company with the two bobbies who, after a quick look round carried on with their drinking. They seemed OK, obviously as thirsty as we were.

After a few drinks we got talking to them, they seemed OK, for coppers that is. We then challenged them to a game of dominoes. Bert, who had been talking quietly with the landlord, asked us to leave him out of the proceedings. This, I should say came as something of a shock to us, but we kept quiet just the same. Bert was always the one who wanted to be doing something, cards darts or dominoes but as he had tipped us the wink we carried on with the game.

About five minutes later Bert slipped out of the back door, returning a short time later with a very satisfied smile on his face.

It was not long after Bert had returned to the bar that the landlord said, "Here you are lads, they are coming out of church so it looks like you are off again. See you after the parade."

The parade reassembled and we started off down the road, the two police horses at the front followed by the band. As we set off it became obvious that something was wrong. It took some minutes before we realised what it was: the police horses were moving from side to side. In fact they were staggering as if they were drunk. I tried to get a look at Bert but as he was in the front rank I could not see his face. All I could see was his shoulders shaking. I thought at first that he was having a fit of coughing but after a few seconds he seemed to calm down.

We had not gone much further down the road when the horses started again. They were still weaving from side to side, but now they started to relieve themselves. It was as if the floodgates had opened up. Straight down the road it came and Bert, who was on the inside, got the full force of it. Up over his boots it came, wetting the bottom of his trousers and, as it turned out, his socks as well. The noise from the basses was something chronic as they tried to sidestep this evil smelling flood. The ranks opened up considerably as we tried to keep as much distance as we could between Bert and ourselves. What had started out a few minutes ago as a reasonable marching band had quickly been reduced to a band trying to do the rumba. Unfortunately, this happened twice more before the parade, after passing in front of the Mayor, who took the salute on the Town Hall steps, was finally over.

As we passed the Mayor I saw a very peculiar look on his face. I would not mind betting that on the following Monday morning he would have the sanitary engineers round at the town hall checking the drains.

It was not until we got back to the pub and had found Bert that we got to know the full story. First of all we had to find Bert who had quickly disappeared as soon as the parade had been dismissed. We eventually found him sitting on the bank of the river which ran through this part of town. Shoes and socks off, feet and the lower part of his trousers in the river. He had soaked his feet in the river to try to get rid of that evil smelling horse water and while they were soaking he was washing his shoes and socks for the same reason. He took no notice of us at all. He just kept on scrubbing and cursing. The words he was using were not at all what the two policemen would have appreciated being called. When at last he had finished and had calmed down somewhat, he told us exactly what had happened.

While the two policemen were having their drinks at the bar, Bert had a quiet word with the landlord. It seems that the ale slops, left over from the night before, were just about to be emptied away. It was at this time that the two bobbies had poked their heads round the corner of the pub and asked the landlord if he would let them have a drink.

Although it was not opening time yet, the landlord decided that as they were policemen - and he he always liked to keep on the right side of the police - he would open the bar for them. So, leaving the slops on the ground where they were, he walked back into the bar and taking the towels off the pumps he pulled them a pint each. It was at this moment that Bert walked into the bar and with a big grin on his face he asked the landlord if we could have a drink as well. The landlord realised that he was snookered, being caught red-handed so to speak serving the two policemen so, directing a black look in the direction of the two policemen, he said, "All right then, I suppose what is good for the goose is good for the gander. What will it be?"

"Reight," Bert said. "We'll have five pints of bitter, and every-body'll pay for their own." Bert moved along the bar as soon as he had got his ale and, as he sat there drinking he'd had a brain-wave. He had thought of a way to get his own back on those two mobile water closets, well now it was his turn.

Bert was an animal lover, or so he said and, being an animal lover he felt that he could not leave those two poor animals standing out in the hot sun without giving them a drink. He thought for a moment. Would they like beer? Being Bert he couldn't think of any reason why anyone or anything would not like beer and so, while the two policemen were drinking and playing dominoes with the band lads, he slipped out of the back door and stopping only long enough to check that there was enough beer in each of the two buckets, he set them down in front of the horses.

He watched doubtfully. Would they drink? What a question, you might as well ask if water flows downstream. With a dip of their heads away they went. Heads down inside the buckets, snorting and sucking so that within seconds, or so it seemed, the two buckets were empty. It seemed that they could shift beer quicker than their masters, if that were possible.

First they rolled their eyes, then their ears pricked up and they stood there stamping their hooves. Was it possible that horses should not drink beer? I'm sure that if they had not been tied very securely to the railings those two horses would have been off like the clappers down the road and away like a couple of race horses.

Bert watched them for a couple of minutes or so, waiting to see if anything else happened to them. Their antics had given him quite a shock. He had never thought that there was any possibility of the beer slops doing them any harm.

"Steady lad," he thought, hoping that the water running down the inside of his leg was sweat. Sure enough, after a few long minutes the horses seemed to settle down and just stood there with their heads hanging down. Bert heaved a sigh of relief and slipped smartly back into the pub, downed his drink and then stepped outside and into the front rank of the band. That's where it all started.

We'd listened in amazement to Bert's explanation and then had a damn good laugh at his expense and the fact that it had backfired on him made it even more hilarious. Not many situations got the better of Bert Fallows.

We were still laughing when the two policemen walked back into the room, which suddenly went quiet. They walked up to the bar and ordered two pints. When they had been served, the landlord quickly disappeared, muttering something about an urgent job that needed doing in the cellar, they turned round and faced us, neither of them looking very pleased. I thought, here we go, trouble.

Now these two bobbies were big lads. I mean they were built like two brick out-houses and if there was going to be any trouble with them, then I was off. We waited, as their eyes swept round the room.

"Right," said the smaller of the two, "I'm Bill Bradley and this is my partner Jock McClain. We are a team so, before we go any further, who got our bloody horses pissed?"

There was not a sound. Bert started to get to his feet. I do not know whether he was going to own up or not but the landlord, who had crept back into the bar, thought he was and he did not want any trouble, so he said, "What are you lads talking about? Who's done what?"

Bill explained what had happened after we had all left the pub earlier on, including what had happened during the parade.

When he had finished the landlord scratched his head and said, "Well lads the only thing I can think of is, when you came round the corner this morning and asked me if you could have a drink, I just left my buckets where they were and forgot about them. When you tied your horses to the railings you must have tied them too near my buckets and they just helped themselves, without so much as a by your leave."

"So," Bill said, "what the hell's difference does that make? What were in the bloody buckets that knocked our horses cork-legged?"

"That's just it," the landlord replied, warming to his excuse, "it were all the ale slops left over from last night's drinking.They must have snaffled the bloody lot, the greedy buggers. Serves 'em bloody right, I thought that one of you lot had emptied 'em for me while I opened the bar."

Bill looked round the room his red police eyes trying to root out any culprit.

"Yes, I suppose it could have happened that way," he said. "But if I find out that some bugger from here fed them that bloody stuff for a lark, I'll string him up by his bloody balls, so help me I will."

As he said it he seemed to be looking directly at Bert, but Bert only grinned and said, "Thank God it weren't the good stuff." He quickly stopped himself and looked away.

"How did he know it weren't the good stuff?" Bill said to his partner.

"He must have heard the landlord say so," replied Jock.

They looked at one another for a moment or so but decided to leave it at that, no one was going to admit anything at all.

The time was now one o'clock. Four of us had promised to play with another band in Within Park, just outside Stolworth town centre, about eight miles away. We could not very well refuse when they had asked us because two of their top cornet players had played with us this morning on the parade.

Anyway that is not the point. What I mean is, we had a full hour and a half before we had to be there ready to play. A full one and a half hours in which to relax. Well, we were in a pub and what better way to relax than having a pint in one hand and another one coming up.

We had transport laid on in the form of a Ford Popular car belonging to one of our borrowed players. Unfortunately we drank perhaps a little bit more than we should have done and, after a rather hair-raising ride along the back roads, we arrived at the park just in time.

The band we were to play with was the Fitworth Old Band, a near neighbour and competitor, but as bandsmen are a bit thin on the ground, especially when it comes to park jobs, we usually help one another out when necessary. Park concerts are always hard jobs, very hard on the lips that is and any help available when we had these engagements was welcomed with open arms.

Just as we arrived the band were going on stage and with a glare from the conductor we quickly got out our instruments and followed them onto the platform. Although the conductor had glared at us for cutting it so fine, he was very glad to see us, but it still left him short of cornet players. On concerts they always took the biggest bashing so the more cornets the merrier.

As we got seated on stage it would be reasonable to assume that we were not in the best condition to play and I am sure that would be correct, but that was not the real reason that we soon began to feel uncomfortable. Beer has its own way of getting back at you.

The afternoon had turned out to be very warm and sunny. Any breeze available was cut off by the numerous trees surrounding the park. Rhododendrons, elm, tall poplars and many more different varieties, all seeming to hold the heat into the green chaired area around the bandstand.

We had a full hour to play before we were to get any rest and it was not long before the large amounts of beer began to effect our bladders as it rolled around in our stomachs. The heat did not help either and the toilets seemed to be miles away, when in fact they were only about a hundred yards across the green but, for the next hour they might as well have been on Mars for all the good that they were to us.

The programme that we played was not all that bad for a Sunday afternoon concert. The opening march, *Death or Glory* was not a lip-bender and that was followed by an Overture after which came Jimmy Tomlin playing his trombone solo *The Acrobat* which went down well with the customers. But time was of an essence, quite a lot of bandsmen's faces were starting to go red as the pressure built up. A couple more tunes and then the last piece of music before the interval. I was not sure that we could last it out. My thoughts conjured up images of us being in the middle of the final number and bandsmen exploding off the stand in a cloud of fermented beer. It did not bear thinking about and the last piece of music did not help one bit. Fancy finishing off the first half with the *Light Cavalry*, my God, was the man heartless altogether?

The conductor closed down the first half with a flourish and we were then allowed off the stage. The panic, as everyone tried to get out, struggling out of the door and going full pelt for the toilets across the green only to find that when we got there the queue stretched for quite a way back, the park-keeper having chosen this particular time to forget to unlock the toilet door. He was not our favourite man of the moment. The next toilets were on the other side of the park and who was going to race to the other side of the park only to find them locked as well? He should not be long because the first person to the toilets had dashed off to find him. Obviously that didn't help us one bit, we were due back on stage in a very short time. There was not much of a break at a Sunday afternoon concert.

It was such a warm day and there were a lot of people walking about in the park relaxing and enjoying the sunshine as well as listening to the band, so we could not just slip into the bushes for emergency release, so to speak. We just had to hold on as best we could so, with faces creased up with pain from the pressure building up inside us, we once more returned to the bandstand with one thought screaming inside our heads, another hour to go. How were we going to last out and what was going to happen if we couldn't? Oh lord, it did not bear thinking about. It was without doubt, the longest and most difficult hour I could ever remember, before or after that particular concert and, at the time I felt sure that we would not make it. The real crisis came when some idiot in the audience shouted for an encore, obviously not a music lover. Perhaps the sun had gone to his head.

I must admit, it was unusual for someone to ask for an encore; probably sounded better because the Burston band lads were playing. Of course the conductor gave them an encore. This was something great. They were actually asking for more. What the conductor did not know was that if he did not finish rather quickly he would give one or two of us cause to make a spectacle of ourselves.

How we stuck it out I will never know, but we did. Never say that bandsmen have no courage. As soon as we had finished we shot off the stage and straight into the bushes behind the bandstand. There had not been time to go down to the toilets so, we just took the chance that no one would see us. Not that there was much to see, just the top of many band hats sticking up above the bushes.

One thing about that concert: we learned the hard way that too much ale before a concert was the most painful way to entertain people and we would not do that again, at least not until the next time. Another thing, it is very hard to keep your eyes open on a sunny afternoon and after a belly full of beer.

Perhaps a lesson had been learned but I doubt it. It's all right to make promises at the time when you are in pain but I wouldn't mind betting that it could happen again and in the near future. The mind soon forgets, especially when there is a pint of shimmering best bitter standing on the bar in front of you.

5

Johnny Martin

After tea sometimes, my dad and grandad would relax in the easy chairs and after opening a bottle of beer they would start recalling some of the old days when my father played with Burston Band. When this happened I always tried to sit somewhere out of the way so they would not notice me and, if I kept quiet they would forget that I was there as they recalled stories of the old days which kept me enthralled for hours.

As the beer relaxed them the talk would turn to various characters who stuck out in their memories. Grandad would say, "Hey lad, d'you remember Johnny Martin? What an idiot he was."

Dad: "Aye he was that. Didn't he used to pawn his cornet for ale brass and when the band needed him to play, they had to redeem it or go short of a solo cornet player?" They both laughed at the thought.

"Aye, he was a bugger right enough," grandad recalled, "but it was worth it. When Johnny Martin played, everybody listened."

So it went on. I had heard it all before but it still thrilled me to hear them once more recall some of the stories about Johnny Martin.

Sitting there on the floor keeping out of the way, I could not very well interrupt but it seemed that every time the stories were told they seemed to have gained a little sort of stretching the truth. I suppose that the retelling altered depending on who was telling the story.

Johnny Martin had been a great character in his day. A

bachelor; he had lived on his own in a little one up and one down terraced house, in what was then called Weaver Street.

Weaver Street was a row of houses down near the river, built by the owner of the cotton mill for his more skilled workers. On the front side were ten terraced houses and back to back with them were ten more. Each of the houses had a small living-room and a tiny kitchen, if you can call a 'slop-stone' sink with a cold water tap hanging over it, a kitchen. This kitchen was situated at the bottom of the stairs which led to a small bedroom.

This may not seem much of a house by today's standards, but you have to remember that these houses were built in the early eighteen hundreds; when mill-owners recognised the skill of their best workers and did not want to lose them. It was to these workers that the houses were rented and were known as 'tied houses'. So it became imperative that the workers did not lose their jobs or they also lost their houses.

It was in one of these houses that Johnny lived. During the day he worked in the weaving shed at the mill, which was very dusty, so on his way home he would call at the pub for a beer just to lubricate his throat. Of course one beer was never enough for Johnny and by the time he came out of the pub he was usually as 'drunk as a lord'.

Because this happened almost every night of the week, even at tuppence a pint, by mid-week he was broke and that is when he would pawn his cornet. When pay-day came round he would pay his debts, which meant getting his 'slate' cleaned at the pub. This was the most important thing. Then he would get his shopping done and try to have enough money left over to redeem his cornet.

Most of the time he would get his cornet back but there were occasions when he could not do so. Then he would be miserable. Having no money and no cornet really got him down in the dumps. There was always somewhere that he could cadge a drink but, if he did not have his cornet he was lost.

His music would be propped up against the jam-pot staring him in the face and the only thing left for him to do was to go and get drunk. How he did it only the landlord of his local pub knew and when pay-day came round again he would still be without money to redeem his cornet. At the time he would vow never to let things get so bad that he would have to hock his cornet but, once he got a drink in his belly he would forget everything he had said.

Neighbours of Johnny Martin were not as keen on his playing as everyone else seemed to be. The main reason for this was because when Johnny had his cornet out of hock he was forever practising. Hour after hour, until at last some friend or neighbour would give him some money to go down to the pub and get himself a beer.

It never occurred to Johnny that everyone did not care for brass band music, especially around midnight when a drunken fool like him staggered from the pub and started practising on his cornet. The fact was that he and his neighbours had to be up at five in the morning to go to work. Enough was enough and it was not the first time that Johnny had his neighbours banging on the door mouthing murderous threats against him and what they would do with the contents of their chamberpots if he did not quiet down.

One story that was told and retold was when Johnny was playing with the Burston Band as usual. The engagement was playing for St John's School in Fowley Village about three miles away. You could get to this school two different ways. One was to go down the main road for about two miles and turn right at the railway station, you then had an uphill climb of about one mile to the school. The other way was across the fields and was the shortest way. Most of the band went by this route. At the end of the day the return was usually along the main road.

The engagement at St John's was a procession and consisted of a short walk to the top of the village and back again, about a mile and a half all told. The children would be dressed in their Sunday best, the girls usually dressed in white and carrying poses, the boys in their best suits. A large banner naming the church and its title to be carried by the men with women or older children holding the four corner stays.

After the walk the procession returned to the schoolroom where a light lunch was served. (A real rock cake and a cup of tea.) The children were then allowed onto the playing fields for games while the band set up the stands outside and played a concert programme.

The only trouble with playing outside is that even if the weather is fine, with this particular village being on a hill above the main road, it was always a bit windy. The more experienced bandsmen, knowing this, always carried some clothes pegs with them for just this reason. Pegging the music to the stand was the only way to keep the music from blowing away.

When the games had finished, which was around four-thirty, tea would be served. At St John's it was always potato pie. It was the cheapest way to feed them all. Those pies were famous throughout the valley. They were said to be made in the the biggest enamel dishes anyone had ever seen. They measured about thirty inches across and it must have taken at least a couple of bags of flour to make each pie crust. Rumour had it that it took a hundred weight of potatoes for each pie, a possible exaggeration of the truth.

On this particular day, after everyone had eaten their fill, there was one dish with still nearly a quarter of pie left over and, as everyone had finished eating it looked as though they would have to throw the pie away. This is where Johnny came in. On hearing about the pie Johnny approached the church committee and asked if they would allow him to take the dish home with him? He would return it the following day. The minister, after consultation with the church committee agreed, saying that it would be a pity to waste such good food, especially since it could provide a good meal for a hard working man.

After the band had finished playing for the day Johnny quietly slipped away, returning about half an hour later with a bag in which were four or five pint bottles of beer. After collecting his potato pie Johnny set off across the fields in the direction of Burston.

The next day, being Sunday, the band assembled at the band-room for practice. Usually Johnny was one of the first to arrive and had never been known to be late but, by the time the band was due to start rehearsing Johnny still had not put in an appearance.

When band practice was over some of the bandsmen decided to go down to his house to see if he was all right. He was the band's solo cornet player and it was totally out of character for him to miss rehearsal unless there was a very good reason.

When they arrived at Johnny's house they found the place empty. There was no sign of him, nor were there any signs that he had been home at all. His door was unlocked but that was not unusual, he always left it unlocked. He had said that there was nothing in his house worth stealing, in fact he said that he had left any thieves a note asking for a donation. His friends were always dropping by and, being an idle devil he left the door unlocked so they could let themselves in.

They went in and made a thorough search of the place without finding hide nor hair of Johnny. Now they were worried and called in the local bobby. They had never known Johnny to disappear without telling anyone where he could be found.

Sergeant Benton, our local bobby, was a bit sceptical about Johnny's disappearance. On more than one occasion he had had to lock him up in the cells for the night when he had been found drunk and disorderly and as he said, he did not want anyone going off half cocked when the possibility was that they would find Johnny somewhere sleeping off last night's booze.

The sergeant did not know Johnny Martin as well as he thought he did. No matter how drunk Johnny was at night, the morning always found him at home or in the police station. This morning he was not anywhere to be found so, where the hell had he got to? At last they managed to convince the sergeant that there was something wrong. After a bit of thought the sergeant decided that they had better form a search party. They knew him best so, while they were searching all of the places Johnny was known to frequent, the sergeant would go back to St John's school and make some enquiries there, because that had been the last place that Johnny had been seen.

About an hour later they returned to the police station after a fruitless search to find that the sergeant had drawn a blank at St John's. Now he was puzzled. They now knew that no one had seen Johnny since yesterday at the school.

After a short discussion the sergeant decided that the only way to find Johnny was to cover the ground between the village and the school and as Johnny had said yesterday that he was going back to the village by the short cut, they would retrace our steps to the school by cutting across the fields, keeping their eyes peeled for their missing friend.

After about half an hour's walking they came to a stream and as it was a warm day decided to rest before crossing and continuing the search. The water looked very inviting, especially when you were hot and tired and the pubs were a long way off.

The stream at this point had been partially blocked with stones and twigs from the trees and bushes scattered around. The banking of the stream had been broken down as well; probably by youngsters from the village, who liked to play with their small boats in the water.

This part of the stream was now backed up like a small dam, forming a wider pool of water. As they sat there resting, watching a beer bottle floating around in the pool, the sergeant quickly got to his feet. The floating bottle had suddenly caught his interest. He bent over and fished the bottle from the stream. He looked at it for a moment. It was a pint bottle, empty of course. It had not been there long or the youngsters, that they had seen playing nearby, would have taken it back to the pub to get the penny back on it.

He looked at the bottle for a while, a look of concentration on his face then, gathering Johnny's friends round him, he explained his theory about the bottle. With one half of the party on one bank and the other half on the other, they set off searching both sides of the stream going upstream towards where the children's voices were coming from.

They had not gone far when there was a shout from one of Johnny's friends. They all rushed up to him, not quite knowing what to expect. What they did find was Johnny's pal leaning against a tree, tears rolling down his face and holding his stomach. What a shock! He looked like he was in agony. As they went closer they realised that it was not agony on his face, he was laughing fit to bust. They tried to question him but he could not reply for laughing, he just kept pointing at some bushes behind him. When Sergeant Benson looked over the top of the bushes he found Johnny Martin curled up fast asleep, his head propped up against a bush. On one side of him was the empty enamel dish that he had taken from St John's the day before, and around him were scattered empty beer bottles. It did not take a 'Sherlock Holmes' to figure out just what had happened though he did fill in the details later.

He had set off from the school with the enamel dish with the pie in it, after having had a couple of pints in the local pub. He had purchased a few pint bottles to help him on his way and he felt in good fettle. The wind from earlier in the afternoon had died down. The sun was warm on his back and he was at peace with the World.

He had arrived at the stream and sat down for a rest as we had done. While resting he had opened a bottle of beer. After he had drunk a bottle he felt hungry so he decided to eat some of the pie. There was plenty so he would have some left over for tomorrow. Then he had another bottle of beer and a little more pie before he set off once more for home. Another drink and another bit of pie and before he knew it the velvety voice of Sergeant Benson was whispering sweet nothings in his ear urging him to wake up. Eventually he realised that the sergeant, who was by now going red in the face, was actually shouting at him. What for? He had not done anything wrong had he? He remembered sitting down by the tree, eating some of the pie and drinking a bottle of beer. The rest was hazy. The next thing he knew was waking up with some of his friends standing round him and Sergeant Benson shouting at him for some reason, calling him all the names under the sun. Anyway the sergeant was wrong. He had had a father. When the sergeant had calmed down, he presumed that Johnny must have got drunk on the bottles of beer he had with him, finished off the pie and fell asleep.

I do not feel that it is appropriate to relate here just what names the sergeant was said to have called Johnny that day, mainly because there were many different versions, some of which were unprintable, they all did agree on one thing though and that was that looking after Johnny Martin was a full time job. If it had not been for his wonderful cornet playing I am sure that he would have been run out of town on more than one occasion. As for now we got the distinct feeling that Johnny had better keep out of Sergeant Benton's way for a while.

Johnny's escapade was the talk of the village for weeks afterwards and he was not allowed to forget it. Not that it bothered him a great deal. In fact the telling of the story brought him quite a few pints. Free at that. There is also the possibility that to bolster his story he may have stretched the truth, just a little perhaps?

Another of the tales about Johnny Martin was when he paid his rent. As everyone knew, trying to get money out of Johnny Martin was like trying to get blood out of a stone and as pay-day came round, Johnny's creditors would be crowding him for payment. The rent man had to make his own arrangements and so it became a battle of wits.

Johnny would come home from work, have a quick wash and

then off down to the pub. The rent man's job was to catch Johnny before he left the house. If he called at the house in time he mostly got his rent money. If he did not catch him in time and his bird had flown then he would have the dubious job of trying to get double the next week and this, he knew, was almost impossible to do.

Having been baulked many times before in his schemes to get the money from Johnny, the rent man decided that the only way to be sure when Johnny was home was to wait at Johnny's house for him to get home from work and catch him as he entered the house. This scheme worked quite well for a few weeks and Johnny was getting very annoyed. Something had to be done.

The next week Johnny left work on some excuse and got home early, he decided that in order to keep his reputation intact, he would have to teach this crafty rent man a lesson. This man was an expert and after getting Johnny's rent last week he had then collected the rest of his money quite easily. He knew all the excuses but had heard them all before and once people heard that he had collected Johnny's rent without even getting out of breath he was then regarded as something of a magician.

After coming home two weeks on the trot and getting caught with money still in his pocket Johnny was past caring. It was war. It just could not go on. Johnny's neighbours were saying that the rent man had Johnny well and truly taped and Johnny did not like to have his hard won reputation dragged in the dirt in this way.

This particular Thursday Johnny arrived home earlier than usual and keeping his eyes open for the rent man he stoked up the fire and put his small steel shovel into the flames. As soon as he saw the rent man coming down the street he placed his two shillings rent money on the now very hot shovel and waited.

The knock came a few minutes later. Johnny immediately removed the shovel from the fire and slid the hot shillings onto the rent book laying on the sideboard. He opened the door and much to the rent man's surprise he nodded his head towards the sideboard and said, "There you are lad, hurry up I'm waitin' to go out."

At this point the rent man should have smelled a rat. The fact that Johnny had given in so easily should have made him suspicious and the burning smell coming from the rent book could have made him stop and think. The over-riding factor was of course that Johnny Martin was paying his rent without a murmur and being a rent man, money was money and he could not get his hands on it quick enough. He quickly scooped up the rent book with one hand and slid the two shillings into the other one. For a second or so there was no reaction and then suddenly he let out a yell that could have wakened the dead. He dropped the two shillings, luckily into his bag, shaking his burnt fingers and cursing Johnny for all he was worth. Verily he swore at Johnny who was now rolling with laughter, tears streaming down his face, and when he eventually could, he said, "It's your own fault tha greedy bugger. Tha comes sooner and sooner every week. I knew that one week tha'd come before I'd finished makin' them reight. Thought tha'd got old Johnny taped did the? Well thy'art one off. Go an' tell that to thy cronies and see if they laugh at Johnny Martin now."

The rent man left Johnny's house cursing and swearing, vowing that somehow he would get his own back on him, but Johnny watched him go and chuckled to himself, his thoughts on all the pints that the story would bring.

How true these stories are I do not know but from the tales that are told about Johnny, I feel sure that it is just how it happened.

6

Christmas Carols

Come Christmas time there was not a great deal of cash to throw around and now that the band had settled down to a certain level of playing - not good, but we were getting better. It was suggested that after Christmas we would try our hand at contesting again. Tom Perkins had told us stories about his contesting days before the war and I suppose these stories had fired our imagination.

First we had to complete our Christmas playing. This was the time of the year when we went round the streets showing the people that we were still around hoping that our beloved public would show their appreciation in the form of cash donations in our collection boxes.

Burston was not a large town but it covered a pretty big area as we were to find out over the Christmas period. The villages were interlocked with one or two large estates and we had some very remote groups of houses and farms to visit.

Having such a large area to cover, Adam Bailey decided to split the band into two parts, in order to get to as many of the villages as possible. We were only allowed four weeks to do the whole lot. Even then it depended on the weather.

In most cases splitting the band into two parts was a good idea and it worked, but sometimes the full complement of players just were not available, due to work and family commitments etc. Then we would not have enough players to share out into two well balanced bands, so we had to go out in one band.

I managed to get into the part band conducted by our bandmaster Ernie Benson, we were to play in the streets around the town centre. At times this could be a bit awkward. Up to eight o'clock there would be no trouble but after that, although the people would come to the door to listen some would ask - I say ask, but sometimes it would be a battle of words before they would tell us to 'bugger off further up the street before you wake the children up' - us to play perhaps a little quieter.

As the evening wore on we tended to play at the end of each street, with the collectors going down both sides collecting as they went. We always continued playing until the collector had finished, then we would move on to the next street.

Some of the hymn tunes we played sounded like the names of streets and one night an old lady asked one of the bandsmen, "D'you know St Marcus?"

Joe Sudders replied, "No luv, but we'll play it when we've finished this tune."

It took some time before we realised that she was looking for St Marcus street, which happened to be the street where we were playing. She could not see it in the dark.

Sometimes when we came to a longer street, we would play halfway down. This was not a good time to play *Christians Awake* or *Good King Wenceslas*. The spirit of Christmas certainly did not apply when they were trying to get small children to go to sleep and we would be told in no uncertain way where we could go to play our Christmas music.

Either way we could not win and, as we became aware, not everyone cared to hear the brass band playing Christmas music. (Peace on Earth, good will to all men?) Thank goodness these people were few and far between.

A lot of the nights when we went round Christmas playing, the air would be keen and frosty, which, if we were wrapped up well kept us moving quite nicely. The thing was, with blowing dampness into the instruments it caused the valves to freeze up if we were not careful, then we would have a devil of a time getting them free again.

This particular year - it was nineteen forty-eight - we had more snow than usual. All the roads in and around town were blocked and anyone who had a job to go to had to set off very early in the morning if they were to get to work on time.

Anyway to get back to Christmas playing. As I said, the valves

c

of our instruments kept freezing up. It meant that in between playing we had to try to keep our instruments warm. We had various ways of doing this, pouring warm water on the valves was one way of doing it, and it was not a clever thing to enquire too closely where the warm water had come from. The favourite way was to breath on the valve casing and at the same time keeping the valves moving up and down as we moved to the next street. The only trouble was, we soon got out of breath and it was particularly hard on the bass-players. The finger ends also got very cold, so that we could not feel them and the best thing we could wear for this were mittens. These were like a glove with the finger ends missing but at least it did keep the hand warm.

After we had had a number of stops for valves freezing up Jim Hogan our E-flat bass player said how he was shattered. He was puffing and out of breath which was very unusual for him, even at fifty years old he was a very fit man but tonight he was making very hard work of it.

When out Christmas playing we usually tried to make sure that at least sometime during the evening we would be able to call at one of the houses of one of the bigwigs of the town,. who we thought might invite us in for a coffee or something. A whisky for the senior members of the band and a mince tart or cake for the younger members. We were always open to offers, besides we always dropped a hint that we would be calling in at some other town heavies over the Christmas period so we felt sure that when we called we would he made most welcome. The easiest way to lose votes was to he known as being tight when the local brass band was doing the rounds at Christmas time.

When it came to our main breather of the evening we were duly invited in for a drink and a short rest and Jim, as usual, stopped just inside the door to relieve himself of his now heavy bass. Walking around with a heavy instrument strapped to your back all night was a wearying task, even when you loved playing it. As was his way Jim stood the bass up on its bell end and doing a few stretches said, "Thank God for that, I've been blowing my guts out all night. I've never felt so knackered. What with the valves freezing over every time I stopped blowing, I must be getting old. I don't think I've played as bad in all my life."

With that he lifted his instrument to move it nearer to the hot radiator. Suddenly Bert Rawlins burst into laughter. We turned round to see what was the cause of his merriment and found Bert doubled up, as he pointed at Jim's bass.

"No wonder Jim's been blowing his brains out all night," he said. "The silly bugger's been trying to blow with his bass blocked."

We followed his pointing finger and sure enough their on the floor where Jim had moved his instrument from were a couple of banana skins and a large orange. Jim spluttered as he denied that the fruit had come from his bass, he felt such a fool, but he had no explanation. The fruit had not been there when he had put his instrument down. We decided that it must have happened when we had played in the streets beneath the windows.

The children, who were supposed to be in bed, must have dropped the fruit out of the bedroom windows into the large bell-end of Jim's instrument and, with it being so cold Jim had not noticed. It was not often anyone got a laugh out of Jim Hogan but believe me it would take some time before he lived it down. I fancy that the story would be brought up time and time again in the following years.

Other things happened that Christmas. We were attacked by hordes of children at different points in our rounds. They would wait for us to pass their back yards before popping up and pelting us with a hail of snowballs. Then they would run like hell. Sometimes we chased them without really meaning to catch them, well, what were we going to do to them? They were the same sort of tricks we had tried when we were younger, mind you, it did keep us warm.

Looking back at some of the hymn tunes we played, I remember that the favourite tune was *Deep Harmony* a lovely hymn but by the end of the evening, after being asked for it over and over again, we did tend to get fed up with playing it, however, that is what most of them wanted to hear and that is what they got. There were many other beautiful hymns we were asked to play such as *Rimingtom*, *Hark The Herald Angels Sing* and *Silent Night* or as it is known in German *Stifle Nacte*. The German name seemed more appropriate if you know what I mean.

My favourite night was Christmas Eve. By now I was allowed to stay out all night with the band. We started with a hymn round the crib in the town centre. The hymn would usually be *Deep Harmony*. The older people used to call it *Great Harmony* though

51

where this came from I do not know. We followed it with a Christmas hymn, this would be *Hark The Herald Angels Sing*, finishing off with *Silent Night* and then we moved off on our round of the pubs. Much ale was consumed in our run up to midnight when we set our sights on getting round as many farms as we possibly could before morning.

Going round the farms died out in later years, possibly because bandsmen did not want to go out all night. I could never understand it, but then I was not married, not even courting. Then again some of the bandsmen having been away for so many Christmases, during the Second World War, wanted to spend Christmas with their families. Well, that was in years to come. It certainly was not because the farmers wanted us to stop. The welcome that we received at every farm proved it.

The last pub finished, it was now time for the farms so, with Tom Perkins in the lead we set off. Tom Perkins being the senior member of the band had in his possession our most treasured farm map. It was not just any old map that could be bought in the shops. It was one which was hand made, though who made it nobody knows, probably made by the first band that went round the farms, anyway Tom had it and after studying it carefully away we went.

If he hadn't had the map to help him and also to show us the shortest way round we could easily get lost. Thank goodness someone had had the sense to make a map, there were no street lights on the moors.

This particular winter was, as I said before, one of the worst winters that I could remember. The snow was waist deep in most places around town and only idiots like us would have ventured out on the moors on a night like this but we were well wrapped up with extra wrappings round our legs. Over our leggings we wore anything that would keep us warm. I wore an extra pair of my grandfathers fustian trousers which were designed to keep the weather out and even these were wrapped with 'puttees' from his army days. Looking back I must have looked like 'Owd Fagin', a character I had read about in a book called *Oliver Twist*. I looked like I had put on three stone in weight.

I protested when my grandfather first brought the trousers. I thought it was daft going out on Christmas Eve looking like that but my father would have none of it, he told me that if I did not wrap up well he would be in trouble with my mother and she was a real tartar when she got her dander up. I was not going to miss my first all nighter for anyone, so I did not argue. At least not much, anyway before the night was over I was going to be thankful that I had not left anything off.

It might have crossed your mind that we were daft or just plain stupid. Well, we were neither. The farmers round Burston district were weather hardened men who never seemed to take time off, even at Christmas. They still had to take care of their stock come rain or shine, or as in this case, snow. Even now some of them were probably out in the hills looking to their sheep and cattle and, as we went from farm to farm that night, I knew just how much they appreciated our calling round.

We always knew which farms to go to. These would be the farms that were lit up like beacons and as soon as they saw our paraffin lamp and candles in jam-jars, they would come out to meet us and guide us safely in.

When we arrived at the farm we played a tune outside the house, then we were invited in with a great Christmas greeting to hot drinks, lots of food and a rest by the fireside. Unfortunately this did not last for long because we only allowed ourselves half an hour inside each farmhouse, this included playing the carols so, it was a quick warm, a bite of food and then the carols, then off again to the next farm on our list which never seemed to go any shorter. Sometimes however, two or three families would get together in one farmhouse, when this happened we could relax and allow ourselves a longer stay.

This happened at our first port of call. Mainly because of the snow, I hoped it would happen for the rest of the night, it was lovely and warm inside the farmhouse. The food was good and when no one was looking I managed to get a drink of the hard stuff which helped to warm my insides amongst other things.

The families would come together at the same farm just because they were friends and neighbours, I suppose, but they said it was mainly to make sure that they would not miss the band. Whatever the reason they made sure that we were well fed before we left. I feasted on mince pies and sausage rolls all night long and the drinks that the older members consumed made them virtually snow-proof.

While we were in the farmhouse we played as many hymns

and carols as possible, in between eating and drinking. It meant that after Christmas the instruments would need a good old fashioned clean out.

When it came time to go one of the farmer's sons said that he would guide the way to the next farm, because the snow, which had now started again, would have drifted across most of the paths and tracks. We accepted the offer gratefully, because although this was one of the earlier calls of the night, we were only about three quarters of a mile from the main road and it had taken us the best part of an hour to get here and that was before we went into the farmhouse.

Our next port of call was Warton Clough Farm, Fred Pearson's place, which was about a mile or so across the valley. We were guided by Joe Paley, the farmer's son from the previous farm, without question. Full of cheer and with a lot of laughter, especially when one or another slipped and fell into a drift, of which there were many. On more than one occasion I am sure that I was deliberately tripped so that I fell head first into the snow but I suppose that was because I was the youngest. A lot of funny things seemed to happen when you were not expecting it and the thing is, they all seemed to be accidental. I wonder?

We carried on working our way through the drifting snow which was deepening as we went. Every now and then there would be a shout when someone slipped and disappeared down a snow covered banking, but they did not seem to let it worry them. They would swear for a while and then someone would take a bottle of whisky from their pocket. After a taste of the Christmas spirit they would examine their instruments for any damage and then we would all stagger off into the night.

At this time we seemed to be taking one step forward and two steps back and we did not seem to be getting any nearer to any farm. The only light we could see was our own lantern and candles that did not shine more than a couple of yards in front of us and still no sign of any farm lights. Tom Perkins broke the silence.

"Hey Joe, as tha gett'n us lost tha daft bugger?"

All eyes turned towards Joe as he trudged silently forward. He stopped and looked around shamefaced, then he had to admit he did not really know just where we were. It was not altogether Joe's fault, we had all been laughing and joking with no one bothering to notice where we were going, but he had been the one specially sent to guide us. Everything went silent for a moment and, as though we all had the same thought, we grabbed poor Joe and upended him into a snowdrift, then amidst the shouts and curses it started to snow again.

"Come on Joe sort thyself out." Tom shouted above the rising wind. "See if tha can get thy bearings, come on shap thyself."

We stood there for a few minutes so that Joe could decide just where we were. He swayed first one way and then the next until suddenly we recognised the calamity. Joe had also partaken of a gradely amount of Christmas cheer and was looking somewhat stupefied and from the look of him we knew that we were lost.

"Well we can't just stay here," Ernie Benson said. "Let's keep moving. Come on Joe you should have some idea where abouts we are."

"You'll be lucky." A voice said out of the darkness. "He doesn't even know what bloody day it is."

"Leave the lad alone can't you?" Tom said, then to no one in particular. "He were a dizzy bugger before he 'ad any drink so I'm beginning to wonder what brainy sod asked him tu guide us now?"

"I don't know what you're shoutin' about Tom, he's lost us out on the moors and can't find a farm, you've nobbut got a trombone an' most of the time and you can't find that."

"Which silly bugger said that?" Tom shouted. "Own up if tha dares an' I'll flatten thee."

"I said it. Tha great puddin'," Jim Hogan shouted back. "Stop shoutin' at the lad and let's get goin', I've a bloody E flat bass to carry not a bloody piddling trombone like you."

"Don't thee call my trombone," Tom shouted back at him. "Thy instrument's a bastard, everybody knows that the trombone is the only true instrument in the band, so shut thy mouth."

At that Jim unstrapped his bass and laid it carefully in the snow at his feet, took off his cap and said, "Reight, big mouth. I've just about had enough of thee. Say one more word an' I'll swipe thee one. Just because tha's got the map of the farms doesn't mean that tha con say anything tha fancies."

With that he launched himself at Tom Perkins, knocking him down and then falling drunkenly on top of him so that they rolled over and over in the snow.

When all this happened we were crossing the side of a hill and as Jim fell on top of Tom they both rolled off the side of the narrow path and went flying arse over tip down the hill, stopping about twenty yards below us when they landed in a huge snowdrift. All that could be seen of them was four legs sticking out of the drift. We slipped and slid down the hill until we got near enough to pull them out, but we were laughing so much that we finished up in the same snow-drift, only we were the right way up. Luckily our paraffin lamp, had stayed lit, though the candles had blown out. How they missed getting smashed up is still a mystery. So, that was it, we were lost in one of the worst snowstorms that I had ever known. Wet through and all helpless with laughter.

After we had calmed down a bit and pulled Jim and Tom out of the snowdrift, Tom said, still chuckling a bit, "Tell you what, let's have a blow! Maybe somebody'll hear us an' come an' get us out of this bloody snow."

So we all agreed, mainly because nobody could think of anything better.

"Reight," Ernie Benson said, blowing furiously into his now cold cornet trying to get some warmth to circulate round the yards of piping, "let's play something rousing."

After a bit of arguing, mainly because Jim wanted *Diadem*, he said that it had a good bass part, and Tom wanted *Blaenwern*, Ernie sorted it out.

"Remember last year lads? Someone asked for *Cwym Rhonda* an' we didn't have it with us, didn't we put it in the book for this year?"

"Aye we did," Pete Barton piped up, he was one of our trombone players, but tonight he was carrying the lantern. "I put it in there myself."

Now as luck would have it we had four cornets in our little group, and we certainly needed them? *Cwym Rhonda* was a fair blow at the best of times but now we needed it played at a double forte. The time had come to see who had a good lip and who had not.

So, there we all were, standing knee deep in snow, lost and ready to blow mightily into our instruments trying to get our valves working. Ernie counted us in and we started to play.

Maybe it was just the time of the morning and the predicament that we were in, but the sound of Ernie's cornet in the night air seemed to me like nothing I had ever heard before. It sounded beautiful. The snow all around us like a great white blanket. The odd snowflake floating down. Now the wind had dropped and the sound was of the band rising and falling as the hills around us echoed to that magnificent Welsh tune. I am sure that it would have brought a tear to a statue's eye that night. I know it did to mine. The only thing is, I do not remember whether it was pleasure at the sound of the tune or the cold night air making my eyes water.

It really did sound great. We played it over and over again until at last Ernie brought us to a halt and we sank down into the snow completely knackered. I am sure that the lips of all the cornet players were hanging right down to their knees. Mine felt like a plumb-bob swinging all alone above my bottom lip. We were too tired even to speak. As we sat there resting I suddenly remembered the words of a song I had heard, *In The Still Of The Night*, this is just what they must have meant.

"Come-on lads," Tom Perkins said. "We can't stay here all night, we'll be frozen stiff if we do, let's get movin'."

Suddenly a voice came from out of the darkness.

"That were great lads, maybe you can play it just as well in the barn."

We all turned round. The shock of hearing the voice was like having a bucket of cold water thrown over you. Pete shone the light in the direction of the voice and there leaning on what turned out to be a gatepost, with his pipe turned upside down to keep out the snow, was Fred Pearson, the man who owned the farm that we were looking for.

"Where the hell did you come from?" Ernie said, after he had found his voice. "You bloody near frightened us to death."

"I've been leaning here on the wall listening to thy playing an' by gum I did enjoy it, it's a gradely tune is that but I wouldn't a liked to have sung all them verses. Anyway bugger this for a picnic it's freezin'. Dern't stand theer gettin' cold, come in the house an get thyself warm. You must be starved."

With that he bent down and pulled the bar fastening the gate which had been covered by a snowdrift and as soon as the gate started to swing open the snow fell away revealing the outline of the farmhouse not more than seventy yards away. When we asked Fred why he had not let on that he had been by the gate he said,

"I thought that you were enjoyin' thyselves and I didn't want to disturb thee."

If I had been big enough I think that I would have strangled him there and then, but his good humour and the roaring fire overcame us as he invited us into his living-room. Fred's wife had a hot drink waiting for us and as we sat by the fire slowly defrosting she brought out a big meat pie and the usual mince pies. It did not take us long to demolish the food and drink. A few more carols and then we were off again. Out into the cold night once more battling against the ice and snow. Scott of the Antarctic had nothing on us that night except that we could see where we wanted to get too. We just could not seem to manage it.

From where we were standing on the hillside we could just see lights twinkling in the distance. It looked so picturesque in the moonlight. We could see the farmhouse standing out against the snow-covered hills and that darker patch must be the woods behind the house. What was it that made it look so different? We all stopped to gape at what we thought was Ganley's Farm! It looked OK at first glance but when we took a second look there was something different. Dick Hardy, our horn player was the first to spot it.

"Tha daft pillock Tom. That's Warton Reservoir an' them's the road lights shinin' on the water. We've come down the wrong side of the hill. You daft bugger, we're nearly in bloody Yorkshire!"

Tom's glazing eyes fastened on Dick as though he was someone not quite right in the head. "I've got the sodden map here," he said. "So we can't be going the wrong way." He waved the map under Dick's nose, gave a weird little laugh and then flopped down in the snow drunk as a lord. What were we going to do now? Tom flaked out in the snow snoring like a pig, in his hand the aforesaid map now crumpled and wet.

We looked at one another for a moment or so and then everyone started to talk at once. I say talk. It was more like a shouting match. They were arguing and pushing one another to try to get their own point of view over but it was Jim Hogan who brought them to their senses. It was quite inadvertent of course because he too was well under the influence of the Christmas spirit, but just when the arguing seemed to be getting out of hand the shouting was interrupted by the sound of one of Jim's infamous farts. All arguing stopped as the sound seemed to strike them dumb.

It is whispered in the back rooms of the local pubs that Jim's father perfected this noisey and loathsome smell in the First World War. Said to have caused the first German retreat of two miles when they thought it was mustard gas. Just how he had managed it no one knows but somehow Jim's father had passed the secret on to his son. He did not do it often, he had lost too many friends that way, but when he did, it was said that he would have won 'The big Farting Contest' at 'Shittam-on-Peas'.

Whatever the beliefs, it did the trick. Everyone stopped shouting and rushed to get as far away from Jim as possible without losing sight of him. When we thought it safe enough, we ventured back. Tom, who had been starting to come to his senses, took the full force of the explosion and was some yards back flung in a snowdrift and looking somewhat dazed. We got Tom to his feet, but just for good measure Jim rubbed a handful of snow in his face. A bit nooky were Jim when he had had some ale.

"Where's the bloody map you drunken sod?" Jim shouted, shaking Tom back and forth like a rag doll. Tom's eyes were rolling round with the shaking. Then suddenly he shook Jim off and gave him a mighty shove which sent him skidding along, in the snow on his backside. He then pulled himself up to his full height and, holding the map out in front of him trying to get his bearings he said:

"Come on, this is the right way." He then set off in the direction of the reservoir.

Bert Rawlins made a grab for him and only succeeded in knocking him into another snowdrift. Then they all dived on him before he could get away, quite forgetting that we were still on the side of a very steep snow-covered hill. It was just like the Keystone Cops, everyone grabbing at each other trying to stop the inevitable. Someone grabbed me in passing and we slipped and slid down to the bottom of the icy slope, the only thing that stopped us falling into the river that fed the reservoir was a big stone wall, built to stop the animals from slipping into the water. I do not think for a minute they would ever have imagined the sort of animals it would save.

What a night! Even more cold and wet, floundering about in the snow with arms and legs sticking up out of the drifts, the curses and shouts could have been heard all over the valley. The curses turned into laughter as a figure heaved itself up out of the snow. It was Tom, once more back in the land of the living. He had his arms held straight out in front of him just like a sleep-walker. He said, "Reight lads follow me. It's straight on," and again with that stupid grin on his face he set off once more across the hillside. This time we were ready for him. I wrapped myself round his ankles and Bert grabbed him round the waist and he again toppled over into the snow.

"Owd on a minute," Bert said, trying to keep his eyes in focus and hold Tom down at the same time. He snatched the map from Tom's hand. "Bring the light over 'ere."

We all gathered round him as he stared down at the map.

"No bloody wonder we'er goin' the wrong way," he said. "The silly sod's had the bloody map upside down. I'll bloody kill him. Having us stuck on this soddin' hillside in the middle of the night, just cause he can't 'old his ale. That's it, next year we'll 'ave somebody else reading the bloody thing." Still cursing the bleary-eyed Tom he stalked off muttering, "He's not fit to carry me bloody cap, the useless pillock."

We studied the map the best we could and then we backtracked up the hill and down the other side, through the snow which had drifted up over the walls so that even with the map the right way up we could not be sure that we were going in the right direction and, being off the paths, every now and then someone would venture into deep snow and we would have to drag them out cursing and swearing and making dire threats against Tom Perkins.

The amazing thing about all this falling and slipping was not one of our instruments was damaged, not even a dent. Maybe it had something to do with it being Christmas Eve, or should I say Christmas Day because it was now early morning and we still had four farms to go to. Three of those farms were much further away from the road and we had not even got to the nearest one yet. I hoped it was like this every Christmas Eve, I would not have missed it for the world. I had never laughed so much in all my life.

We struggled on through the snow in the general direction of Bracknell's Farm. We could see the lights from the farm as we slid down the icy slope. It was only half a mile as the crow flies, but we were not crows and we were getting very tired. In fact we

60

were knackered. It was only the thought of the liquid refreshment at the farms that kept us going. I also heard more than one voice say that this was going to be the last time that they would be hiking over the snow-covered moors at Christmas time. They said it every year so nobody took any notice of them, they knew that when next Christmas came round they would be looking forward to it once again.

Eventually we got to Bracknell's Farm and as we slipped and slid into the farmyard, a door was flung open and a shout of welcome came from Nat Bracknell.

"Well you're here then? I didn't think you'd make it this year, what with the lane bein' covered over, I don't know when we'll get it cleared, anyway come in lads, have a warm an summat to eat, grub's on the table so get stuck in an I'll get thee some drinks."

With that he ushered us all into the farm kitchen. It seemed uncommonly quiet as we took our coats off and moved closer to the roaring fire. David green said, "I don't know what's going on, but things aren't usually as quiet as this. Nat's normally got the place bouncing by this time."

We had been wondering, but when we asked Tom Perkins he wouldn't say anything. He knew that Nat must have something up his sleeve. Tom had sobered up quite a lot since his roll in the snow and was now sitting in a chair by the side of the fire. He had taken the hot poker and was dipping it in his glass of stout which Nat had pushed into his hand. He said that he was mulling the ale, but as for what Nat was up to he did not know, at least if he did he was saying nothing and he had known Nat longer than most of us. He just sat there eating a piece of homemade meat pie with another bottle of stout within easy reach.

We got stuck into the food left out for us and as the fire warmed us we relaxed. I got myself a glass of ale and was just about to drink it when I felt a hand on my shoulder. It was David Green our secretary.

"Just you take it easy young Joe," he said. "We've let you have an odd glass of ale because it's been a bad night, but that's it, from now on it's tea or lemonade. Your dad will skin us alive if he gets to know that we've been letting you have any ale at all so, no more OK?"

I nodded my head and sulked for a bit and then thought 'so

what?' what he didn't know wouldn't hurt him. I'd just have to be more careful. To be fair though I was only just in my teens and I had had a good do up to now and what with all the food on the table I wasn't sure that I would have room for ale as well. Would I?

We sat there eating and drinking for a while then Ernie said, "I think that we'll have to be going soon. We've still the other farms to do and time's getting on."

"We're reight," Tom said. "Ale's good, food's good and we haven't had time to dry out properly yet, and anyway we haven't given Nat his carols yet."

We looked around. We had not seen Nat for some time now and we had been here for nearly half an hour. We decided we could stop for a bit longer, the idea of moving went against the grain. The warmth of the kitchen made us realise just how cold and wet it had been out on the hills. We would get moving shortly when we had given Nat his carols.

It was just as well that we had not decided to move, outside the door we could hear voices. The door was thrown open and in trouped all the other three farmers and their families.

To say that we were surprised would he an understatement. We were totally astonished. Two minutes ago we had been talking about getting ready to move on to the next farm, now we need not move at all. This was great. What a turn-up for the book! At that moment Nat and his wife Elsie came into the living-room to welcome their friends and also to explain how it came about that it was not just a coincidence that the other farmers had just dropped in.

When we had arrived at the farm all wet and frozen stiff, Elsie had suggested that Nat ring up the other farmers and tell them the condition we were in, that we were all wet through and may not be able to make it to their farms so, if they wanted to come down here to Bracknell's Farm, they were welcome. Also the farmers knew the hills better than we did and would not get lost. Nat had not told us because he did not know whether his friends could make it or not. Obviously they had, with all the children well wrapped up against the winter's cold breath. It was very late for the children to be out but they were full of excitement at the prospect of being at someone else's farm. It was an adventure and they were delighted to be part of it.

After Nat had contacted the other farmers, Elsie had then set too and prepared beds for the children. We could not believe it that the farmers would go to so much trouble just for us, but they did and the other farmers had brought plenty of ale with them making quite sure that the short time we would be able to spend here would go down as one of the best 'Tommy Kelly' do's we had had for years. One other good thing was that we did not have to go out again until eight o'clock, the only point being that it was nearly five o'clock now. At least we had three hours before leaving to meet the other members of Burston band in the town centre later on at nine o'clock.

When all the greetings were over and everyone had been supplied with a drink we decided that it was time for carols. The children had been put to bed but it was quite obvious from the noise upstairs that they were not going to go to sleep. We started with *Hark The Herald Angels Sing* mainly for the children then the requests came in thick and fast. *Crimond* then *Great Harmony*, *We Three Kings* and many more. That farmhouse vibrated with their singing. I am sure that there was a slate or two lifted with the sound of the voices of those families singing their hearts out with the praises and to welcome the birthday of Jesus Christ. The happiness on their faces was something to behold. Whoever thought that farmers and their families were not religious should have been there. The exultation shown on their voices that night was something that I would never forget. Everything was sung with gusto, even when we were busking *Jingle Bells* for the children. Later on there were versions of *Paddy Mcginty's Goat* and *My Brother Sylvest*. I think that everyone there sang something. Even the youngest gave us a very shy *Twinkle, Twinkle Little Star*. This Christmas had been something special for the children. The excitement of moving down to Bracknell's Farm had left them too excited to want to sleep so they had been allowed to come downstairs to sing. Now the tiredness was catching up with them and even as they sang some of them were nodding off and with others who were too tired to stay awake Elsie had them carried up to the beds she had prepared and, though it was something of a squash, they were soon tucked up and we heard no more from them.

Now that the children were in bed the rest of the company decided that it was time that they got down to some serious drinking, though what it was they had been doing up till now I will never know.

With the house now filled with people laughing singing and topping up with even more of the Christmas cheer, the party started to go with a merry swing on into Christmas morning when, at eight o'clock we had to make our departures. We were supposed to meet the rest of the band at nine o'clock but I doubt that we would get away before ten. There was the possibility that the band would split up into two bands but that depended on how many players turned up. We always tried to fulfil our Christmas Day commitments but after a Christmas Eve of drinking and parties, bandsmen were not always in a fit state to go out playing.

We had left Nat's farm and had been pointed in the right direction, so, after struggling through what seemed another thousand snowdrifts, we eventually arrived on the main road. Then it was only about a mile to the town centre. I was the only one not under the influence of the 'farmer's farewell'. Possibly through not imbibing so much in the overpowering grape-juice I wasn't feeling as warm as the others. In fact I was what is known as 'frozen tut marrer' which in good English meant that I was very cold.

I made a mental note that next year I would try some punch, maybe even some more whisky. It had not done the rest of the lads much harm, in fact they did not seem to feel the cold at all and so if it could keep them warm it could do the same for me. I decided that I had time to slip off home and, after much fussing from my mother and a change of clothes, I was once more allowed to go and join the band for the day's caroling. I did not want any breakfast much to my mother's disgust. I could not face any more food just now, so she put me up some sandwiches chance I starved during the day.

It never occurred to my mother that the other women who stood around listening to us playing carols, were just like her. If they saw a youngster playing with the band they felt that they had to give them something to eat. A mince pie or a piece of cake. Even a warm by the fireside. They seemed to think that we were forced to go out playing with the band and nearly all of them felt sorry for us, and although I was in my teens I was still one of the youngsters. Little did they know that the best time of the year for us was Christmas with all those goodies and also, when no one was watching, a quick slurp of ale.

The following week seemed to go very quickly. We were out playing with the band every night, stopping every now and then to rest and have a warm in someone's hallway or kitchen, a quick bite and a drink of something, mostly tea, sometimes coffee then we would be off again.

Up until now I had not realised what Christmas playing was all about. We had so much ground to cover and, although we worked very hard over the holiday period, in the coming months there would still be people who would complain that they had not heard the band over Christmas.

Suddenly New Year's Eve was upon us and once again it was round the pubs. I had not counted them but it seemed that there must have been a pub for every house in the town. Something that the band would never complain about.

As the evening progressed nearer to the New Year, we were being invited into more houses than usual. Drinks came our way in the form of pop for the youngsters and something with a little more bite in it for the older players. Like in most bands many of the youngsters got money pushed into their pockets from enthusiastic listeners and they did not forget the collection box either, even if it was mostly coppers. At the end of the day it all contributed, how much we did not know, it would be about a week before all the tins were counted and added up.

The counting of the cash collected at Christmas was done at a special meeting of the band committee in the first week of the New Year when all the boxes, which had been sealed up before we had started collecting, would be opened with all the committee present so that it was seen that everything was above board and that none of the seals had been broken before the tins were emptied and counted in the band-room.

Once again the committee were to report that the town had shown its appreciation for the band by digging deep into their pockets. The one thing about public subscription bands was that if your town did not appreciate the band, it showed up in the size of the donations in the collecting boxes. If the town did not care much, they did not give much, whether we worked damned hard for it or not.

I did not see the conclusion of the New Year's Eve playing because my father came at about ten thirty and hooked me off home. He had done all this Christmas playing himself when he had been playing with the band and, as New Year's Eve was one of the bands most booziest nights he was getting me home before I got too involved in the drinking. He was quite aware that the senior members would not be in any state to watch me as the night wore on and he was also aware that I liked a little taste of the golden hops, so one more year was to pass before I could indulge in the drunken sprees of those beer soused bandsmen. Well, roll on next year! Only ninety minutes to go!

7

New Year's Day

New Year's Day morning came and we met as usual at the band-room. Nine o'clock was the time for setting off but it was nearer to nine thirty before all the stragglers arrived. We never seemed to start out on time. There was always someone arriving late, not quite recovered from the night before, so, although not quite as planned, we set off.

This year we had a reasonable band out. Three basses, two euphoniums, a baritone and all three horns. We counted ourselves lucky this morning in that we also had five cornets plus two trombones, plus of course Bert Fallows on tenor and Tom Perkins on bass trombone. Tom had never been known to miss a New Year's Day, there was too much ale about for that, even though it had been in the early hours of this morning before he had staggered home.

We set off eventually for The Golden Ball which was the only pub in the village of Fowley. The walk to the village wasn't more than a mile and Dick Hardy, our solo horn player, had his potent pick-me-up. This was a potion of vile repute. It has been said in the past that Dick's pick-me-up was more potent than all the ale they had supped the night before.

In a moment of lucidity, Dick had once disclosed that the mixture was made up of a small amount of brandy, a good measure of whisky and then topped up in a quarter sized bottle with dry ginger. He also mentioned something about pepper, but not very loudly. From the looks on the faces of those who were foolhardy enough to taste this concoction I think that Dick had got the portions mixed up - more like eight parts spirits, one part ginger and two parts gunpowder, but go easy on the ginger beer. Either way, in some cases it did the trick.

Jim Tubbs, our solo baritone player, had one small sip and immediately directed his morning's breakfast over the wall bordering the river. When he finished being sick he leaned weakly on the wall trying to recover, his face looking decidedly green, once he had stopped heaving he vowed that before the day was over he would surely separate Dick from his breath but by the time we got to Fowley village he had recovered and forgot all about his threat.

We set up the band in the usual formation on the road leading to the village. Adam Bailey asked Jim Tubbs if he had recovered and was ready to play? The reply was a wheezy gasp as Jim searched his pockets for a handkerchief.

"Come on Jim," Adam said. "We're all waiting for you. What's up?"

We all stood there in the snow waiting while Jim hurriedly searched his pockets, his face going crimson.

"Tha'll 'ave tu start bout me," he said. "I've lost me teeth."

We all looked in his direction in disbelief, but he wasn't lying, all we could see was the rubbery face of 'Gummy Jim.'

"You daft bugger," Adam shouted. "Did you have them when you came out this morning?"

"Course a bloody did," Jim replied. "A must a lost 'em when a were sick comin' down the lane just now."

"Well you'd best go back and find them you drunken sod," Adam said. "You're not much good this morning even with them in, but without them you're useless."

With a crestfallen look and his face ten shades of red Jim stalked off down the lane in search of the missing choppers, as he did so we had the distinct feeling that we would not see him for the rest of the day.

We could not march into the village as we usually did due to the snow being uneven on the ground so, we stood in a circle and played our first tune of the day. It was the same every New Year's Day morning, *Hail Smiling Morn*, and while the collectors were getting sorted out we gave a couple of verses of *Good King Wenceslas* so that they could get a bit in front. Then it was off another hundred yards and so on, until we got to the Cenotaph. Here we always stopped to play *Abide With Me*. Then away again towards the top of the village.

As we moved further up the village road it started to snow again. Not the large feathery flakes but the more sleety wet stuff. It did not take long for us to be soaked through. Stopping here and there for hot drinks was OK and for these we were very grateful but it did not stop us getting wet.

We carried on playing until we reached the top of the village and then started the return journey by the back route which would bring us out at The Golden Ball. Though the way back was done in quick time I felt that the last hundred yards was done at a gallop.

By now the sleet had turned into snow. We could barely see fifty yards in front of us. The wind was rising and it was obvious that the early morning snowfall was turning into a real blizzard which forced us to take shelter in the pub. We had been offered shelter in a number of places. One bloke offered us shelter in his garage but the offer was politely refused, I mean, how much ale would he have in his garage?

At last the shelter we had been patiently striving for all morning, The Golden Ball, came into sight and never had it looked so welcome. I had been there a couple of times before but this morning with the sleet and then snow getting us wet through I could not wait to get near to that roaring fire in the tap room.

We were just about to dash straight in when Adam shouted, "Hold on a minute you bloody lot. I don't care if your fingers are dropping off, we play outside first."

"Aye we do normally," Joe Sudders said. "But surely with the weather like it is shouldn't we better get inside."

Adam looked Joe up and down in disgust and then with a glare that would have stopped a charging elephant, he said, "The only thought on your bloody mind Joe Sudders, is boozing but, as Bill Jackson usually lays on good food and ale once we get inside, I think that the least thing we can do is what we always do on New Year's Day at this pub, and that's give him a tune before we clutter up his pub for the rest of the day so pucker up your lips and shut your silly gob, we play first and sup later."

That overlong statement left no more room for argument so we quickly gathered round Adam and with the snow now coming down in earnest we played *Hail Smiling Morn* followed by *See Amid The Winter Snow* the last hymn being very appropriate. Then at a nod from Adam we rushed into the pub for a well-earned rest.

After a quick de-frost we turned our attention to the shouts of greetings coming from mine hosts and the other occupants, our favourite one being: "What'll you have lads?"

It seemed that our playing outside the pub had not fallen on deaf ears as drinks started arriving from all sides, the first one being from the landlord, Bill Jackson, who brought in the tray of drinks himself. It took all of David Green's active watchfulness to stop the younger end of the band from getting too involved in the drinking spree that was obviously going to follow.

With devious dexterity I managed to collar a pint and had swigged about half of it down before feeling David's hand on my shoulder, "Come on you young sod-pot, put that bloody ale down before you make yourself sick. Get into the kitchen and get those wet clothes off. I'll not tell you again, lay off the ale."

With that he dragged us off to the kitchen where there was a big blazing fire surrounded by a large fire-guard. Also in the kitchen there was a clothes rack hanging from the ceiling and once we were divested of our wet clothing it was lowered and and our clothing laid on the wooden bars to dry. Being as there was quite a lot of wet clothes to dry some of the smaller things were hung on the fire-guard, but the hot fire dried them so quickly that we could not see for the steam rising from them and in next to no time they were dried and hung on a clothes-horse at the back of the room.

The sulks that we had on our faces at not being allowed to stay in the bar-room, were soon replaced with triumph as the food arrived. We were plied with hot soup and lots of bread followed with the usual mince pies. The only unfortunate part of it was that we were only drinking hot soup and oxo's while the older members were sat in the bar drinking hot toddies.

As we settled down in the warmth of the kitchen we realised that we had not been expected to turn out this morning, what with all the snow that had fallen, and of course with all the roads being blocked, but they had not reckoned with the redoubtable Burston Band. People round the village and in the bar had been heard to say what a brave set of lads they were, turning out in this terrible weather just to play for the folk of Fowley Village, and did we not lap it up?

The people of the village thought the world of the band and always gave us a great welcome whenever we played for them but they never suspected that the band would have gone twice as far and played twice as much, even if getting more soaked than they already were, rather than miss New Year's Day at The Golden Ball. It wasn't every day that so much free ale was flowing and who was going to miss that? It was a well known fact that the band that played at The Golden Ball on New Year's Day never payed for any ale.

Drinking was not the only thing though. Once the warmth had penetrated and the inner glow had been returned the band were once more ready to play. Now it did not matter what they wanted us to play, carols, hymns and quite a bit of busking, now was the time to relax. After a while the noise of the pub would rise and that was the time for us to play something rousing and if they could talk above that they were welcome, and the band lads did not mind, the more they played, the more they wanted to drink. Tom Bibby reckoned that it was the blowing that did it, that we actually blew away any drunken effects.

Now Ernie Benson, as well as being our solo cornet player, was a very good pub pianist. This did not mean that he could play *The Warsaw Concerto* or anything like that, though I suppose that he could have done so if he had known it off by heart. You see, Ernie could read brass band music but he was not conversant with piano music, which is very different. From a very early age Ernie had been able to play the piano without music and now all he had to do was to listen to a tune carefully and he could then play it off by heart, this made him very popular when it came to a sing-song.

In the meantime, I, being one of the youngest members of the band, had to stay in the back room out of the way. I hated this. I felt that I should be allowed to stay with the band all the time, instead of just being allowed in the bar when they were playing. Being in the back room had its compensations though, shandies and lots of food were sent in, the only thing that I had to do was to keep an eye on all the clothes left to dry in the kitchen.

As I sat in the kitchen my eyes alighted on the clothes-rack now pulled up against the ceiling. What a marvellous thing it was. It had two iron parts, not unlike coat hangers, with four square holes in each one. Into each of these holes were threaded four long poles which were about seven or eight feet in length, one iron piece at one end and one at the other end. Two pulleys were screwed into the ceiling and ropes were passed through these pulleys and attached to the two iron hangers. The ropes were threaded in such a way that the rack could be lowered at will to enable the clothes to be spread on them and then the rack would be pulled up to the ceiling where the warm air would dry them very quickly.

The clothes-horse on the other hand was a wooden frame of two or three pieces with three bars in each piece. Each part was joined together with either metal hinges or in some cases with pieces of strong cloth making each piece flexible. It was then stood on end so that the bars could be used to hang the cloths on and placed round the fire.

Being left on our own in the kitchen was not our idea of a good thing though. We liked being with the band and this was going to be remedied very soon or my name was not Joe Clayton. I had been listening to all the singing and merriment coming from the other room and I was not about to miss out on the best part of the day.

The singing was very good too. Occasionally I would hear and enjoy a very good singing voice, both male and female. Usually all the good singing came from our very good Amateur Dramatic Society, of which our small town was justly proud. Like most towns we had a theatre for films and a Mechanics' Institute where the amateurs practised and also held their shows. Amongst them, as you would expect, there were some very good singers and, come New Year's Day when they knew that the band finished up in The Golden Ball, they congregated there and what a pleasure it was to see and hear them. In between their singing from the shows there were one or two locals adding to the festivities with their own brand of entertainment with songs such as *Put Another Chair At the Table* and *My Old Man said Follow the Van*, the talent was endless.

As the beer and spirits moved them there would be singing quartets, duets and trios all trying to harmonise, sometimes getting it right but most times getting it wrong, as the alcohol took effect, much to the delight of the audience. There would be catcalls amidst the laughter as they stepped away from the piano, with a parting shot of anyone who could do better were welcome to try. Then it would start all over again.

All this we could hear from the kitchen. Eventually, getting fed up of being on our own, we ventured into the bar, trying to keep out of David Green's sight. David was the blight of our life. I feel sure that my father must have put the fear of God into him if he let us near the beer. One quick look round assured me that for the moment I was safe, as my eye alighted on the luckless David slumped head down on the table in front of him. It was obvious that he had partaken muchly of the dreaded hops and grape. He was not in any state to keep an eye on anyone.

I was mistaken if I thought that I was now free to do as I pleased. Hughie Mack decided to take me in hand as he pulled me down onto the bench beside him. The other youngsters were equally being looked after. If only I had known at the time I would probably have left the pub and most likely grown up to be an ordinary citizen but, I was young and inexperienced and my early drinking days took an ominous downwards trend.

Sitting by the side of Hughie did not help me one bit. Every now and then someone would put a gill glass of ale within easy reach and pretend not to notice when I quickly emptied it.

After a short while I began to relax. The soothing effects of the beer took over so that for one brain storming moment I thought that I would have to pay for a round of drinks. That would have been a catastrophe, I was broke. Luckily someone stopped the gesture just in time. The band did not pay for its own beer on New Year's Day, or any other day if it could he helped.

Suddenly the dreaded shout, "Time gentlemen please."

With that shout the landlord, Bill Jackson, a great character with everyone and a still greater favourite with the band mainly because it had been he that had instituted the rule that the band did not pay for its own ale on New Year's Day, started to collect the empty glasses. At the same time trying to get the customers to drink up and leave, as it was well past closing time. It took Bill about half an hour to get the last customer through the door which he then locked. The only people left in the pub being himself, his wife, the staff and the band who, if anyone was daft enough to ask were still drying out from the mornings playing.

The quiet of the now empty pub was broken by a wild shout, just like in the 'Tarzan' films as Bill appeared from behind the bar

d

dressed only in a Leopard skin. I do not know how he did it because Bill was a large man, certainly no chicken, but Bill had seemed to vault over the bar. He must have had a stool on the other side. You have to imagine the size of the man, very large with most of his weight centred around his middle. I mean he had not seen his feet for years.

From then on it was just mad-cap fun. Bill doing his cavorting up and down in his leopard skin, grabbing everyone he could in his mad dance. All of us that where left, the band and the bar staff, trying to get out of his way. The noise was tremendous. It is a wonder that the police were not called in. The funny thing is that according to Tom Perkins, all the time that he had been going to The Golden Ball and no matter how much noise there had been, not a sign of the police had there ever been seen.

After about twenty minutes or so Bill showed signs of slowing down, probably because the smile that had been on his wife's face at the beginning was now beginning to look decidedly sour, especially after seeing Bill grab one of the barmaids in the wrong place. I fancy that afterwards, when she got Bill alone she just might grab Bill in one or two awkward places and could even put the squeeze on him.

Nevertheless they were both great sports and when the hilarity had died down a little and Bill had changed back into his normal clothes, he appeared from behind the bar with two gallon jugs of ale. He plonked them down on the table in front of us and said, "Get stuck into them, lads, you've earned it."

With that he once more returned behind the bar under the watchful eye of his wife May. (Peace on earth, good will to all men.)

After all the cavorting and fun that we had just had, we must have been in a daze because it must have been a full two seconds before Bert Rawlins grabbed the jug and did the honours, filling up his own glass first, he filled every glass in sight, and without his realising it, mine as well. Within a very short space of time both jugs were empty. No one could say that our lads were backward at coming forwards. Seconds later they were both filled and back on the table.

I suppose that it was with a little regret that Ernie decided that we had better get back to singing before we drank ourselves silly so, planting himself at the piano he blasted out a few old tunes and off we went again. In the meantime Bill and his staff started clearing everything away ready for the evening opening time, pausing now and then to add to a chorus or two. They would have to be quick because it was nearly that time now.

It was about this time that it dawned on Dan Parker, one of our front row cornets, that I was still in the pub. Not only that, but that I was getting a bit tiddly. He said, "David, I thought that you were supposed to be keeping an eye on the lad?"

The only reply he received was a very incoherent mumble and then bump as David slid unceremoniously under the table.

"Oh hell," Dan said. "Joe's dad'll have us guts fer garters if he sees him in this state, come on let's get him into the kitchen an' get him sobered up."

I sat there smiling to myself. By now the room was beginning to move round a little bit. Dan, who was standing in front of me seemed to be leaning to one side, the daft devil. Then other things seemed to take over as a volcano started to rumble in my stomach. There seemed to be certain places that I needed to be and one of them was the toilet.

I stood up and the room started to alter shape again. I could see the door quite clearly but as I started to walk towards it, it moved and my legs just would not go in that direction. It was as if they had a mind of their own. I knew that I was making for the door but it kept moving and I finished up doing a sort of crab walk until my legs went funny and I finished up sat on the floor. What was happening to me? My legs felt like jelly and, no matter how I tried, I could not make them obey me.

While I was having this most traumatic experience, never having been drunk before, the rest of the band were rolling with laughter. They could not help it. They were three parts cut themselves. Then Dan took pity on me and came over. He grabbed me under the armpits and lugged me to my feet. He put one of my arms over his shoulder and dragged me out to the toilets.

"Come on lad, we've let thee get sozzled so, we'd better get thee sorted out."

He'd no sooner opened the back door than the fresh air hit me like a sledge-hammer, but Dan had taken a firm hold of me and we made it safely to the little room out the back.

I don't think that I should relate just what happened when I got to the toilet, but I do remember loosing all that lovely ale.

I'm glad that Dan was there because the toilet was one of those toilets we called a 'long drop', which meant that although it was normal in shape with a wooden seat, the inside of the toilet went straight down into a sewer pipe and, if Dan had not been there to hold on to me I would have been head down and up to my ears in sewage, even if it was about ten feet below me. The thought does not bear thinking about, I certainly would not have smelled of roses for a long time. It gives me a shiver every time I think about it.

Anyway I must have passed out, because the next thing I remember was sitting in the pub kitchen and having coffee poured down my gullet, no milk, no sugar just black coffee.

It seems that the landlady, who was a lovely woman, had not thought about me being so young, I was a big lad for my age so, she decided that I had to be brought back to the land of the living and, with the aid of an old remedy, she took me in hand. (I did not know this about this until some time afterwards.) What a remedy! If I had known what was coming I would have sobered up on the spot. Two raw eggs in vinegar, beaten up and then poured into a glass then, with Bill holding my arms and Dan holding my nose the whole concoction was emptied down my throat.

Once again I found myself back in the toilets emptying my stomach then back in the kitchen for more of the same until they were sure that there was nothing else left to bring up, only then was I allowed to sip the next cup of coffee quietly. One thing was for sure, it was not going to happen again and I told them all so. When I eventually got back into the bar Bill and May smiled at me knowingly over the pumps as Dan steered me groggily out of the pub and headed towards home.

The evening walk home was normally straight forward but tonight the road seemed fraught with things that were hell bent on tripping me up, but the long walk and the cold night air sobered me up very quickly and as I got nearer home I found myself much more in control. I vowed again and again to myself that there would never be a recurrence of today's happenings. I would never again get so drunk that I could not control myself and at the time I am sure that I meant it.

My dad was not as daft as I thought either. As soon as I walked into the house he must have known. He shoved a couple of butties in my hand and ushered me straight upstairs with a warning that he would deal with me later, but at that moment I could not have cared less and when I eventually woke up in the morning I was undressed in bed and still clutching the two butties from the night before. I do not know whether my dad forgot or not but he never mentioned it again and nor did I. I thought that I had been punished enough before leaving The Golden Ball, who would have thought that two such nice people as Bill and May could have thought up such an awful sobering remedy. Anyway enough was enough, at least until the next time.

8

Contesting

Now that Christmas playing was over, we once more settled down to normal practice nights. When I say normal I mean that there would only be three or four players missing at practice. This state of affairs could not carry on. Adam had told us that as soon as Christmas playing was over he would be entering us for our first post-war contest. Only the local ones to start with, but before he could do that he had to find out how many he could expect at rehearsals? If most of the band could not be there it would be pointless in entering any contest.

In the past we had tried a number of old contest pieces. When Adam had come to the band-room for his audition for band conductor, he had tried the band out on a piece of music called *Lorenzo*, a piece of music used as a test piece at Belle Vue before the war. Needless to say we had not played it very well, *Lorenzo* was a hard test for any band let alone for a band of our doubtful ability. But at least it had shown Adam all our strengths and weaknesses.

At the next rehearsal, which was on Sunday next, Adam produced his bombshell. He had spoken with the band committee and they had agreed with him, we were to enter a contest at Rempton; about four miles away. The contest was to be held at Rempton Town Hall in seven weeks time. We had been entered in the lowest section which was for third and forth section bands.

These local contests were open to any band in the north-west really but what with petrol rationing and cash being in short supply we tended to keep as near home as possible, on top of which the prizes were nothing to write home about, usually a silver cup and a tenner in cash, so it was only bands who had only a short way to travel who entered, and who could afford to lash out on a charabanc just to take them to and from contests. It was not cut and dried yet but if we did go we would be hard put to to afford a charabanc which could cost as much as ten quid and that was ten quid too much.

Finding the correct piece of music was going to be the hardest thing for us. It had to be a piece that we could play confidently and well and it also had to be well within our capabilities. One good thing was that it was an 'own choice' contest. This means that we could choose our own music. If our choice was too easy we would get slated and if it was too hard we would get slated again so Adam had to make the choice very carefully.

Sunday morning arrived and we sat in the band-room wondering and waiting for Adam to break the bad news. Would it be the dreaded *Lorenzo*? Adam had frightened us to death with that music when he had first put it up on the stands. One or two of the older members had a small wager on what it would be and we listened to their studied thoughts. Would it be one of the old favourites from before the war? *William Tell* perhaps or it could be *Lohengrin* but, because it was written by the German composer Wagner and the time being so early after the Second World War, that was quickly discarded. Tom Perkins turned to Jim Hogan in the bass section and said, with a mischievous grin, " 'appen it'll be *Life Divine*? That'll put the cat among the pigeons. They'll spit feathers."

They laughed together at their secret joke. We younger lads had only heard tell of this musical masterpiece. I once heard two bandsmen talking about *Life Divine*. They agreed that there had only been one band that played *Life Divine* near perfect and that had been the great Saint Hilda's Colliery Band from South Shields, World champions five times before the war. I decided to ask my father about it, he would know, he had been there.

We sighed with relief when we were told it would not be *Life Divine* and it was not what some wag suggested, *Labour and Love*. No other band could ever have had the wonderful remarks from the composer and attributed to the great Irwell Springs Bacup Band after they had won the trophy at Crystal Palace in

1913. Speaking of the playing of the piece when played by 'Springs' he, (Percy Flecher, the adjudicator) said . . . "They were solid, heroic, with a big organ tone, wonderful attack and release: An inspiring and arresting performance with which I was delighted in every way." Can you imagine the pleasure in receiving remarks like that from any contest? And from the composer's own mouth. It must have been one of the greatest moments of any of those bandsmen. I wondered, would anything like that ever happen to me during my banding life?

Once, after I had walked over half a mile to the Radio Relay shop in town to collect our accumulator (a rechargeable wet cell battery, used to power our radio at home. When it ran low, as it often did, I had to take it to the shop to get it recharged), I had been allowed to listen to a concert broadcast on the radio by one of the great brass bands of the day and I had heard them play *The William Tell Overture*; it had stirred me deeply and I never forgot it, so my bet was on *William Tell*.

Adam came slowly into the centre of the room. I am sure that he was stringing it out just to get us going.

"Here you are lads," he said. "Pass them round."

There it was in black and white. I looked at the title, I had never heard of it before *A Souvenir of the Opera*. What a let down. We had all been sat here thinking about all the famous names and pieces of music which were bywords in the brass band contesting world and here we were with a piece of music that even Tom Perkins had not heard of and he was old.

Still Adam was not daft. This we came to realise. What was the point of putting something up that we could not play. We did not even know if we could play this yet. It looked OK. We just had to wait and see - perhaps there was more to this piece than we knew. We had been deceived before by innocent looking music.

Well, we played the piece through just to get the feel of it. It had a good lilt to it and it did not seem too difficult. Then Adam really got down to it. He had given us time to look, we had run through it once and now it was time to start the real practising. Taking the music bit by bit, he made us grope through it and by the end of the night Ernie Benson said that his lip was hanging down like a sow's tit. He decided that soaking it in beer would do the trick. I do not know whether it did or not but by closing time he had stopped complaining.

Things were about to change in the band. For one thing Adam had decided that the only way we were going to play this piece of music was by taking a section of the band and rehearsing the individual parts with them.

The first section was of course the cornets, so the next evening, which was Monday, the cornets turned up at seven o'clock as had been arranged and didn't he give them some stick? By nine o'clock they could hardly play a middle 'C'. It was about this time that everyone realised that Adam was serious.

Like most conductors, when he decided to get the band into shape he turned into a monster. Gone was the nice guy and in his place was a shouting, sarcastic, venomous creature, the like of which we certainly weren't used to. That night I think that I came of age. I learned words I had never heard of before, not even at throwing out times on Saturday night. He did not know when to stop either, until someone suggested that he might be reported to the watch committee for practising late at night. Every night he was there at the band-room with one or more sections. I have to admit, he worked damned hard and by the end of two weeks sectional rehearsals, things did seem to be sounding better.

On the next Sunday morning Adam decided that it might help if we heard all the sections playing together, not that he thought we were good enough, just that it would possibly give us a better idea of how our parts fitted together. I looked forward to this as I am sure that the others did and when Sunday morning came we all sat down quietly while Adam gave us all a pep talk. After that we once more got stuck into the *Souvenir*.

What a difference it made. It still needed a lot of work but now we could feel that at least we could get through it in a reasonable style.

Adam was disappointed. He growled at us, swore and threatened us, but it was no use, he still didn't like the results of the practice. I think that at this point he was ready to kill but, after a bout of jumping up and down, of cursing and throwing things at various people he just glared at us in exasperation and moved on to a different piece of music altogether. That did the trick. We relaxed and when he eventually returned to the *Souvenir* again he seemed in a better frame of mind. We did seem to play it better and at least he had stopped throwing things at us. In the weeks that followed he said that he was reasonably satisfied with the progress that we had made. It was just up to us. Home practice was the thing, but when we played together as a band it was still up to Adam to knit us together as a team. By the time we arrived at the contest we would be able to play *A Souvenir of the Opera* in our sleep. Even now the difference was terrific. You would not recognise it as the piece of music that we had tried to play just a few short weeks ago.

Now Adam really got the bit between his teeth. Crescendos, diminuendos, slowly, quicker, waken up, watch the stick. God would it never end? One minute well done and the next minute he was going red in the face with frustration. When would he be satisfied? The answer to that question was never and it did not take me many years to realise that this was an unhappy trait that many conductors suffered from. At last Friday night arrived. The final rehearsal. If we could not play it now, we never would.

Tonight was different. Just before the start of the rehearsal there was a knock on the door of the band-room. David Green answered it. There were seven or eight people standing in the doorway asking if they could come in and listen to the band having the final rehearsal before the contest. What a turn-up for the book, none of our public had ever shown any interest in the band's rehearsal before, well, not while I had been in the band anyway. The general opinion of the public seemed to be that we were just another 'ale and baccy' band. I suppose they were right really, and it was going to be a long time before that opinion changed. I wonder who would be blamed for that?

David invited them in and seats were found for them at the back of the band-room. A buzz went round the room as the visitors sat down. Here was some of our public who actually wanted to listen to us, even though they had heard us play before. They must be the local masochist club doing penance. What other reason could there be? It was obvious that things were now different, that someone other than band personnel were interested in our contest performance. It made a difference. The band sat up straight and seemed more attentive than at any other rehearsal.

The rehearsal went well and the band played the piece a lot better than at any other of the previous rehearsals. That did not stop Adam from stopping the band and going over a part that had not been played just as he thought it should have been played.

Saturday was a day off from rehearsing. But Sunday was

different. We had to be at the band-room at nine o'clock sharp for the final touches, not much, just a last minute blow, like a hymn tune to start with and then when we were well and truly warmed up, the final tuning of the band.

David Green was not there so we had to hope that his cornet was correctly tuned. Being the secretary of the band gave him the duty of being at Rempton Town Hall to see that everything was organised and to attend the draw.

At the Town Hall, where the bands were to play, the adjudicator, who was to judge the contest, had to be shown into a large box or small room adjacent to the contest stage. Once there he was not allowed to leave until the contest was over. It was not especially comfortable but he was not there for comfort and it could be awkward when he wanted to use the toilet. A pot was provided, so what more could he want? Anyway it served him right. Adjudicators were as popular as referees, football or otherwise, and were usually just as wrong, especially if we were not in the first three.

This was the best way they could think of to stop any hanky panky like cheating. The idea was that if he could not see the band he could not be accused of favouring one band over another, or so the principle goes. There are more ways of skinning a cat! After he had been shown into the box, a steward was placed at the door, to guard against any intrusion and to take in any food or drinks. I wonder who would be watching the steward?

After the enclosure of the adjudicator into the box the draw was taken. All the names of the competing bands in each section were listed in a programme and each secretary would go and draw his own number from a bag, so it would be band number one would play whichever number the secretary drew out of the bag. In this way the adjudicator was not supposed to know which band was on stage at that particular time, (unless someone told him!) No band knew before the draw what number they would be playing. This was to be the way contests were run for quite a number of years.

When we got to Rempton David was waiting for us, he told us that we had been drawn number five. This gave us about an hour after the contest had started before we were due on stage. As we were in good time it gave us about an hour to do with as we wished.

We could go into the main hall and listen to the other bands playing or we could go and have a look around the various music stands set up in the entrance hall where there were sets of new and old music for sale. If we were lucky we could even go outside and perhaps find a publican who could be persuaded to open up and give us a wee dram. As there was not much time to get involved in a drinking session we decided to have a look round the music stands.

When we arrived in the entrance we found that an instrument stand had been set up as well. The instruments had been provided by a large music shop just outside Rempton. They were all brass band instruments and accessories, mouthpieces, valve oil, etc. Valve oil was new to me. I had always relied on saliva for my valves when they needed lubrication. Well, maybe it would catch on, but I doubt it, who was going to pay good money for valve oil when a mouthful of spit was free.

The salesman of the instruments had been very brave placing the instruments in that very prominent position, with not even a sign of a dent in any of them. They were beautiful with the light glinting off the highly polished surfaces. Some instruments were plated silver and some brass, depending on how much you could afford. Either way they looked great. They were the first new instruments I had ever seen never mind being near enough to touch.

The salesman stood there watching us very warily. One wrong move against the table and all his carefully placed instruments could come crashing down onto the floor.

Dan Parker, one of our front row cornet players, asked if he could try one of the cornets out. The salesman looked at Dan for a moment, trying to weigh him up I suppose, and then hesitatingly lifted a cornet down and handed it to Dan who, after examining it, produced his own mouthpiece and inserting it in the cornet and put it to his lips. This was going to be good. We did not think that Dan was that good a cornet player, but then we had only known him a short while. He had only been with the band for a few months.

Dan blew into the cornet, just to warm it up he said. Then he played a chromatic scale, which made more than one or two people stop and stare. As I said before, we stood well back and waited, until we had heard a bit more we were uncertain whether to be known associates of Dan. He sounded like he knew what he was doing but then, I suppose, that was the idea. We did wonder if he was just showing off, then he shook us all, even the ones who thought that they knew him. He started to play an old cornet solo called *Silver Threads Amongst The Gold*. This, as well as being an old solo, was also a well known song. After he had played the tune he carried on and played the variations. I had heard the song before but never played on the cornet.

As his fingers caressed the valves with an expertise we had not known he possessed, we listened as this beautiful tune rang round the entrance hall. Somewhere in between some of the people gathered round, started to sing, stopping only when Dan moved on to the variations. When he eventually finished playing and lowered the cornet from his lips the crowd gave him a good clap. Dan gave them a wave and handed back the cornet to the open mouthed salesman with a comment, "It's a bit flat on't third valve, but not bad." With that he turned and walked away, the rest of us following close behind.

The conclusion was that after that demonstration it was firmly agreed Dan, after all, should be one of us. Some people, who had just heard Dan play, asked the salesman who Dan was. Did he play with a famous band? We moved closer to him. If they thought that Dan was someone famous we were not going to miss this chance There might be a drink in it!

When we had removed ourselves from the entrance hall we asked Dan why he had kept a low profile when he could play like that? He just grinned and said nothing but after a little friendly persuasion, he told us that it was the only tune that he could play with all the variations, even though it was not the musically written version. He had learned to play it in the army, just the basic tune that is and the rest he had added when practising at home.

Needless to say, we were very chuffed with Dan. He had carried it off like a professional. We realised that there was more to him than met the eye. Perhaps we would find out more when we had played our contest piece and Dan had a few pints inside him.

We returned to the main hall because it was getting near to the time for us to go on stage. The rest of the band had gathered outside the main hall, near enough to the time that Adam had stated earlier on. We had about twenty minutes before we were due to play but before that we had to sign in.

Signing in is one of those things that came about because in the earlier days of contesting a good soloist could earn himself a great deal of money by playing all the solos in the contest piece, for different bands. If there were any difficult solos or cadenzas in a contest piece a top soloist would be engaged to play just these parts.

In a big contest, say for instance the great Crystal Palace contest in London this happened quite a lot. A top soloist would go on and play with one band, playing only the solos and cadenzas and then as the band came off stage he would wait for the next band that had hired him and go on and play for them.

During the nineteen twenties it was decided by the governing body of the brass band movement that this was an unfair practice. Then a rule was brought in that all players had to be registered with one band only.

This was done by registering all the bandsmen in their own bands, by putting all the names of the bandsmen who were playing at the contest on a register and getting the bandsmen to sign their name opposite. When the band registered at the contest, prior to going on stage, the bandsmen had to sign again opposite their own name and their signature checked with the one done in the band-room. Only then, when every signature was passed as correct, was the band allowed onto the contest stage.

This is where we came in. There were stewards on duty to direct us to the signing-on room in which three people were designated by the contest organisers. One had to check that you were the person indicated on your personnel card. The next one had the register where you had to sign opposite your own signature, this was then checked with your card and the signature on it and the third person there had to see that no fiddling went on. (They never did say who was watching him!)

It sounds more complicated that it really is. You just file past, give your card in to be stamped, sign the register and wait while the signature on your card is checked with both your signatures on the register and when told OK you were ready to go on stage.

On each door that you have to pass through to go on stage a steward stands guard to make sure that you do not go before your turn and also that no one has any contact with the band before they go on to play. If, unfortunately, a signature does not match, the player concerned would not be allowed to pass and also, depending on the circumstances, the band could be disqualified. Fancy, all those weeks of practice and then to get disqualified before even getting a chance to play. To most bands it just was not worth it, but still some bands did try.

To return to the contest, here we were standing at the door waiting to go in to sign when Brian Dale, our repiano cornet player said, "Hang on, where's Joe Sudders? We can't go on bowt him." Joe Sudders being our second euphonium player. Adam tried to appear calm and sent three of the band to look for him with instructions to return in the next five minutes whether they found him or not. Some of the band were getting extremely edgy. Our first contest since before the war and our second euphonium player missing. Where the hell had he got to? Now we were all beginning to get worried. The time was short and nerves were starting to show and that was the last thing we needed. Suddenly one of the lads rushed up to Adam.

"It's all right we've found him. He's on his way now."

Adam's face lost that tense look, but as Joe came towards him I thought that for a second he would clobber him. Instead he turned away and said, "Right lads, in you go and get signed on. We'll sort this out later." He stood to one side as we all trooped past him, but by the look on his face I decided that I would not like to be in Joe's shoes after the contest. We were all accounted for now but Joe's excuse had better be a good one when he had to explain to Adam why he was late.

It was a great thrill for me to be signing on the dotted line in my first contest. I hoped it would not be the last time. No one had asked for my autograph before, not for anything.

We seemed to sit in that room for ages before the door was opened and the steward poked his head round the corner and said, "Reight, come on tha con go now." Then turning round said, "Foller me."

This was it. We followed him down a corridor which led to the bottom of some stairs.

"Go up the stairs and through that door and tha'll be on the stage."

I walked onto the stage conscious of every eye in the crowded hall being on me. The butterflies in my stomach were trying to escape. Oh God is it always like this? I could play my part of the piece OK, my dad had seen to that. I gaped at the audience like a country bumkin. I was so nervous that I could have walked straight across the stage and off the other side if it had not been for Bert Rawlins grabbing my arm.

"Are tha all reight lad?" he said, pushing me forward.

"Just a bit queasy Bert."

"Dern't thee worry abeat that lad," he said. "That's good, we all feel a bit like that, it puts an edge on thee an' maks thee concentrate more. Once we start tu play tha'll be al'reight, tha'll see."

With that he pushed me onto the stage where the rest of the band were getting settled in their seats. I walked round to my seat with a feeling of trepidation, now everyone seemed to be watching me. Perhaps if I sat down it would be better. I sat down quickly, my father's words coming back to me.

"Remember lad, when you get on stage you'll be nervous. Don't let that bother you, just sit down and set your music straight, don't look at the audience, keep your eye on the conductor and warm your instrument up ready to play."

Well, I tried. My instrument was so warm it could have set on fire, or so I thought. I fixed my eyes on Adam as he helped the band to settle down. He glanced round and saw me looking at him. He smiled but it was only his mouth that smiled as his gaze shifted from one player to another. At last he seemed to be satisfied with everything and his face relaxed just a little.

Seconds later the whistle sounded from the adjudicator's box. Adam raised his baton. I thought for a second that I was going to miss the beat and then we were off.

I do not remember much about the performance I was too busy watching my music and Adam's beat. Suddenly it was over as Adam finished off with a flourish. There was total silence. I thought for a moment that they had all gone home but after what seemed an age the clapping started. Then the cheering. Adam waited for a moment and then turned round and bowed low to the audience, then turning round to us again he motioned the band to their feet, turned, bowed to the audience once again and left the stage as if he owned it. We followed with the sounds of clapping still ringing in our ears.

When we got back to the changing room the questions started. "How d'you think we did? Did it sound all right? Who was the daft sod who fluffed that opening note? Who came in early at 'C'?" The questions went from one to the other. Adam coughed. It was clear to see from the look on his face that he was not all that pleased, but he just told us to be back in the hall in time for the results at the end of the contest.

Well, the playing was over so what were we going to do for the rest of the day? We found the answer to that when we got outside a few minutes later. We decided that it would be better if we kept together but as some wanted to stay and listen to the rest of the bands and the others wanted to go and find a pub open, we agreed to meet back at the hall in about three hours.

Those of us left decided to try to find a pub or club where we might get a drink, preferably a club where the drinks would be cheaper. It would not be long before they were officially open and we had to find a watering hole before then. Pubs and clubs tended to get very crowded around a brass contest. With this in mind we turned to Tom Perkins. When it came to finding a pub or club open during closing hours, he was the king.

Tom Perkins was one of those people who you come across just once in a lifetime. His uncanny sense of smell had been the basis of many discussions around Burston. The feeling was that somewhere in his distant ancestry there must have been traces of a bloodhound. There were many suggestions about Tom's distant ancestry, most of them from pub landlords and all of them unprintable, but never in Tom's presence.

Tom had said that he did not know the district very well but he would give it a try. It was unlikely that we would find a club open yet but we might find a pub that would let us in the back door. Tom was the boss so we stood back to give him room.

He stood in the middle of the road sniffing the air, that is when I became convinced about the bloodhound bit, then after a couple of minutes he turned and set off down the road. After walking about fifty yards he sniffed the air once again and turned down a narrow street. We had no idea where he was going but, trusting in Tom's nose, we followed him. Every now and then he stopped to sniff the air again. It was around this time that we thought that he was having us on but we decided to trust him a bit longer, he had not let us down yet. We followed him further down a side street, round one corner and then another till suddenly he stopped.

"This is it," he said.

What was he talking about? We were in an alley with tall backyard gates every so often and we could not see over the top of them.

"We're here I tell you, I can smell it, move out'a me way. Let the dog see the rabbit." He gave one more sniff and then pushed a backyard gate open. We gaped at him for a moment but there was no doubt about it, he had done it again. There were beer barrels stood in the yard and that back door did not look very secure.

"There y'are," he said triumphantly. "What did I tell you, follow me."

With that he walked straight up to the back door and pushed it open. It was like stepping straight into a den of iniquity. (I'd heard my mother say that once when she'd caught my father playing cards late one night in his local, when he should have been home with his wage.) I'd looked it up in a dictionary, 'a particular thing that is evil', it said. It certainly seemed to fit the description of the place we had just entered.

The air was thick with smoke even at this early hour and most of the tables were filled with glasses of beer belonging to bandsmen in various uniforms who were playing cards or dominoes. We could hardly get to the bar and no one challenged our right to be in here. The place was heaving with bodies, most of them trying to find a seat. We did not care, the first priority for us was ale.

It was only half past eleven in the morning and although the pubs were not supposed to be open yet our champion beer sniffer had done it again. Here we were in what we now knew to be the Black Dog, with pints of ale in our hands. What more could we ask for? The answer was nothing better, but we did start to wonder. Had Tom really found this pub with his great sense of smell? The answer came a minute later when we heard Tom greet the landlord.

"Hello Fred, when I 'eard we were comin' to Rempton I knew tha'd be open."

Fred laughed, "Aye an I knew tha'd be showin' up when tha found all't rest o't pubs shut. Tha drunken 'owd bugger. 'Ow are tha keeping?"

We left them trading insults as only long time friends can do and looked around for any available seats. Unfortunately there were too many of us to find enough seats in one place, so we sat down anywhere we could. There were six of us who had come into the pub to start with but, as the day went on we were to see a few more of our band arrive.

I enjoyed myself for the rest of our time in the pub, especially since David Green was absent and not there watching everything I drank. But I had not forgotten New Year's Eve yet so, although there did not seem to be anyone in particular keeping an eye on me, I watched what I was drinking.

Instead the lads decided that it was high time that I was introduced into the dubious art of cards and dominoes. By this time we had managed to get a table to ourselves in a corner of the tap-room. Here beginneth the first lesson!

We started off playing dominoes. Tom Perkins playing as partner to Bert Rawlins and me playing with Ernie Benson. It was a massacre as was the next game. It was not until much later that I noticed that Bert had developed a twitch in one eye. Tom had a slight catch in his throat. Of course by the time me and Ernie had caught on we had been thrashed over and over again, much to the delight of Bert and Tom.

It was Hughie Mack who eventually put me straight as to what was going on. The winks and the clearing of the throat from Bert and Tom were all part of the strategy. We played them once again, warning them both that wink, nods and coughs were not part of the game. It made no difference. We still lost. I swear I had never seen two men develop so many mannerisms in so short a time. It did not matter that we stopped them doing or saying anything new, they still had a fund of other signals that they were able to make to one another. I suppose it was understandable, they had been playing together for donkey's years.

We went on to play a game of dominoes called 'five and threes'. This game was so called because as you laid your dominoes, to score you had to be able to divide your total, both ends, by either five or three exactly. For instance, if there was a double five at one end and a single five at the other end you would score as follows, three into fifteen goes five times and five into fifteen goes three times so, three plus five equals eight which is the score.

This score was marked on a special board by one player from each side, using matches for markers. The play first was slow, but as we learned more about the game so we quickened up.

As you can imagine, a great deal depended on the dominoes you picked up. As they were picked up face down and you would not know the dominoes you picked up until you turned them over. It was pot luck. Or so we thought. After we had been playing for a while we realised that luck did not enter into it, as far as Tom and Bert were concerned.

The thing to watch with care was not just the dominoes, but what the marker was putting onto the scoreboard. On a marker board there are four lines of holes drilled into the board, thirty holes per line making a total of sixty holes for each team. As it was explained to me later on that day, when we had been beaten for the umpteenth time, a good marker is better than a good player.

What would happen was this. One player would lay his dominoes down when his turn came and call out the score, his opponents, (us), would check to make sure that he was not claiming more that he should and the other player would mark his score on the board. If not watched carefully, while we were checking the score on the dominoes the marker would gain a few holes on the board.

One time when I was watching Bert play, I decided not to watch the dominoes being laid down on the table, instead I kept my eye on Bert marking the board. Money was on the game so Bert was making sure that he would not be on the losing side. The score was called out and Bert, instead of moving his marker down the board and marking the three points that had been called out, moved his marker across the board into the adjacent line of marker holes and so gained about thirty points in one foul swoop.

The moves were done so smoothly and quickly that no one noticed. Had anyone noticed he would have been in trouble but as he was playing with friends it would just have caused a big shout. The arguing would have started but after trading insults Bert would have said he had done it on purpose to see if they were watching. There would be threats of breaking off his arm and beating him about the head with it, but none of the threats came to anything, mainly because they would all have been cheating and they knew it, they were just annoyed at being caught out.

The same thing would happen at cards. The funny thing being that if there were any newcomers in the pub where we happened to be then everyone stuck together, and as Bert put it, "If there's any fiddling to be done, mak' sure it's on thy side."

My education continued on into the afternoon. The drink seeming not to have any effect on me. I had got one pint when I first came into the Black Dog and I had kept on drinking steadily since then. Although I did not know it at the time, Tom had arranged with his friend the landlord that after the first pint, I was to have only shandies, and weak at that. Being as I was such an experienced drinker I did not even notice. So, even without David Green, they were still keeping an eagle eye on me.

Why this was I could not begin to think, they should mind their own damn business. I was in my teens now and quite tall for my age. I could sort myself out. I decided that an odd pint now and then would do me no harm. Thinking that I was one of the lads made me feel good but I could not keep away from their prying eyes.

It was Ernie Benson who first noticed the time. "Hey lads, have you seen the clock? We said that we would be back by four o'clock. The results should be coming in about now."

Tom looked up at the clock on the wall.

"T'lad's reight," he said. "But yuh know them buggers in t' box, they've tuh 'ave their scoff and tea afore they con mak their mind up oo's won, an yuh know 'ow power mad they are, even in a bitty contest like this'n, they 'ave tuh mak thee wait, even if they'd a been ready straight after 't last band'd played."

There were knowing nods from the rest of the bandsmen in the room. It was a well know fact amongst bandsmen that the long wait after the last band had played was totally unnecessary. The adjudicators had plenty of time without making you all wait. Even then they strolled leisurely onto the stage as if they had all day. It just was not fair. They had been sat in that box in their easy chairs all day, waited on hand and foot. Food taken at regular intervals and with all the mod cons. I would be most surprised if they were able to walk out of that box with all the food and drink they must have guzzled. I would not mind betting that they would come out kettled.

We finished off our ale. Well, we could not be seen leaving any could we? Then we set off for the Town Hall. When we got there we learned that the results were not in yet, Bert had been right all along. The contest had finished and they were just waiting for the adjudicator, who was said to be sorting out his notes. We knew that they would let us know when the adjudicator left his box.

The waiting was awful as all the waffling went on before the actual results were given out. The stage was full of officials and of course the man who would be presenting the prizes, usually the Mayor.

We did not hear the announcement because of the noise in the hall, we just heard a cheer and the ribald shouts from the crowd.

"As tey bin 'avin' a kip in theer?"

"No," comes a reply. "He's bin finishing off all that scoff an ale they've bin takin' in all day, carn't leave the evidence con they?"

The same sort of banter followed him all the way to the stage. The man smiled and said nothing, it was all 'grist tut mill' to him, he had heard it all before. Anyway it was all good natured fun and said with a laugh. Anything to fill in the time before the results were announced. There were three prizes for all the bands to play for so some bands were going to be disappointed. I hoped it would not be us.

This is where the waffling started. First there was the contest secretary giving his speech of welcome to the dignitaries on stage. Then the Mayor said a few words. Would he never stop? After the Mayor the adjudicator gave his comments on the playing etc.

The crowd were getting restless. You could feel the tension. They could not be blamed, everyone had tried to get back into the Hall for the results and were blocking all the passageways leading to the stage and making the people who had stayed through the contest angry at having their view of the stage blocked. It was like trying to get a pint into a gill glass.

"Get on we it." A shout from the now impatient audience. "Cut thy prattling an' gis't results."

Cries of agreement followed. I was sure that there was going to be a riot. But no, the contest committee took the hint with a statement that the results would be given out in reverse order.

Third. No, that was not our number, but it would have done. Second. No, we were not mentioned for that prize.

"Come-on," I muttered under my breath, surely this must be it. The suspense was killing me. We had played well enough, could it be that we had got first prize? What a triumph that would be, winning the first contest that we had entered since the war. We were to be disappointed. The first prize was announced and it went to a band called Bexhill Colliery from Yorkshire. We had heard them play just before going to the Black Dog and they were nowhere near as good as us. It must have been a fiddle. Surely there must have been some mistake. It was no use, we just had to accept it, a damn Yorkshire band had up and licked us and on our own midden too. Well, that was it, we had played well and got nothing so, amid cheers from the winning band's supporters and catcalls from the rest, we left the hall.

"Who the bloody 'ell were th' adjudicator an' what the 'ell did he know abeat soddin' music?"

It came to me then, that this was to be the usual format at most contests. There had to be winners and there had to be losers and we certainly were not winners, at least not this time.

This was a catastrophe. Where had we gone wrong? Ernie had played those solos with such passion. It would have brought tears to the eyes of a statue, and Jimmy Belfor's euphonium playing had been magic.

What was that adjudicator's name? Was he like all those other judges and referees, deaf, blind and dumb? Could he not tell a good band when he heard one? Fancy, picking a Yorkshire band over a Lancashire one. Everyone knew that the best bands came from the red rose county.

Walking back to the charabanc, Adam kept telling us not to worry because there would be other contests and we would just have to try harder next time. When he had got the adjudicator's remarks he would see just where we had gone wrong; David Green had gone to get them.

As we waited at the charabanc for David, Adam said that we had played very well but he felt that there was room for improvement. He was pleased with some of the playing and disappointed in others who he knew could play better. He seemed to be looking straight at me when he said that. Just then David arrived with the adjudicator's remarks.

We watched Adam closely. It was evident that even though he had said that we had played well, he was not pleased, surely it could not be all that bad? I began to wonder what that so-called judge had written? We were about to find out.

"It looks like we finished fifth, according to the points," he said. "We were only six points behind the winner. Not bad for the first contest but we'll have to do better than this if we are going to win anything. There's some good bands in this section and they'll all be trying to move up a notch or two."

With that he handed the remarks to David with a wry smile.

"Don't get downhearted, it's the first contest with me and now we know why we didn't win today we can do something about it and try not to make the same mistakes next time. This is only one adjudicator's opinion but his remarks could help us. The next adjudicator could give an entirely different opinion. Either way we've a lot of work to put in before the next contest. We'll get better, you'll see, or my name's not Adam Bailey."

He let his words sink in and then said, "Let's make sure that we've learned from our mistakes. When I've had a word with the committee, we'll see about doing some more local contests just to get you into the right habits like, a bit more home practising."

By now we were feeling very disgruntled and I personally thought that we had walked it, but obviously we did not and I did not know as much as I thought I did.

We bucked up a bit when David said that we were to call in at one of our local pubs on the way home and when he mentioned the Coach and Horses we knew that we would have to put all our gear away in the band-room first as our pub was just round the corner. We still felt that we had done enough to get a prize of some sorts. Mind you, I suppose all the other bands felt the same way. I think it rankled us more because, in Bert Rawlins words, "It were a bloody furrener frey o'er's border ut filched top prize. I wouldn't a bothered as much if it'd a bin one o' our'n."

When eventually everything had been returned to the band-room and we were soaking in the atmosphere of the Coach and Horses with decent beer in our hands, we began to feel better. Ernie started to play the piano in the singing room and before we knew it we were singing our heads off. The disappointment of the contest was now in the past.

We had some more contests to come and, armed with the adjudicator's remarks perhaps we would do better in them. Well, we could only try, and the more contests we took part in the more we would learn.

When the contest music is first given out, the only part that interests you is the part in front of you. My first thoughts were what have I got to play? Are there any twiddly bits? What key is it in? Usually my mind is in a whirl until I get it all sorted out. Then comes the first run through. What a load of rubbish. Then we run through it again, this time a little slower in order to get most of the notes in the right place.

At first I tried to fool the conductor by playing my part very quietly, so that I could give myself a chance of taking it home and having a good look at it. Eventually it has to be played and, if the home practice has not been good enough, then there could come a time when I would have to play it on my own in front of the whole band, and if I had not got it correct by that time I would feel awfully foolish, especially if it was not a very difficult passage.

Usually what the conductor will do is to run through the piece once or twice and then leave it alone until the next practice, having expected you to have taken it home in the meantime and practised it in the privacy of your own bedroom, or wherever you practise.

Contesting made you practise more. In my case the more I practised the more I got it right and the more I enjoyed it. Playing at concerts was not my favourite pastime but concerts are our bread and butter and when the sun is shining on a Sunday afternoon it can be quite fulfilling.

e

9

Mayday

The time seemed to have flown and now I had left school my mother had found me a job at the place where she worked almost before I had put my school books away. I had finished on Friday and I had started work on the following Monday.

It was while I was working at the slipper factory that I was made aware of the girls. The female of the species is much more dangerous than the male and it was while I was moving about the factory that I learned all about the female form. I discovered how to manipulate bra-straps, why I could get an aspirin from any of the girls and it still be warm, (they used them as a button with their suspenders to keep up their stockings. Sixpences and buttons were used as well but aspirins were favourite).

My experiences at the factory lightened up the working day but I was young and not very interested in girls. The only thing I wanted to do was to get down to the band-room. Girls would have to wait, there was brass banding to be done.

Time seemed to pass much quicker now that I was working. It seemed no time at all before winter had come and gone. Spring was past and we were getting ready for the Mayday processions.

On the Sunday in question, which was the first Sunday in May, the band were to meet at the band-room at eight o'clock sharp. We had to check the instruments that were left in there, the basses, the bass drum and its kit. The bass drum was only used on parades and should be ready, having been cleaned and checked at the last rehearsal. There were other things too, the music and stands for the afternoon concert and also of course the band itself. It would not be the first time we had arrived at our destination short of players.

This particular day we were travelling in what is loosely described as 'own transport'. It meant that we would be riding in Jim Tubbs' old truck. This was an old ex-army fifteen hundred-weight vehicle with a loose canopy and although very draughty it saved the band a lot of hard earned cash. Into the truck went all the stands and music, bass drum and all its accoutrements, after which anyone who could not get a lift piled into the back. Talk about a squeeze!

Now came the tricky bit. It was eight o'clock and Adam was showing signs of impatience. He had made it clear that he expected everyone on parade at the time stated. Poor Adam, his Sergeant days were well and truly over. This mob that he had taken over were far below par. He expected his small shower of men to respond to his enthusiasm. It would not happen, at least not with this crew and certainly not for a while yet.

Back straight, chest out, stomach in. What a fine specimen of manhood he looked. Adam had developed a small moustache waxed and twirled at the ends. I had seen a drawing of a chap they called 'Colonel Blimp', a caricature of a bumptious upper class twit used in cartoons during the war and Adam Bailey could have been the prototype.

"Who's missing?" he growled.

"Only Jim Tubbs an' your Joe," Bert Rawlins replied. "I'm sure they'll be along in a minute."

Adam looked at his watch for the umpteenth time. "We're due on parade at St Albans at nine o'clock and I won't set off late," he said. "If they aren't 'ere in five minutes they'll 'ave to find their own way theer."

Adam cast a puzzled glance down the street. He still could not understand how his son Joe could be late. He had sounded reveille at six that morning. What he could not understand was that Joe was young and times within forty-five minutes or half an hour seemed pretty reasonable to him.

Because his dad had to be at the band-room early to sort out the music, Joe had been left to get his own breakfast and then get ready for the church parade in a more leisurely fashion. Adam should have known better, but that morning he had other things on his mind and for once he had left Joe to come on his own.

Joe's mother had made him a few sandwiches just to keep him going, these he had packed into his cornet case, squeezing them in with his cornet. At about five minutes to eight Joe set out to walk the three quarters of a mile to the band-room. Three quarters of a mile in five minutes seemed plenty of time, but at the pace he walked he would not have made it by eight thirty. Luckily Adam, knowing Joe, had put the clock forward thirty minutes, but even then Joe arrived five minutes late. Adam noted the time Joe arrived but decided to leave the admonishments till later, he had proved his point. Now only Jim Tubbs was missing. He had come earlier and left his truck at the band-room and then nipped away on an errand. He should not be long and anyway we could not go without him, it was his truck.

At fifteen minutes past eight Adam told the other players, who had already organised lifts, to carry on and make their way to Beldon so, away they went. As the last of the vehicles, a ramshackle old van, on its last legs but still able to carry ten or eleven players, disappeared round the corner, Jim Tubbs dashed up with his band jacket over his arm, his shirt collar wide open and swinging about on his collar stud, his peaked cap perched precariously on his head and his face crimson from the effects of running. He paused for a minute to get his breath.

"Sorry lads," he said. "I 'adn't realised what time 't'were."

"What happened, tha wife grab yer shirt flap?" Adam said sarcastically, but still pleased that Jim had eventually arrived, even if he was a bit late. He cringed at the thought that crossed his mind, of players arriving late after the procession had started and trying to slip unobtrusively into the band ranks. If it happened to him he would be mortified.

In the past the band had always marched up the road to St Albans. They would stop about quarter of a mile from the church, rank up and then march smartly up to the church where the congregation would be waiting.

This morning we were to meet at the Tin Bobbin Inn, just round the corner from the church. We would get organised and then march smartly up the road. The idea was good but, as I mentioned earlier, our band was not renowned for its marching ability. The thought was there and we hoped we could put it into practice when the time came.

We arrived at the Tin Bobbin pub with only a few minutes to spare and while the band was getting sorted out Harry Rawlins slipped round the back to see if he could get a quick pint. The time was a quarter to nine in the morning and Harry was not used to being without ale between meals. It had been six hours since he had staggered out of his local in the early hours of this morning, and he was more than ready to take up where he had left off. Like 'the hair of the dog' it helped to clear the mind after a long drinking session. Not that there was much to clear in his case.

Harry had been here before and said that he knew the landlord so, he knocked very quietly on the back door. Nothing happened so he knocked a little harder, Betsy was usually ready and waiting at the door for the band to arrive. Although it certainly was not opening time yet, Harry had said that we could usually get a quick snifter if we went round the back.

After a minute or so he heard the bolts being drawn back from inside the door. The door opened just enough for him to see a woman's face peer round the edge.

"What d'you want?" she said.

"Er, is the landlady in?" Harry asked.

"I'm the landlady so what d'you want?" she insisted.

"Where's Betsy Parsons?" Harry asked. "I'm with Burston Band. We're playin' for St Albans t'day. We usually set up 'ere at the pub afore marching up t' church an' while we were settin' up Betsy used t' give us a quick drink afore we set off."

The landlady peered at Harry for a moment as though he was some sort of nutter and then seemingly making her mind up said, "OK, wait a minute while I get some clothes on." She shut the door and Harry heard her put the bolt back on. This lass was not taking any chances at all.

After a couple of minutes he heard the bolts being drawn once again and the face of the landlady appeared.

"Well, don't just stand there like cheese at fourpence, come in." Harry quickly stepped inside before she could change her mind, closing the door behind him.

"Right, what's all this about a band and who are you?"

Taking a deep breath Harry said, "I'm Harry Rawlins. I'm sorry that we got you up but you see we didn't know that Betsy had left."

101

"That's OK," she said. "I'm Carla Mason. Me and my husband took this place over about five months ago but nobody has said anything about a band being here today."

"Well, now that that's sorted out how're we fixed for a drink an' can we 'ave the same arrangement with you?"

Carla thought for a moment. "I'll have to have a word with my husband first but I think that we can work something out. I suppose you want a drink now before you go?" she asked. "The pumps aren't on but you can have a bottle. You must keep quiet though, my husband's still asleep." With that she whipped a bottle off the shelf and taking, the top off said, "That's all you can have for now but it you come back at lunch-time we'll sort something out."

Harry thanked her for saving his life, downed the glass of ale and with a "Thanks luv, see you at dinner-time," he slipped quietly out of the back door.

When he returned to the rest of the bandsmen, who had been waiting anxiously to see if they could get a drink before starting off on the mornings march, they all started to shout at once. In answer to their questions Harry could only shake his head, "Sorry lads but the landlady is new and didn't know about us coming, but she's quite a dish and she's told me that when we come back at dinner-time she'll work something out with me for next time."

Time was getting short now so Bert Rawlins said, "Come on Harry get in'tut ranks, we're ready for the off."

Harry grabbed his trombone and music and stepped into the front rank of the band, all the trombones being at the front. The set-up was four trombones at the front followed by the basses. Behind them were two euphoniums and two baritones. The forth rank had three tenor horns and a cornet, the rest of the cornets bringing up the rear, that is with the exception of our bass drummer Jim Baxter who was the band librarian and sometimes, when we could not get anyone else, he filled in as the bass drummer. For once we nearly had a full band. All we needed now was a flugelhorn and if possible extra cornets. I wonder how many times this season we would be able to turn out with a full band?

"Reight Jim," Adam shouted, holding up his arm as a signal to Jim Baxter to lead off with the drum. Jim started with two short, three long, then three more taps and we were away.

The first march we always played was *Old Comrades*, a good easy march to start the day with. Unfortunately the march was marked to start off very loud, in fact it was double forte and it wasn't until we had gone about fifty yards that Harry remembered that Carla had said that her husband Ben was still asleep in bed. 'Oh lord,' he thought, 'that's buggered it. He'll not be asleep now. We'll be lucky to get through the door in opening time never mind get a drink after closing. What a disaster!'

Unaware of what had happened the band marched up the road to the church, arriving just in time. The Vicar had nearly finished arranging the order of the procession so, we marched straight to the front ready to go. Once in position we relaxed for a few minutes before moving off again.

The procession was not such a lavish affair, but like all other processions the children, parents and teachers were done up in their Sunday best. The result was very gay and colourful. We started off on a route which would take us down the main street and round the cenotaph. There a short service would be held after which we returned to the church hall by a more roundabout route.

Over all, the walk had taken about two hours and luckily the sun had been pleasantly warm, let us hope the rest of the day would be the same. Mayday walks were not always like this and when it did rain many weeks of work for the church could be spoiled.

After the St Albans ladies had served a light lunch, everyone would go to the playing fields behind the church. There would be games for the children plus a few stalls selling any items given to the church who would benefit from the sale. Where did the band come in? We would be playing light music in a shady spot reserved for us on the playing fields. All that was later on in the afternoon, for the next hour we were free to do as we pleased and that was already arranged. All they said was to be back at the church hall by one-thirty.

There were no prizes for guessing where we would be spending the next hour, the point is would we be made welcome at the Tin Bobbin?

Bert Rawlins, using his powers as band-sergeant said officiously, "Only a couple'a pints remember."

We all agreed, of course, but when you get into a pub and the taste of the 'hops' is gargling round your tonsils and the moreishness of the golden elixir is invading your senses, promises are very hard to keep. We did try to keep our eyes on the clock but sometimes a couple of pints is not enough and we had drunk these with still half an hour left before we were due back at the church. I was OK. Not yet being a recognised drinker, two pints were enough for me but I noticed that one or two of the older end decided that another pint or two would he all right.

"Time to go lads," Bert announced.

"Oh, bugger off," Andy Carlton growled. "One more pint won't make any difference."

"I said, drink up." Bert was getting shirty now. "Look, if we beggar this job up just for the sake of an extra drink we will have to look for another to take its place and if that happens there might not be a pub for miles. We can come back after we've finished playing and then we'll be OK for the rest of the day."

For once even Andy had to agree with him and we all drank up. We were being paid for the job. If we went back to the church looking the worse for wear with drink, I do not think that the Vicar would look too kindly on us. The unfortunate thing is that people who are not brass band players cannot realise that when you blow a wind instrument you use up a lot of water and it has to he replenished somehow. Obviously from our point of view a pint of ale is the perfect solution.

We arrived back at the church in good time and after collecting a chair each we then carried them onto the playing field to the roped off area set aside for the band. We arranged the chairs in the usual playing order and then set up the music stands after which the music was given out and we were ready to start the afternoon's concert.

Though the day had started off nice and sunny, a breeze had started to blow. Gently at first and very welcome to us in the band. The woollen uniforms that we had to wear fair made the sweat rise and the breeze helped to keep us nice and cool. Unfortunately this breeze was getting a little too strong, and we knew that we were in for some fun and games of our own before the afternoon was out.

Because we had returned to the church with time to spare we had time for a cup of tea and a bun which the church ladies were delighted to serve us. It wasn't until we had bitten into the buns that we realised why they were so delighted to serve us. The buns were rock hard. We could have used them as door stops. The children, having found this out had left them well alone and so there were plenty left. What could we do with them? We just could not throw them away, especially since the ladies were practically forcing them into our hands, they had to, no one would come near to their table. We were well and truly snookered.

At last we managed to sneak away to a corner but we still had to eat the buns. Having unsuccessfully tried to break them up, we tried dunking them into out watery tea. It worked like a charm and the taste was pretty good too but, unlike 'Oliver Twist', we did not go back for more.

The time had come for us to start playing so we repaired to the playing fields with a sigh of relief, for once the thought of getting away from the church hall and especially the ladies buns and onto our temporary bandstand on the playing field appealed to us.

For anyone who has not played for a Sunday School after walking day you have to remember that the chairs were designed for small children and not large bandsmen. The worst ones effected were of course the players of the larger instruments, especially the basses. Sitting on small chairs barely eight inches off the ground was to say the least very uncomfortable.

In most cases sitting on the small chairs was not the most comfortable positions but at least you could put up with it, but bass players usually rested their instruments on their knees when sat down so that the mouthpiece was comfortably opposite the mouth. On these small chairs they had to open their knees in order to get the bass into the required position. Anyone who has tried to play a bass instrument in this position for a long time will realise just how difficult and painful this can be.

After we had been playing for a short while we became aware that the nice breeze which had been keeping us cool was now becoming stronger. We were playing a piece called *The Grasshopper's Dance* when a sudden gust of wind sent half the music flying off the music stands scattering it in all directions across the playing fields. This was disastrous. Some of the band had not realised what was happening so they carried on playing, and what with half the band trying to play *The Grasshopper's Dance* and the other half trying to catch the music the result was chaos. There was music flying all over the place, with chairs being knocked over in the haste to grab a piece of music.

105

It is well known that a tornado creates terrible damage to everything in its path well, the devastation caused by a small wind on a playing field where an outdoor concert is being held has to be seen to be believed.

The church officials glared at us as if it was our fault that the catastrophe had occurred. (It was known that we had been down to the pub at dinner-time but even we could not have produced that much wind.) But all was not lost. With a howl of delight the children took up the chase and began a far better game than they had ever imagined. Pieces of music being gusted here, there and everywhere by a wind that seemed to be trying to make sure that we would never see them again. (Possibly a message from the heavens hinting at our playing and choice of music.)

At last, as the wind seemed to abate, the children cornered the last elusive piece as it caught on a rose bush, and raced back with it to Adam who was trying to sort the torn and wrinkled sheets into some order.

Thankfully, after what seemed an age, everything was returned to normal. All the music had been rescued, some obviously beyond repair, mainly through being torn in half as the children argued about who was to return it to the band.

Adam waited most impatiently, his foot tapping on the ground, the flush on his face turning more crimson as the pressure rose with each passing minute. At last.

"Which silly buggers forgot to bring their pegs?" he said. "Yer mothers should have tied them to yer damn shirt tails, so that when yer sat on 'em, you'd know that they were there. Mind you, they say 'where there is no sense there is no feeling', but you should know better, it's letting things like this happen that gets us a bad name." He paused and shrugged his shoulders with exasperation, "I don't know why I'm bothering to get so steamed up, It'll happen again next time, if yer name wasn't written inside yer collar you'd forget that too." With that he reached into the bag with all his music and pulled out a handful of clothes pegs and handing them round to what he called the miscreants. He scowled as he did so.

"If this happens again someone is going to suffer. I'll have his guts fer garters, I promise you."

As for the clothes pegs, the experienced bandsmen always carried at least four spring loaded pegs in his pocket, one for each

106

corner of the music to stop it blowing away on a breezy day, the thing is that sometimes in the rush to get off the stand and into the pub, they would get left behind, this Adam knew, so I had a feeling that when we finished today there would be no rushing off, he would see to that.

We finished playing without any more interruptions, though I did see Jim Hogan nodding off behind his bass and only a quick jab in the ribs from Tom Bibby saved him from toppling off his small chair; that extra pint must have got to him. I think that it was with a sigh of relief that half past four arrived and we spent the next half hour packing everything away, including the Sunday school gear. Adam had told them that we would help before we went away and it was only after everything had been removed from the playing field that Adam let us go.

We said our not too sad farewell to the Vicar and then made our way quietly back to the Tin Bobbin. Although it was still closed we hoped that Carla would let us in the back door. When we got there she was waiting.

"Just keep it down lads, I'll be with you in a couple of ticks."

Suddenly the door of the tap-room was thrown open with a bang and all eyes turned towards the noise. This looked like trouble. There was a figure standing in the doorway barring any chance we had of escaping. The figure was of a smallish man but was very thick set, the hair on his head was going thin and his eyes were wide, wild and bloodshot.

At first I thought it was a very ugly pregnant woman, what with the belly sticking out it must be something big. I then saw the braces dangling down by his side and decided that it must be a man and obviously no 'maid of the mountain'. He looked mad. He grabbed Harry Rawlins who just happened to be nearest, by the lapels and lifted him clear off the floor. Harry was only small, about six stones wet through so it was an easy thing to do. All Harry could do was struggle to get free. No chance. This bloke was built like a brick out-house. It seemed for a moment that he would shake the stuffing out of Harry and then his mood changed and he dumped Harry down on a stool and said, "sit." I think it was 'sit', it could have been something else, but neither Harry nor anyone else in the room was going to argue with him. He reached over the bar and grabbed a pint of ale that had just been pulled. He plonked it down in front of Harry.

"Drink."

Now this was something that Harry was very good at. He was only small and thin but he could put away great quantities of ale with apparently very little effort. No one knew how he did it or where he put it in that small frame of his but he did, it was suggested that he had hollow legs but there was not enough room in them to take all the ale that he could sup.

Harry looked at the pint in front of him thinking that there must be a catch, strangers did not buy him drinks just like that, but this fellow was too big to argue with.

'Here goes,' he thought, and wiping the sweat from his brow he lifted the pint to his lips and downed it in one. He put the glass down on the bar and looked up at the brick out-house ready to apologise for anything he thought he might have inadvertently done to him. He need not have worried on that score. His apprehensive look turned to relief as he saw the smile on the big man's face.

"Well done lad," he said. "I didn't think tha could manage it. Have another one. I'm a great brass band fan and *Old Comrades* is one of my favourites, but please don't wake me up like that again. I nearly jumped through the ceiling, when you blasted off reight under my window, it's enough to give a bloke a heart attack. If you're coming this way again give us a ring the night before. Anyway, that's sorted out now, so what'll you have?" With that he went round the side of the bar and removed the other towels from the pumps.

When he had served us all with ale, even me (the lads had told him I was old enough), the Landlord (we hoped that's who he was), said, "Let's get sorted, I'm Bert Mason and this is my pub. I see you've met my wife Carla. By the way Carla's in the kitchen making some sandwiches, I take it you're all hungry?" The murmur of assent proved he was correct. "Reight then," he said, "I'll get some more ale and then I'll go and help Carla get some tea for you all."

We could not believe our ears, it seemed too good to be true. Being allowed to drink after time was great but getting fed as well was something totally unexpected. Only nine of us had come to the pub. All the others had gone back to Burston. They were the wise ones.

At the shout of "tea up" we all trooped into the lounge bar and there laid out on a table for us were meat pies, sandwiches and pickles. Hell, what a feast! We had not seen so much grub on the table all at one time for years. So, without wasting any more time we got stuck in and by the time we had finished eating, the only thing left on the table were crumbs. After that it was time to open the bar officially and get down to some serious drinking once again. This was our main hobby and we were good at it.

We played cards and dominoes in between drinking and at about nine o'clock Ernie Benson went into the singing room and started to play the piano. Ernie was a good pianist and knew all the old songs so, as we were getting a bit fed up of playing cards, we decided to join him.

As usual it did not take long. In about five minutes flat the singing room was full and bouncing. One after another of the customers were getting up to sing and everyone seemed to be having a great time. Then Tom Perkins, our bass trombone player got up to give a song. This was something new. I, along with some of the others, could not remember having heard Tom sing before. Not that it mattered, we were in good company and the beer was loosening everyone up so why not? We had already heard some weird and wonderful sounds that had passed for singing so surely Tom could not be any worse than them.

Tom informed Ernie what he was going to sing and then stood by the piano with his hands on his lapels, just like in the photographs of olden day singers with their large handlebar moustaches, and that was the women! To any of the older generation watching it must have taken them back about fifty years, but not one of us dared to laugh even if we were bursting our buttons to do so.

We waited while Ernie played the introduction and then Tom started to sing. We sat still and quiet not knowing what to expect, but after a few bars of the song we were flabbergasted. The glorious deep voice emanating from Tom Perkins blended superbly with the words of that wonderful old song *The Old House*. The noise in the room died down suddenly, as though someone had pressed a switch. You could have heard a pin drop as they listened to Tom sing, and when he finished he was clapped and cheered in appreciation of a good song well sung. This went on for some time but although they clamoured for more Tom, thanking them, sat down. We did not push Tom to sing again, good as it had been, it had taken a world war and nine pints of ale just to get him to sing one song, only God knows what it would have taken to get him to give us an encore.

When we had got our flabber back from being gasted we decided that we would give the natives a touch of culture. We decided to sing in harmony, at least it would give Ernie a breather and time to get a drink. We had tried this type of singing before and although it sometimes sounded like a cat in agony, this time we got it right. We sang a hymn called *Cwym Rhonda* sung by the Burston band choir and company. I cannot begin to believe that it was sung correctly but it sounded great. Perhaps the quantity of ale that we had consumed may have effected our hearing, it always sounded great after we had drunk a few pints of ale. Maybe it was pretty good, then again so was the ale.

The singing and drinking cannot have been too bad because Bert Mason invited us back any time we wanted to come. I had the feeling that he would come to regret that invitation.

We said our goodbyes and were getting into the truck when someone said, "Hey, we haven't paid Carla fer't grub." I think it was Jimmy Belfor, our solo euphonium player. He went on, "An' we can't go wi'out payin' can we? If we ferget to pay they might not let us come back again, an' it's too good a watering hole to lose."

So, it was agreed we go back to the pub. Mind you it was not just as easy as it sounds, getting out of the back of the truck in our state could have made for a good clowns act in a circus what with slipping and falling over one another. It was like 'Muldoon's Picnic'. It took us so long to get sorted out that we thought that they would have been in bed long ago, but no, the lights were still on, we were all right. We tried the front door, but no joy so we went round the back. This was more our style, going in by the back door. We tried the door and luckily it was still open so we walked into the tap-room.

"Bloody hell, what's ta fergetten now?" Bert Mason exclaimed, thinking that we had left something behind.

"It isn't like that," Bert Rawlins said. "But you see, we forgot to pay Carla fer the grub."

"Aye lads," Carla said coming back into the room, "you could have called in as you were passing, an' anyway I'm not sure what to charge."

"Well, we had a damn good meal an' we're glad tuh pay," Ernie Benson said, with an eye to the next time we were around these parts. Carla tried to shrug the food off as a one off thing but after a bit of arguing she accepted that we meant what we said and told us how much the food cost her to buy. It worked out at two shillings each so we decided to give her two shillings and sixpence each. We were satisfied and so was Carla.

Once the money for our tea had been sorted out, Dick Hardy said, "Well bein' as we're back in't pub we might as well 'ave another pint."

"OK then, just one fer the road," Jimmy Belfor agreed. "But that's the last, then it's time fer movin'."

Once more we settled down in the tap-room and started playing cards. As the game had not finished before our drinks came, we decided to have just one more and before we knew it we were relaxed into the old routine. The next time we looked around the pub it was empty except for us, and of course Bert and Carla. Bert looked up at the clock and said, " 'Ave you seen the time lads? It's gettin' on you know. Haven't you got any homes to go to?"

When our befuddled eyes at last focused on the clock we were stunned and it took some time for it to register that the clock showed one-thirty. We had been back in the pub for well over an hour. I was in trouble with a capital 'T'. Carla and Bert were not aware that I was under age for drinking beer but my father was. I could only imagine what he would say and do if he caught me in this state and coming home at this time of the morning. It certainly would not be hello.

As it happened my father was still out playing with the dance band and my mother was in bed when I eventually did get home. How we got home is just a hazy memory of being thrown from one side of the truck to the other, I think it was pure luck that we arrived home in one piece. We were not the quietest of people when we had had a drink and as I tip-toed into the house I thought that I had got away with it, that no one had heard me come in. How I got away with it is still a mystery. As I crept up the stairs to my bedroom I thought I was making more noise than a herd of elephants but nobody seemed to hear me.

The next morning my mother asked me what time I had got in. I told her that I was not sure, that I had been so tired after helping

Jim Tubbs when his truck broke down. She gave me a funny look but did not say anything else, I felt that she was not quite in harmony with my thoughts but was giving me the benefit of the doubt, at least until she had spoken with Jim Tubbs and I knew that I would have to get to him before she did. She left it at that, but the warning was there. Phew! The lies. I would be in confession for a week the next time I went. Still, I do not see why my mother should have been so quick to doubt my explanation, it could easily have been the truth.

10

Mayor's Sunday

Over the next few engagements that the band had I had been banned from staying out with them. My mother had decided that I was getting into bad ways and even threatened to bar me from the band if I did not buck up. Even then I managed to get a few pints down me. I was having to do all sorts of things to get rid of the smell of beer on my breath.

Even though I could not stay with the band lads after a parade for a couple of weeks, it did not in any way put me off banding. If anything, it made me more determined than ever to be a better player. I still practised every day and only stopped when my lip became too swelled for me to play, but no matter how hard I practised I felt that I was not improving. My father still kept me doing musical scales for at least an hour at the beginning of my home practice as well as blowing long notes, but even I had to admit that my tone was not getting any better.

About this time Carl Dobson, our first tenor horn player, had to leave the band. He had been transferred from his job at the Post Office where he worked as a counter clerk, to another Post Office in foreign parts, namely Bradford in Yorkshire. We felt regret that Carl was going and offered him our heartfelt condolences. Although the Post Office said that he was being promoted, we did not think so. What trouble had he caused to be punished by being sent to Yorkshire? Whatever it was he never said, he took his punishment like a man, but why Yorkshire? They did not even have 'radio' there yet and they were not cultured like what we were.

Through the fact of Carl leaving the band, the main problem was the hole he left in the horn section. I mentioned this to my father and he said that I would be better off on the larger mouthpiece of the tenor horn. This would be a good move for me if I could pull it off. Cornet players, even me, were not pushed to leave the cornet section but I had a word with Adam and the result was that I moved onto the first tenor horn.

This was a move that did not please Andrew Makin our second horn player. Andrew had thought that he would be able to move up onto the first horn and someone else would start on second. Well, he was one off. Adam obviously thought that I was the better player. He was a bit miffed but after a while he got over it.

After a week or two of getting used to the new instrument my father said that my tone on the horn was a great improvement to the tone on my cornet. The difference in the size of mouthpiece was not too bad, the horn mouthpiece being just a bit larger, but it took me longer than I thought to really get into playing my new instrument correctly. Scales and still more scales. Lord when would it end?

About this time the band committee decided that the bandroom needed repairing. It was time too. The room was becoming a bit dilapidated. The roof had started to leak in places and once they started on it they knew that other necessary repairs would come to light so the decision was taken to remove and replace the whole roof.

The argument as to how we would practise and how to keep the instruments and music dry was becoming a telling factor and it was not until the argument started getting heated while we were having a pint in the Duke of Wellington, that the question was resolved.

The landlord, Alf Worthington, heard bits and pieces of the argument in between serving them and asked them why they did not move out of the band-room altogether? The argument stopped there and then. It had come up, but the question had been where could we go. Of course Alf had the answer, they could rent his upstairs room?

A special meeting was called in a corner of the pub and after agreeing on the rental, it was decided. Next Saturday would be the day when the band would move out, lock, stock and barrel.

Music, stands and all the paraphernalia associated with it. We were delighted with the decision and Alf, obviously with an eye on the profits to be made from his offer, was quite pleased with his suggestion. At least twice a week he would have a full house with the band itself after practice and the fact that he had been a bandsman himself had something to do with it.

The following Saturday arrived and once again Jim Tubbs proved his worth. He said that the band could use his truck for the move as long as they paid for the petrol. David Green nearly bit his hand off in his enthusiasm. This was a bargain that the band could not refuse.

Nine o'clock and nearly all the band members had turned up with just a few exceptions. By lunch-time, with the aid of some unexpected volunteers from the pub, we had moved everything from the band-room to our new temporary headquarters in the upstairs room of the Duke of Wellington.

The temporary room at the 'Duke' proved a great success. Straight after the band practice all we had to do was to go downstairs into the bar. Ale on the premises, what more could we want?

During our time at the 'Duke' a number of us would gather round the piano in the 'singing room'. There was Jim Tubbs, Bert Fallows, Harry Rawlins, Dick Hardy and me with Ernie playing the piano. The reason we gathered there was that we enjoyed singing and as there was a piano easily available we decided to make the best possible use of it, and as this was the age of the skiffle groups it was also inevitable that we made ourselves a 'tea-chest bass fiddle'.

Skiffle, is folk or jazz music played by a group of people using non-standard instruments. Usually the groups were made up of a guitar, banjo and an old washboard which was played by strumming up and down the washboard with the fingers which were tipped with sewing thimbles. The group could be inaugurated with odd instruments like a 'Jew's harp' or anything else that anyone could think of that would make a noise. Many weird inventions were tried out in this way.

One of the top stars of skiffle was a man called Lonnie Donegan who sang such great hits like, *Ham'n'eggs*, *Losing by a Hair*, *Does Your Chewin'gum Lose Its Flavour On The Bedpost Overnight* and dozens more. How could we ever forget those memorable songs with names like that, we felt that they would last forever.

The fiddle was made out of an old tea chest which was turned upside down. A hole was bored in the base of the tea chest and a string passed through and fastened onto a long board which was in turn fastened to the side of the tea-chest. Once the string was tightened you had yourself a one string bass fiddle.

That was when the trouble started. Who was going to play it. Ernie Benson was the pianist so he was out but everyone else wanted to try the new plaything. The result was some of the best fun I had ever had. What lengths we went to just to be able to make a fool of ourselves trying to play a one note fiddle and what excuses we found in trying to persuade everyone why each of us was better than anyone and everyone else.

The best one was Harry Rawlins, he was the one who had thought of and built it in the first place. After a week or two he augmented it by putting a hinge at the top where the string was fastened and by bending the hinge he tightened the string and so claimed to be the best because by tightening the string he could get more than one note out of it. That clinched it, no one else could think of any more innovations so we just left it to Harry to prove himself the maestro, which he tried to do, even through all the cat-calls which accompanied him every time he tried to play it. He carried it off like a good-un. He had made his point.

That particular year we did not have a great many jobs with the band. One we did have was the Mayor's Sunday. This happened every year when the new Mayor was sworn into office. A procession would take the new Mayor from the Town Hall to his own church where a service would be heard and then back to the Town Hall.

The Mayor's church this year was about a mile out of town. It sounds OK, but what I have yet to mention is that it was all uphill.

We started off from the Town Hall and for about a quarter of a mile everything was OK, the road being reasonably level, then it started to gradually steepen. It's bad enough playing and walking on the level but as the hill steepened I began to feel it.

It started with the backs of my legs beginning to ache and breathing and playing became a problem. It did not seem much of a hill to look at but that mile up to the church was one of the hardest miles I have ever had to do, by the time we got to the church I was shattered, and I was only playing a tenor horn, when

116

I looked round for the bass players they were laid out at the side of the road gasping for breath, I decided that it would not be a very good time to complain about the march up the hill.

I did think, just for a moment, that one of them had had a heart attack, but it was only the effects of the hill climb. The thought had crossed my mind that someone would have said 'well done lads' but they were all too knackered to even speak. When you are playing an instrument and walking it is hard enough, but when you have such a great hill to contend with it is ten times worse.

The fact that the cemetery was only on the other side of the road made some of them revive very quickly. Mind you they made sure that their eye-lids were moving when the Vicar went past. The one consolation we had was that just about half-way between the Town Hall and the church, was a pub. We had not missed seeing that. When the Mayor's procession had filed inside the church for the service, we stayed outside and as the last person entered the church we laid our instruments down on the grass verge and ran like hell back down the road to the pub.

It was like a beacon in the night. The Wheat Hotel, that was the name of this wonderful building. All we had to do now was to get in. We knew the Landlord of old, him being a friend of Hughie Mack's. At various times we had spent many happy hours in the tap-room playing darts and dominoes with, of course, the inevitable pint.

It was recognised as one of our better watering holes, so it did not surprise Vinny Barker, the landlord, when we raced round the back and hammered on the door. When Vinny eventually answered, it was with his usual grating sarcasm.

"Don't knock the bloody door down," he said. "When I saw the procession going past the window I knew it wouldn't be long before you bloody lot were 'ere."

"Well, are you going to serve us or do we die of thirst?" Hughie said, plonking a pound note on the bar.

"All right, you soddin' gannets, keep yer shirts on, I've hardly had time to switch the damn pumps on, what'll you have? An' stop yer damn moaning. If there's owt I can't stand it's seeing grown men cry."

We all crowded up to the bar, trying to be the first to get his drink. We had about an hour before the church service finished.

Five minutes later, with the ale disappearing like there was no tomorrow, Vinny said, moving away from the bar.

"Well, are you satisfied now? Can I get on with me work?"

"Owd on," Hughie said, grabbing his arm before he got away, "we've only got an hour, let's have some more ale. You can do your work when we've gone."

Vinny grinned, his face lighting up as he turned back to the bar.

"I thowt I wouldn't get away so easily you drunken sots. Get yer money out."

"Reight," Bert Rawlins said, "tha con start wi' me. Fill 'er up again."

"Aye an' mine as well," Tom Perkins chipped in, putting his now empty glass on the bar. So it started all over again and for the next half hour Vinny was kept busy filling the glasses. He did not get a minute's rest.

Suddenly the tap-room door was flung open and there in the doorway stood a man with more scrambled egg on his hat than I've ever seen before, even in pictures of Generals. He turned out to be the police commissioner.

"What the hell's going on here?" he snapped. "Drinking during closing time, dear me it must be my birthday catching all you lot in one go."

The room went deathly quiet. You could have heard a pin drop. We were stuck. Caught in the act. God, I was in trouble, especially when my mother found out. I was not supposed to be going into public houses, being under-aged. I could see the headlines in *The Courier*, police catch local band drinking in the Wheat Hotel during closing time. Of course it would not come as any surprise to some people. Now the fat was really in the fire. The voice of the police chief broke the silence.

"You are very lucky, if it wasn't for the fact that it would take all day to get your names and addresses . . ." He let the words hang in the air for a moment.

"So," he grinned, enjoying the game, "as it's my birthday, who's going to be the first to buy me a drink?"

I could feel the tension in the room relax, as voice after voice volunteered, the relief showing in their scramble to be on the right side of the police chief. Vinny averted the panic that seemed to be descending on the room.

"This one's on the house chief," he said. "Happy birthday, if that's what it is, what'll you have, whisky?"

118

A nod from the chief. "Thanks." he said. "It'll do to be going on with."

"How did you know the back door was open?" Vinny asked him.

"I didn't. I just followed the band-lads. I kept my eye on them and when they didn't go into church I knew that something was up, so I made an excuse to the Mayor and followed them, they always know where to get a drink."

For the next half hour I think that Vinny did more business than he had done all week. Some of the bobbies had followed their boss into the pub and could they sup? Their chief could fair stand his corner as well. Drunken sods!

By the time they left for the church the chief had downed half a dozen whiskies without blinking an eye, not bad for forty-five minutes boozing. I would not like to have to take him out for a full night on the town. No wonder he was the chief, all that booze and he had not even paid for one drink.

We left the Wheat Hotel in time to catch them just coming out from the service and we got some dirty looks from the Vicar as he passed us.

The procession reformed and we marched back to the Town Hall. Thank goodness it was all downhill. At the Town Hall the new Mayor thanked us all and we were then dismissed, so straight back to the Wheat Hotel we went. We had started the day well enough at the 'Wheat', so we decided to do our best to finish it there. The only thing was that Vinny did not have much in the way of food, at least, not for us. He had some crisps and nuts but that was all. The band decided to make do with hops and barley.

Unlike most of the other members of the band, I was a growing lad and when it got to tea time I found that it was too much to go without eating all that time. I decided that I would go home for some tea. That was the end of my Mayor's Sunday. One smell of my breath and my dad put the brakes on me for the rest of the day. I pleaded innocence, having had a mint before I went home, but he had done it all before, so, that was that.

Our last procession of that year was Armistice Sunday. The band was to meet outside the British Legion in Burston, the outside was emphasised, it was the committee's way of making sure that we did not get too much to drink before the procession set off. They tried it every year, it had not worked then and it did not work now. It was not that we got drunk, just that there were few toilets near the Cenotaph and also it did not look at all good seeing members of the band sneaking off to the 'Gents'.

As always at the 'Legion' everything was done in a military fashion and after a few jars in the club we found ourselves lined up outside on the roadway. The man who was in charge of the procession was ex-RSM Flint, late of the Royal Artillery. Most of the ex-soldiers on parade wore their war medals, some even wore their old berets. Also in the parade were some old soldiers from the 1914-18 war and although they were getting on a bit now, they still had enough spring in their step and bearing to make most of us look sloppy.

This year, just for the parade, we had borrowed a side drummer from another band, and very smart too. His name was Colin Hargreaves. He did not look much older than me but as it turned out, he was twenty-two. Colin was waiting in the 'Legion' when we got there; all ready with his drum kit in immaculate condition.

His immediate needs, after he had put his drum safely out of harms way, was to get himself a pint and, that's how we found him, with a pint in his hand. Most impressive. Visitors usually waited until we got there so that we would buy the first drinks. As we ordered our drinks we naturally ordered a refill for Colin and introduced ourselves. He seemed a decent bloke. Not our sort at all but, as we had arrived early, we found time to get to know him better.

It was now one o'clock and we were not due off until two fifteen, so we decided to go easy on the beer. The fact that we did not have much cash was also a deciding factor, and when we got back from the parade we could always rely on a few free pints coming our way. Also we knew that throughout the parade there were no places where we would be stopping for a 'Jimmy Riddle' except at the Cenotaph.

Out of the corner of my eye I could see Colin knocking back the ale. He certainly liked his beer and he could get rid of it in quick time.

"Tak' it easy lad," Bert Rawlins said. "We've all day to go an' there aren't many toilets before tha gets back."

To be fair Colin did slow down a bit, but by the time we were ready for off his eyes had a definite twinkle.

"Outside everybody," shouted the ex-RSM. "Get on parade."

Our position in the parade was, as usual, near the front leading the main procession. The only things in front of us were the Mayor's car followed by the cars carrying the disabled ex-servicemen.

The RSM took charge when everyone was assembled.

"Parade! Parade shun! Parade will move to the left in column of route, le-eft turn! By the left, quick, march!"

The RSM had started us off in the direction of the town centre They were all there. Ex-servicemen, Scouts, Guides, Legion members and other people from many different organisations. In all, the procession must have covered a few hundred yards in length.

The band was set up as normal, with trombones at the front followed by the basses, then the baritones and euphoniums, the horns and then all the cornets. Right at the back were the bass drum and our borrowed side-drummer Colin.

The road, as we started off, was straight but about three hundred yards further on we had to turn right in order to follow the road into the town centre. As we came to the turn the inside men took shorter steps and the outside men lengthened theirs. That was the intention, but it was not to be, at least not to our borrowed drummer Colin. As he came out of the 'Legion' the fresh air must have hit him like a sledge-hammer and by the time we had got moving his eyes had turned to a glazed expression.

His drumming must have been on automatic because when the band struck up with the first tune he was with them all the way, that is, until the band came to the right turn. One by one the rows of bandsmen turned right in correct order but when it came to Colin's turn he just kept straight on and tripping over the kerb he fell on his side on the grass verge. As it was told to us when we got back from the parade, he lay on his side like a mechanical toy soldier still drumming. Someone must have taken pity on him because we did not see any more of him on the parade, neither was he at the 'Legion' when we got back and it was quite a few years before we saw him again. When asked about that parade he disclaimed all knowledge of the incident and I for one do not blame him, I would not have wanted reminding of an incident like that. It makes me cringe to remember it so I can not imagine what he must have felt like.

We approached the Cenotaph playing a nice steady march and,

f

as everything seemed to be going reasonably well, apart from the loss of a borrowed side drummer, Bert, in his wisdom, decided that as soon as we passed the Cenotaph, we would counter march. We had tried this countermarching once before and the result had been disastrous, so why Bert had chosen today as the one to try it again I will never know, and in front of the Mayor as well.

What was supposed to happen was that on a given command, the front row would turn right and right again having done a full about turn, and as each row came to the same spot they too would do an about turn, so that when the countermarch was completed the whole band would be facing the way they had come, and would be facing the oncoming procession who would stop at the Cenotaph as would the band.

That in theory was what should have happened. Perhaps it was a day for brainstorms, what with the side-drummer going missing. The thing is, you cannot always count on everyone knowing his left hand from his right, and, there is always one silly sod who would turn the wrong way. How, I do not know? Because he only had to follow the man in front of him in turning right so, why the hell had he to go and turn left causing untold pandemonium. Well, it happened. I think it was Joe Sudders our second euphonium player. Not only did he turn the wrong way, he stayed turned the wrong way so that everyone coming facing him had to move out of the way causing the man on the outside to move out as well. It happened and I do not think too many people saw it happen but Bert was livid and I thought that for a minute he would explode.

"Band, halt!" he screamed.

No one could say that they did not hear him, you could have heard him ten miles away. Even ex-RSM Flint came to attention at the sound of Bert's voice. The band stopped dead in their tracks. Not a soul moved. Out of the corner of his mouth, Bert cursed the useless idiot who had turned the wrong way, before remembering where he was and who was there. He told them to get back in the correct ranks and after a bit of shuffling around, order was restored.

The service went off as usual with the Vicar making pointed remarks at Bert's whispered cursing. The last post was sounded and all the wreaths were laid. The band was marched to the front of the parade, this time without mishap, and we were ready to start the return to the 'Legion'. Waiting only for the ex-RSM's command the band led off with the march *It's A Long Way To Tipperary* then *Pack Up Your Troubles In Your Old Kit Bag,* the last one being more appropriate to the our band today than for an army leaving for the First World War.

Bert was fuming when we arrived back at the 'Legion'. RSM Flint dismissed the parade and everyone started to make their way into the 'Legion' club.

"Hang about you bloody lot," Bert growled. "Which dozy bugger turned left on the countermarch at the Cenotaph?"

No one answered. Bert was not a man to be trifled with when he was mad. Out on Parade as our band sergeant he was boss.

"If I find out who it was I'll tie a bloody ribbon on his right arm and see how he goes on then."

"Steady on Bert," Tom Perkins piped up. "Tha shouldn't 'ave tried that sort o' stuff wi'out givin' us some sort o' warnin'. You know that we got it wrong afore an' we never thought that tha'd be daft enough to try it on a parade afore we'd had a chance to get it right."

Bert turned on his pal and for a moment I thought he would bang him one.

"I'll show thee who's daft," he said, his voice rising as his temper took hold. "Get back in formation an' we'll see if tha con do it reight now."

We gaped at Bert thinking that he was joking but he was serious, he really was in a temper and although Tom Perkins was a friend of his I thought it would be some time before he forgave him for making him look foolish by calling him daft.

Deciding that it would be easier to do what he said, we got back in formation and he marched us up and down that road, countermarching and countermarching again. Not one mistake was made and after about half a dozen turns and turn-abouts Bert had to concede that we could do it. This made him even more mad at us.

"Why couldn't you silly sods do that in the town centre instead of making me and yourselves look such twits, it isn't hard to tell left from right, all yuh 'ave to do is think about what you're doin'. Right, yuh might as well bugger off, you're a bloody waste o' time, but make no mistake I'll take it up with the committee an' yuh con be sure that they'll be some more practice in countermarchin'. 1 won't be part of another fiasco like this again." With that warning ringing in our ears we walked self-consciously into the club.

We ordered our pints at the club bar and settled down to a drink. Bert was once more arguing with Jim Robins our other double bass player, who was obviously trying to calm him down.

"I know we were wrong Bert but tha should a known summat 'ud go wrong, it al'us does if there's somebody watching us, we should of practised some more afore we tried it out on t' street."

Bert would not be put off. "We've done it before an' we should be able tu do it at anytime. I wouldn't mind but it's not that hard."

"We're not bloody Grenadier Guards tha knows," Jim answered.

"Grenadier Guards," Bert spluttered, nearly choking himself. "Grenadier Guards! Yu couldn't even be mistaken fer the bloody Home Guards an' that's a fact. When I've 'ad a word with the committee an' we've done some more practising, 'appen there'll be no more 'balls up' like this morning I con tell thee, at least not while I'm band sergeant." With that he supped up and stormed out of the club.

We followed him to the door and Jim stood for a minute watching Bert stride angrily down the road then he followed him, calling over his shoulder as he did so, "Look you lot, go and get some ale in, I'll be back wi' Bert when he's cooled off."

We carried on with our drinking and after about fifteen minutes Jim returned with a more calm Bert and once in our company and a few pints under his belt Bert slowly reverted to his old self but still adamant that the band was going to be put through their paces every so often to make sure that nothing would go wrong in any future countermarching.

When we had walked into the 'Legion' after the parade, a bag was thrust into our hands. In the bag was a tea-cake (some people call them balm-cakes or muffins), a small meat pie and a cake. This happened every year. These, I think, were paid for by the British Legion, but whoever paid for them they were very welcome. Also a cup of tea was available for anyone who wanted.

At the top end of the room a table was set aside for the dignitaries such as the Mayor and our local Member of Parliament and the councillors and officials of the British Legion club committee etc.

I could not understand this - a table or tables covered with a tablecloth, being set aside for dignitaries while the rest of the common herd were left to find any place they could. It was as though the armed forces class system worked just the same in civvy street.

It so happened that when the children left and if there were enough of the band left in the club, we would give an impromtu concert, a sort of busking session. Usually this happened after the consumption of a few pints of best bitter, which put us in the right sort of mood.

It would start with perhaps a song and then one of the band would give a solo, usually Ernie Benson. Bit by bit as the ale flowed ever so smoothly, everyone would join in singing and playing. Mostly it was recognisable but that did not matter because by then we would most likely have got to the point where nobody cared anyway.

The afternoon passed with everyone seeming to be having a good time and before we knew it, it was opening time again, though I had not been aware that it had closed. This was the point when we would go. On Sunday evening the 'Legion' held concerts and as the club did not have a games room where we could play cards etc., we decided to adjourn to the Duke Of Wellington where we could play all night if we wanted to. Funny that it was the only place that we ever left of our own accord during opening times, but just the same Remembrance Sunday was both a sad and happy day. Sad because the ex-servicemen remembered old comrades who were not here any more and happy when they met someone who they had not seen for many years, but it was a good time when the remembrance was for all the men and women who had died for us in the two World Wars.

11

Another Christmas

Christmas playing once again came around, but this year for a change it was raining instead of snowing. Most of the time the band could not get out to do any playing because of it. The rain ran down collars, soaked through our raincoats and made us feel miserable all round. Most of all it soaked our music making the thin pages stick together, and although we tried to stay out as long as we could we had to give up, our health being considered more important. We did get a few evenings when it was dry and believe me we fair moved along, not stopping at any of our usual watering holes.

The fact that we stayed in the pub when it was raining did not really have much bearing on our Yuletide playing. As much playing as possible had to be done in order to collect the cash which was needed to pay for the repairs to various dents and leaks necessary on old instruments. Spending time in the pub when we should have been out playing only made the coming year more difficult.

By Christmas Eve we had missed about a third of our playing in the town. This could not be retrieved because we were only allowed a certain amount of time to get all the town and surrounding district covered, so what was lost had to stay lost and we had to keep moving. It was decided by the committee that if we were to go round the farms this year we would have to use a vehicle to get from one farm to another. It was hoped that Jim Tubbs would be available for the nights when we would be out playing. It was his old faithful truck that we would have to use and if Jim could not come then we would just have to walk.

We met as usual at the 'Duke', played them a few carols, had a couple of beers, just to keep us warm you understand, then off we went. We walked round the pubs in the town centre and for once it was a dry evening.

This year there were not as many of the band as we had hoped for. Tonight there were only ten of us. We had a bass, two euphoniums, two baritones, two horns and three cornets. Not a big band but quite a reasonable balance.

There were a few grumbles at the start of the evening as we went round the pubs but the smell of the hops and the taste of the golden nectar soon dispelled all of that and by the time we had finished visiting all of the pubs in and around the town, we were in a far better frame of mind, in fact there were one or two of our ensemble who had a distinct rock on as we left the town centre behind us, and there were still the farms to do.

Half past eleven found us playing round the 'crib', *O Come All Ye Faithful*, *Hark the Herald Angels Sing* and finishing off with *Silent Night*. It did not feel like Christmas except for the music.

We finished the last carol and moved on to the car-park where Jim had parked his truck earlier in the evening, ready for us when we had finished in town.

"Reight lads," Ernie Benson said. "Let's get going. We will have to move some if we're to get all the farms in tonight." So, piling into Jim's truck away we went. It was agreed that the weather would hold and we would have a dry night, but you never could tell in this valley. It should be easier than last year without the snow and as long as the rain held off we should be OK. I knew rain was easier to deal with but I could not help feeling that the sight of snow makes it feel more like Christmas.

Maybe it was me, I was not in the mood to play that night, which is very unusual; I would play with the band every night if I could. Maybe it was the dark clouds gathering and blotting out the moon that weakened my enthusiasm or a cold coming on?

It was too late now; we were on our way and I had heard the clink of more than one glass as the rest of the lads climbed into the back of the truck making it obvious that we would not be 'supping bowt', at least some of us that is.

This year we started by taking the road to Todmorden, a nice little town about ten miles away. We did not intend to go all the way there, we were to cut off about three miles or so up the road. We had decided to make the first stop at Dan Paley's farm, because the snow had stopped us last year.

The farm was about five hundred yards off the road and the track leading to it left a lot to be desired. Personally I thought that Jim was a bit 'gam' taking his truck out tonight of all nights. You see, Jim liked his ale and did not like to turn down any drinks. Still it had been Jim who had first raised the subject of using his truck so who were we to turn it down.

The truck swung off the road and down the pot-holed track towards Paley's farm, with Jim conscious of the fact that if he drove too fast his axle could go. It was not that Dan Paley was poor, he had money. It was the fact that he would not part with it. Like a duck below the waterline, he was watertight.

Why were we going to play for him tonight? Well that is a fair question, because he really was a crabby old sod, but the one thing Dan liked was a brass band and, tight though he was, he never 'jibbed' at putting his hand in his pocket for the band.

As I said before, Dan liked the band above anything else. He did not care what other arrangements we had on at Christmas as long as we called at his farm on Christmas Eve. Last year had been a bad one for getting round to all the farms but Dan would not except any excuses. We told him that if he spent a bit of money on the track leading to his farm we might have been able to get there but he would have none of it.

"If I put a good road down, every bugger'll be comin' an' I'll 'ave all the bloody relations o'er every week. I'd 'ave tuh feed 'em yuh know, an' not one o' 'em'll put their bloody 'and in their pockets. They think I'm made o' bloody brass."

Nothing we said would change his views about the track but he still raised a rumpus about us not going last year even though he had been snowed in for at least a week. I think he expected us to ski to his farm. Well, he was one off. Do not get me wrong, he always made us welcome and we did not go short of ale or even a drop of the 'hard stuff'. Of course, the fact that his wife Mary was just about the best cook throughout the valley made a difference. She had to be good, Dan just would not shell out for any 'fripperies', as he called bought cakes.

Mary Paley grew all their own vegetables in her large garden.

What herbs and stuff there were in there she would not divulge but I had to admit her and Dan looked well on it. They had been blessed with two children but Dan said that to his shame they were two lasses and he could not afford any more. He had always said that to anyone coming around, but only when the two girls were near, just to keep them in hand. They had both married farmers and lived very near so with any help that he might need near at hand Mary said that he should not grumble.

After all his moaning and groaning we knew that Dan was pleased that we had managed to call this year. Mary had said that the reason that we did not call last year was because he was too tight, well, he was not tight tonight. After we had played for them they had said how glad they were that we were here and, of course, we were treated to some of Mary's delightful cooking. Meanwhile, Dan had got the bottle moving and we had quite a few body warmers after which it was time to say our farewells, our collecting box having received an addition which, had it become public, would have put paid to all those stories about Dan's tight-fistedness.

Our next stop was at the farm of the redoubtable Fred Pearson and, as we turned down the lane towards his farm, it started to rain. The truck bumped and bobbed down the pot-holed lane and I wondered if we would meet Fred still leaning on his gate as he waited for us. Hearing the rain lashing on the truck canopy, I put the thought right out of my mind. I was sure though that he would be waiting at the door with a bottle in his hand and a big welcoming smile.

As we pulled into the farmyard, the farmhouse door was flung open letting a blaze of light illuminated the whole place, and there standing in the doorway was Fred, pipe in his mouth, bottle ready in his hand and a great big smile on his face.

"Come on in lads, dern't muck about out theer or tha'll get thy death a cowd, leave the water outside."

This we did and our enjoyment was just as good as last year when we thought that we were lost out in the snow. He laughed when we reminded him how near we had been to his farm all the time. I suppose that the story would be remembered every year. He was still chuckling when it came time for us to leave. He topped up our glasses before we left and the compliments of the season were still being shouted as the truck pulled out of the yard and we pointed our nose towards Ganley's Farm about half a mile away.

He was a funny bloke, Harold Ganley, and we did not stay too long there, just a couple of tunes and then off to Bracknell's Farm.

The approach to Bracknell's Farm brought back warm memories of last year when Nat had done such a grand job of arranging for the rest of the farmers to come down to his place because he thought we had got ourselves lost. This year there was no need to do that. In fact we were a bit in front by the time we got there so we were able to stay a little longer. Maybe it was true that his wife Elsie had something in her eye just as we played her favourite hymn, it must still have been there all the time we were there as we played tune after tune.

When we did stop for a rest and a drink, Elsie told us about a strange bloke who had called there last summer, supposedly looking for work but, as Nat was sorted out with the same help every summer, he told the bloke that he had no need for more workers. He did tell him where he could probably find some work so the man thanked him and left. Just a few days later as he was getting into bed Nat thought he heard a noise outside. He told Elsie that he would go and have a look round just to be sure that everything was all right.

Nat quickly dressed again and tried to let himself quietly out of the back door but unfortunately he just was not built for that sort of thing, he was sure that the noise he made could be heard by the whole valley. Once outside he stood stock still and listened. The noise was coming from the chicken coop. Nat crept up to the coop and as quietly as he could he opened the coop door. As he opened it a figure leapt out trying to push Nat aside, but Nat was ready and grabbed him round the waist.

Nat was not a tall man but he was stocky and with all the work he did around the farm day in and day out it did tend to build up the muscles and, mild mannered as he was, if the moment warranted it he could be a terror. This must have been one of those moments because once his hands gripped the waist of the intruder there was little chance of him letting go; he just held on tighter and no matter how hard the intruder struggled he could not shake Nat free. They struggled so violently that they both fell over on the grass with Nat on top. At that moment Elsie arrived on the scene. With the lantern swinging crazily as she ran across the grass she pulled up sharply in front of the two figures struggling before her. She gasped as the light shone on the intruder who Nat had now got under control.

"Nat, it's that bloke who asked you for a job the other day."

Nat pulled the miscreant to his feet, thinking that it would be obvious that he could not get away now that he had been recognised but, as Nat was dragging him towards the house he made another bid to escape, as he did so he caught Elsie with his elbow, making her cry out. At the sound of Elsie's cry Nat seemed to lose all control. Still with his grip on the man's coat Nat swung him round and round eventually having to let go as his foot slipped on the wet grass. Elsie took hold of Nat's arm as she helped him to his feet, keeping hold of him till the dizziness went away.

"Are you all right love?" she asked in a worried voice.

"'Aye lass," he replied still staggering a little. "Just a bit dizzy, but where the hell's the bugger gone? Has he got away?"

Just then there was a plaintive shout which seemed to be coming from the other side of the yard.

"Get me out of this lot, please."

Nat and Elsie made their way slowly towards the voice which seemed to be coming from the tank where they stored their liquid manure. Every farm had one. It was saved to spread on the fields in the spring. They approached the tank with great caution.

Elsie shone the light onto the tank and there in the middle of all that stinking mess was a figure covered in the horrible stuff. Lord what a stink. The more he struggled the worse the smell seemed to get, the clinging manure splashing everywhere.

He stopped shouting and they found out afterwards that it was because when he opened his mouth to shout it got filled with the watery fluid.

At this part of the story Elsie had to stop to wipe the tears from her eyes and cheeks. "Oh lads, you should have seen him, he was such a mess. Oh, I did feel sorry for him." She stopped to wipe her eyes again. "You tell them the rest of it Nat."

There were tears in Nat's eyes as he recalled that night. He wiped his eyes then continued the story. "That weren't all. We left him there until the police came. Well, he couldn't run away from there could he?" Nat paused, unable to continue the story for laughing. "Mind you, if he had done we wouldn't have needed the help of any tracker dogs, we could have smelled him out

131

ourselves." He burst into another bout of uncontrolled laughter. Eventually he continued the story. "When the police came they refused to allow him into the police car dripping with liquid manure, so I had to stand him in the middle of the yard and hose him down, and after sending Elsie indoors we stripped him down and hosed him again, and all this with cold water. I found him an old boiler suit to put on but it didn't make much difference he still smelled to high heaven and the police still refused to allow him in their car so, after a bit of arguing I agreed to drop the charges against him. In the meantime Elsie had washed his clothes in her old boiler and had hung them out to dry. The police stayed until the clothes had dried and returning them to the intruder moved him off the farm with a stern warning. The police sergeant had not wanted him stinking up his cells and they all agreed that he had been punished enough. That," Nat said, "was the last anyone saw of him again, but I still think that he got off lightly and I don't think that he'll go near anyone for a while, they won't let him."

We left Nat and Elsie still laughing over the memory of the incident and I must admit it did sound funny. The other side of the coin was that Nat could have been badly hurt but he wasn't and the story would sound just as good next year.

It had stopped raining by now and we made our way down the hill in the direction of Tufling Copse Farm, our next stopping shop, just about a mile away.

The farm had got its name from what was called Tufling Wood. There may have been quite a lot of trees around at one time but now there were only a smattering and you could see right through to the other side.

As the truck dipped down into the trees the track became very muddy and the truck started to slide from side to side as the worn tyres failed to get a grip. Suddenly there was a bump and the truck stopped dead. Jim started the engine again but the wheels skidded and the truck would not budge. We were well and truly stuck, and to cap it all it started to rain again and this time with a vengeance and, although we were only about three hundred yards from Tufling Farm, we didn't realise it because we could not see a thing, it was pitch black.

"Reight, everybody out," Jim shouted. "We're well down at this side."

We started to get off the truck, jumping down onto what we

thought was the track. What a performance, as each one jumped down he landed in mud which splashed everyone else and even came over the tops of the boots of some of us. There were shouts as everybody blamed everyone else when they got splashed.

"Round the back of the truck everyone," Jim shouted. "When I give the word, everyone push!"

We all got behind the truck and leaned with our shoulders against the tail-board. Jim revved up the engine and leaning out of the door of the truck shouted, "Push!"

We heaved and strained as hard as we could, the truck rolling backwards and forwards as we tried in vain to get it out of the hole. At last Jim shouted for us to rest and get our breath back before we tried again.

"Reight lads let's try again, this time we'll try to rock it out. Each time I shout push and then let it come back and then push again. Ready? Push!"

We again put our shoulders to the truck tail-board and pushed. All at once there was an angry shout.

It is at this point that I must tell you that whenever Jimmy Belfor went out anywhere he felt that he must try to look good and tonight was no exception. Although he had his wellingtons on like most of us, he still dressed like a dandy. He had a dark blue suit on over which he wore a Burberry raincoat, a red scarf round his neck and a check trilby on his head with a jaunty coloured feather sticking from the hatband. That, to us, was being a dandy.

"Stop, yuh big daft bugger," he shouted at Jim. "Look what you've done, you've covered me in bloody mud."

As one we turned towards the angry voice and the figure that we could just make out. Jim Hogan told us to calm down while he got a light. A match was struck and we all looked at Jimmy Belfor. For a moment there was complete silence and then we all started to laugh, we just could not stop as we gazed in awe at the mud covered spectacle before us. Jimmy was not laughing.

"What the 'ell do you think you are doing you dozy pillock?" He raged at Jim Tubbs. "Look at me, I'm shit up to the eyebrows, I'll bloody flatten you if I get hold of you, you useless bloody idiot."

Then the match went out. Still the laughter went on. Jim Tubbs got out of the truck and another match was struck. He took one look at Jimmy Belfor dripping with mud and then he too burst out laughing.

"What's there to laugh about?" spluttered Jimmy. "Here I am covered in bloody mud an' all you bloody lot can do is bloody laugh."

We tried, but it was no good, we were helpless with laughter and we just could not stop. I know it is not funny when you are the one covered in mud but the sight of dandy Jimmy standing there in the rain covered in mud from his little feathered trilby to the tips of his wellingtons, was just too much.

After a while we calmed him down and scraped most of the mud off his clothes and then Jim Tubbs said that we had better walk the rest of the way to the farm where maybe we could get some sort of help to pull out his truck. We trudged up the track and coming to the farm gate we found Bill Stacey standing by the gate.

"What the 'ell's goin' on down there?" he asked. "You're makin' enough noise to wake up the dead. Are tha all pissed or summat?"

We told him what had happened and, as the bedraggled figure of Jimmy came into the light, he burst out laughing.

"Sorry Jimmy," he said. "But if tha could see thyself, tha'd laugh as well." Still laughing he took the still angry Jimmy into the house to get cleaned up. When he returned a few minutes later and we told him about the truck he went and got his cart-horse from the stable and we all returned to the truck. It did not take his great horse long to pull the truck out of the mud-hole and still laughing at the hapless Jimmy we returned to the farmhouse to find Jimmy wrapped up in a blanket while his clothes were drying round the range in the kitchen.

As it turned out Jimmy's clothes were not as bad as they first looked. Once they had been dried and brushed most of the mud came off. Of course he would still have to have them cleaned, but they would do him for tonight. It turned out that his trousers and his raincoat had been the worst but they were OK now, as for his scarf and that cocky little trilby they had come up somewhat better than before but the poor little feather would never be the same again. Still, no one got hurt except perhaps Jimmie's pride, and as we sat having a final drink before setting off again, we noticed that the drinks that had been poured down Jimmie's neck earlier on were now beginning to take effect. He began to see the funny side of it and laughed as he said, "I must have looked like the 'Monster from the Deep'." We all laughed with him. It really had been funny. I wondered if he would still see the funny side of it the next day?

We had now been held up just a bit too long at Bill Stacey's, so it was time to press on. The time was now four o'clock in the morning and we still had two more stops to do. First of all there was Felix Carter's farm, about three quarters of a mile down this same track. It would be easy to get there, the track was wide and it was all down-hill.

When we got to the farm, we found that the party was in full swing. As far as I could see everyone seemed to be drunk, or well on the way. Drinks were pressed onto us, even me. I finished up with a large glass of spirits. It was a mixture and tasted of whisky, brandy and rum, but not being an experienced drinker of spirits, I could not really be sure. Whatever it was, it sure warmed the cockles. I cannot remember just who gave it to me but I remember someone thrusting the drink into my hand and saying, " 'Ere lad, get that down yer neck, it'll keep the wet out, an' if it doesn't you'll be well past caring by the time it 'its the bottom." Then he had staggered off in the direction of the kitchen and I don't remember much else, because it began to take effect and that warm glow started to spread all over me.

I was not used to drinking spirits and as the band lads said that they were not staying long I just gulped the concoction down. It was like setting my throat on fire. At that moment David Green noticed me; I had been keeping out of his way all night. He rushed over and I had the distinct feeling that he thought I was about to have a 'fit'. He told me afterwards that I had suddenly gone red in the face and my eyes started to pop out. He grabbed me by the arm and rushed me out into the kitchen where I collapsed onto the floor. He sloshed water on my face and in a few seconds I started to come round. Although my speech was slurred for a while, I seemed to be no worse off for that cocktail.

After a while I made my way back into the living-room where the party was in full swing. I soon found myself next to a table piled high with food of every kind, and although I was still a bit woozy I was quite able to answer the nagging requirements of my stomach. The next thing I remember is David pulling me from under the table, where it seems I had retired with a couple of pies

135

and some sausage rolls.

"Come on Joe, we're away now," he said, and grabbing my arm he dragged me struggling from the table. Not, however, before I'd stuffed my pockets with food.

Outside once more we moved on to what we thought was our last call that night, or should I say morning. This was Peter Dodson's place, Lower Fold Farm. Now although Peter had only been at the farm since the end of the war, he was a keen supporter of brass bands, especially ours. He had invited us many times to call at his place and this time we were able to oblige, the only thing was, we had not told him that we were coming.

Jim rolled the truck into the farmyard and shut off the engine. Everything was quiet and there were no lights showing. Still, we were here now and we decided that even though we were three parts cut, he would have his tune.

We started quietly but *Hail Smiling Morn* is not a quiet tune and not the best one to wake someone up with. The bedroom window opened with a crash and Peter stuck his head out and seeing who it was he yelled, "You bloody nutters. What bloody time d'you call this to be blowing yer bloody 'eads off, it's half past four in the bloody morning. I've ony bin in bed an hour."

Only Andy Carlton, who was carrying the lantern tonight, seemed to hear him and he had drunk too much ale to let a little thing like that bother him so he just waved to him and we carried on playing, only stopping at the end of the hymn tune, by which time Peter had put some clothes on and was just opening the door.

"By 'ell lads, yuh certainly know when tuh call. I know that I'm always asking yuh to come and play fer us but yuh didn't have to make it in the middle of the bloody night did you? Why didn't you tell me that yuh were comin', I would 'ave bin ready fer yuh?"

"Sorry Peter," Jim Tubbs said. "We didn't come at an inconvenient time did we? I mean you an't the missus weren't in the middle o' summat were you?"

Peter stood there looking at us, and we part stupefied stood looking at him until at last Jim Tubbs said, "Well, you've asked us tuh come an' 'ere we are. Tha can't grumble, we 'aven't that much time tuh spare around this time o'the year, tha 'as tuh be glad we found any time at all."

Peter stood with his coat wrapped round him. Personally I

thought the ungrateful sod was not glad to see us. Then as his family appeared at the door, with the children still rubbing the sleep from their eyes, trying to kid us that they had just woken up and found that Father Christmas had been, at last a grin appeared on Peter's face.

"You useless lot o' prats. Come in. Let's put the kettle on."

We all went into the living-room and in seconds it was as though we had entered another world. Instant gaiety. The children were shouting as they discovered their presents under the tree, ripping and tearing at the wrappings in their eagerness to get them open.

Peter's wife said nothing, she just glared at us. When she did talk to us she said that she would never forgive us for wakening them up. There was very little chance now of getting the children back to sleep with so much excitement. Nevertheless a brew was made and in between drinking and other liquids, we played a few carols including the evergreen *Jingle Bells*. It was nearly six o'clock when we left and by that time Peter's wife had forgiven us and made us all breakfast. Ham and eggs being a very nice change from turkey and chicken. As we left to the shouts of 'Merry Christmas', I had the distinct feeling that Peter would be ever so careful before inviting us to play again.

After leaving Peter's it was back to town. A short rest and then out for the Christmas Day carolling.

This time of the year is not a good time for any bandsmen's families. They, like us, were never sure what time we would be home for our Christmas dinner and keeping Christmas dinner in decent eating condition taxed the patience of most bandsmen's wives, the result being many Christmas dinners spoiled with everything dried up, and we had to eat it, that was the least we could do. We did manage to get plenty of food on our rounds but we dare not say that. We had to appear famished when we got home.

There followed a frantic week to get in the last of the Christmas playing. We had to try and get to all the districts on our lists before New Year's Day which ended the Christmas playing for another year.

Early in the New Year we had entered a contest which we felt that we had a good chance of winning. It was again at Rempton Town Hall. It was also again an 'own choice' test piece. I wondered what Adam would dig up for us this time. I hoped it was something different than *A Souvenir of the Opera* again. It had not been a bad piece for us to play but it did not exactly send the pulses racing when we had to play it over and over again.

12

The Big Engagement

Sunday morning rehearsal arrived and we waited for old Jim Baxter to find the music that Adam had asked for. While he was waiting, Adam decided that we would tune up our instruments after all our Christmas playing, hoping, of course, that we had cleaned out all the bits of food before coming here today.

Adam looked pointedly at Jim Hogan, remembering the time when Jim had played most of the night with an orange stuck in the bell end of his instrument. Jim did not bat an eyelid when Adam asked him to blow a middle 'G', he just picked up his bass and blew into the instrument. A note of sorts came out but it was not a very good one and Adam said, "What's up Jim? Has all that Christmas playin' buggered up thy lips?"

Jim's face went as red as a beetroot. "Well no it's not that," he spluttered.

"Come on Jim we 'aven't got all night, spit it out. What's up?"

By now Jim's face was a picture. He just did not know where to look, he had not been caught out like this since one of the committee had come into the band-room unexpectedly and caught Jim fettling one of the lasses from the village, mind you that was some years ago. That did not make any difference, it was 'water under the bridge'. About his predicament now though, he did not quite know how to say it because he felt so stupid, he was right in 'Dicky's meadow'. There was only one thing to do and that was to come right out with it. Sweat poured down his face as he squirmed in his seat, he just knew that they would laugh.

"I've fergetten tuh put me choppers in afore I came out."

There, it was out now. He waited for the laugh. The room went quiet as Adam, thinking that he had heard wrong said, "You what?"

"I said, I've fergetten tuh put me bloody teeth in afore I come out this morning. It could 'appen tuh onybody tha knows an' if tha wants tuh 'ere me say it again ye're one off, if I say it any louder they'll 'ere it all o'er Burston." With that he got up from his seat and stormed out of the band-room. He only just got to the door before the laughter started, which did not improve his humour one little bit.

Adam looked round the room, not quite knowing what to say.

"Dern't worry," Tom Perkins said. "He'll be back shortly. Tha's lucky he remembered tuh bring his instrument. He were out on't razzle last neet an' the last I saw of 'im he'd 'ad a belly full o' ale."

"Right then," Adam replied, dismissing Jim's petulant display from his mind, "let's get on. Get your hymn books out. Let's see what sort of form you are in this morning?"

With that the rest of the band settled down.

"We'll start with *Cwym Rhonda*, it seems that you've getten yerselves quite a name with this hymn, at least that's what old Fred Pearson said the last time I spoke to him. He said that they could probably hear you in Yorkshire, so you can try it again. Happen it will help blow all the cobwebs away."

Adam then raised his baton and away we went. I think that he kept us on that particular hymn tune for about an hour, on and off. While the rest of the band were stopped he would take the basses, then he would give the basses a rest while he listened to the cornets, after that the middle of the band got a roasting. By the time he had finished with *Cwym Rhonda* the band was not only warmed up, it was boiling.

"Right!" He said, as he put down his baton. "Give the music out Jim and we will try to sort out a piece for the contest at Rempton. This year I mean to win, so get ready for some real work." To us he said, "I have had the librarian dig out some old contest pieces and we are going to have a run through them before I decide which one we will use."

Jim Baxter passed out the music. The titles of some of these pieces were totally foreign to me. We started off with *Nabucco* by

Verdi. This was really something to get our teeth into. Everyone in the band had some sort of solo, every section that is. I must admit, I really enjoyed it, but I knew that we would have to do a whole lot better if we were to play it at a contest.

It took us a bit longer that Adam thought it would on *Nabucco* and therefore we only had a short time in which to look at other pieces that had been handed out this morning. The only other piece I liked was one called *L'African* by Meyerbeer and that was also a hard piece. All the soloists had a chance to show just what they could do and, come to think of it, they did not make a bad job of it. It was the first time that some of us had heard of some of these pieces of music, let alone played them.

As we were leaving the band-room and muttering about how hard the rehearsal had been, Jim Baxter told us that he had been asked to dig out some more contest music for the next rehearsal, one called *Eroica* and another one called *Ernani*. That alone gave us something to think about before the next band practice. *Eroica* I had heard of but *Ernani*, that was a new one on me. I would have to have a word with my dad about that one. Maybe he could tell me more about it.

The next couple of weeks were going to be very busy for us. The band-room was not quite ready for us to return to and if the rain kept up, like it seemed to be doing, it might be weeks before we got back there and did the roof. All we had to do then was to raise enough money to pay for all the materials we had used. Being as we were the town band we had been allowed to have the materials on 'speck' and pay for them later.

When I got home and told my father about the morning's rehearsal and the music that had been put on the stand, he just laughed and told me that the best thing I could do was to go up into my bedroom and start practising, I was going to need it. It seemed that Adam was getting quite serious about it being time we won a contest, so after the next rehearsal I would have to see if I could take some parts home with me and get them practised, then perhaps I would not feel so foolish when we next rehearsed these pieces. Mind you I felt I had better keep quiet about it or the lads would not let me hear the last of it.

In the next few weeks, what with coming home from work, a quick tea and then out again to the band-room to give a hand in replacing the rotted timbers, both in the roof and around the walls, we fair had our hands full. When I look back at the job we had set ourselves to do, I shudder to think what might have happened had the walls not held when we were doing the roof. It might have been better if we had replaced the whole band-room en block. I don't think that there was one part of the roof or walls that had not been affected by rot. If we got some good jobs in the summer, perhaps we could put some cash aside. What a dream. These days money was hard to come by and the possibility of having some money to put aside after uniform and instrument repairs was just not a reality but, you never know. They do say that when you are young anything's possible.

On the following Wednesday evening we tried out the two contest pieces. When we had played them Adam said that we were going to try to win the coming contest with *L'African*. This would really be something if we could manage to get the piece right and, if we did, we would surely have a great chance of winning.

Things seemed to be looking up. Nearly all the band members were turning up at rehearsals and we seemed to be getting into a good routine. Perhaps Adam's enthusiasm was beginning to rub off on us. Who knows? Anything could happen, it is just that it was not something that usually happened to us. Well, the important thing was that, although the contest piece was not perfect, it was getting better and, as we got nearer to the contest Adam decided that sectional rehearsals would help to clear up some of the points which seemed to be troubling the players. This, of course, included the soloists, they carried the main parts of the music. Euphonium, cornet, horn and baritone all had solos, including a trombone and later a horn cadenza.

If, on the day of the contest, our soloists got their parts right, we felt that we had a good chance of winning, or at least coming in the prizes. All the rest of the band had to do was to get their parts right and be as good as the soloists.

This meant of course, taking our parts home and practising them as much as we could. It was boring for the underparts but the counting and the reading of the music was of paramount importance, whether we got it right would only be heard when the whole band practised together. We kept at it, and as we practised it more and more so our confidence grew as the date of the contest drew nearer.

142

The only worry came in the last week before the contest. Adam decided that in order to put a fine edge on our performance we would rehearse every night. What with work, some of the band could not make it but they would have to get there as much as possible. This was very hard. Some of the band had only just settled in after their war service and did not want to chance losing their jobs by refusing to work overtime. Adam asked them to do their best.

All in all we did not get the band on a completely full rehearsal until the Friday night before the contest. This was not altogether unusual with a village band and let's face it, that is all we were, but this year we felt that for once we were in with a shout especially after the final rehearsal. Adam still wasn't satisfied though. He said that if the draw had us playing late, he would want another rehearsal.

The draw did not always suit everyone. Some wanted it soon and then we could get it over with and go for a bevy, others said that late was better then we would have time to have a late practice to put that final edge on our playing. The main argument for early playing was that we would not have time to get sloshed, although they had promised Adam that they would lay off the beer until afterwards.

I could only but hope that we got an early draw, this lot could not keep off the ale for too long, no matter what they had promised. I knew that one or two of them would not even be able to blow if a pint was not forth-coming before the contest, the excuse was that it quietened their nerves. Perhaps it did but my hope was that it would not quiet them too much.

When we arrived at Rempton and had made our way to the Town Hall, David Green was there at the entrance to meet us. He told us that we had been drawn number ten. The moans and groans could have been heard back at Burston, but Adam soon got them sorted out, he just had to keep the older members away from the bar for the two and a half hours before we were due to play. David Green supplied the answer.

"Because we've been drawn so late I've managed to book us a room to practise in. It's just down the street at a pub called The Black Dog and we've got it for two hours."

This announcement did not go down at all well, especially with Tom Bibby.

143

"Damned draw!" he said, half to himself. "If we practise any more we'll over the top an' us lips'll be knackered. My mouth's as dry as a bloody desert, if a don't get a drink soon I'll die o' bloody thirst."

Jim Hogan gave him a sharp dig in the ribs. "Shut thy bloody clack." He whispered in Tom's ear. Didn't tha 'ear the name o' the pub we are goin' to, The Black Dog, remember, it's Fred Dalton's place so, keep thy trap shut, Fred'll sort us out bout Adam knowing owt so, 'ush thy mouth afore he smells a rat."

The two conspirators moved away pretending to be checking their instruments but mainly to keep out of Adam's way. It would not do to let Adam get suspicious, at least not until they had had a pint or two.

They all got back into the coach as David gave instructions to the coach driver on how to get to The Black Dog. Long before we got to the pub some of the band realised that this was the same pub that we had been to last year. Whether David had done this knowingly I had my doubts but no one said a word, not if there was a chance of a drink.

When we got to The Black Dog we unloaded the coach and took all the gear upstairs into the large room. Well, it seemed large but once we got all the band tackle in there did not seem to be enough room to swing a cat and Adam had to stand in the doorway in order to conduct. This turned out to be very unfortunate for the lads who wanted a drink. How the hell were they going to be able to sneak out for a drink with Adam blocking the doorway?

Once again it was David who unwittingly came to their rescue. He argued with Adam that he allow the band lads to have one pint before practice and they would then be in a better frame of mind for the practice. After a few minutes of argument Adam agreed, better to have the band content then he might get better concentration from them. As they were stampeding downstairs to the bar, he shouted after them.

"One pint mind you and no more. You can have another after the practice."

Poor Adam, he might as well have talked to the wall. At the first sign of Adam agreeing to them having a drink they had shot off down the stairs and into the bar. As they got to the doorway into the bar they were pulled up short by the sight of the two men

144

standing there. How had they managed it? Tom Bibby and Jim Hogan just finishing their first pint and the barmaid just putting another two down in front of them.

"Owd on," Bert Rawlins said, " 'ow the bloody hell did you two get down here so fast? I were one o' the first to get through the soddin' door."

Tom's grinning face turned towards him. "It were Adam's fault, 'e told us tuh go an' check the coach, an see that nothin' had been left be'ind, we did that an' when we were comin' back Fred shouted from the tap-room that he'd put a couple o' pints on the bar fer us an' we couldn't leave them there could we? They'd a bin flat as a fluke by the time we'd a got back, then we 'eard you lot charging down the bloody stairs an' by the time we turned back tut bar Fred'd put two more pints on it, so we supped 'em."

Who could argue with such logic? With the argument so suspect that even Bert had to grin. It did not really matter, the crafty sods, they would have got their drink from somewhere, he felt that those two could have got a drink out of the 'Sally Ann'. Mind you, the rules of the Salvation Army would have to be changed before they let those two in.

After about ten minutes Adam shouted from upstairs. "Come on you lot, let's be havin' you, we've a lot to get through and the sooner we get goin', the sooner we finish. We've still got a bit of time before we go on stage, so let's make the most of it."

We all finished our drinks and trooped upstairs again, sat down and we were ready for a good blow. Perhaps this year we stood a better chance of winning, what with having time for a practice just before we went on stage. Of course, if Adam used his head he would be able to keep us practising until it was nearly time for us to play.

We had wet our whistles, now we were ready to practise. Who was missing? We looked round the band. No soprano cornet! Where the hell was Hughie Mack? It was not like him to be late. This we did not need. Our soprano player missing and the contest well into its stride.

Adam carried on without him and we had already played the piece through once when Hughie stepped through the door. I say stepped, more like staggered. He looked a mess. His face was all swollen and his right eye was beginning to close, by tomorrow he would have a bobby-dazzler of a black eye. Even worse than that,

g

his lip was beginning to swell up. How the hell was he going to play a soprano cornet with a fat lip?

"What the blazes has happened to you?" Adam gasped, visions of the contest cup floating before his eyes. "Did you fall downstairs or what? I only let you out of my sight for two minutes and you come back looking like a walking disaster."

Hughie sat down and as we rendered what first aid we knew he told us what had happened.

It seems that when he had gone downstairs to the toilet, to answer the call of nature, there had been two other bandsmen having a very heated argument and Hughie, being late and also in a hurry to get a pint, pushed past them and with a, "Come on lads, let the dog see the rabbit, I haven't had a pint yet," he proceeded with his urgent call. The two men, feeling very aggrieved at being so rudely interrupted, turned round and gave Hughie a push and told him to mind his own business. Then one thing led to another and the result was that, although Hughie could look after himself, he finished up with a fat lip etc.

Hughie's black eye was not the thing that worried Adam, it didn't stop Hughie from playing. Even the swelled face did not upset him much, but the lip, that really was too much. He let fly at Hughie with both barrels and a string of invectives that would have made his own Regimental Sergeant Major stick his chest out with pride. At the time I do not remember him repeating himself once and at last, when he had calmed down, he sent Hughie down to the bar for some ice for the fat lip.

This, we decided, was not a very wise thing to do, taking into consideration the blasting he had just given him, in front of the band too. We waited, feeling sure that the chances of Hughie returning were, to say the least, quite slim. If he did not return, the chances of winning the contest were minimal. Hughie was a very good soprano player and the only one we had.

In the meantime we had to get on with the rehearsal. After about fifteen minutes a very dejected Hughie returned, looking very sorry for himself and with a great bag of ice pressed against his fat lip. He did not play during the final rehearsal, just sat there trying to get the swelling down. I hoped he would succeed, we did not want to lose either him or Adam but I had the feeling that if he did not play in the contest the row he would have with Adam afterwards could possibly mean the departure of one or the other from the band and that could be disastrous.

The time seemed to be slipping away at an ever increasing rate so that Hughie had less and less time to get his lip in shape to play but, in the meantime he would not be able to practise. No wonder Adam was mad. All that work that he and the band had put in and now the chances were that we would be without a fully fit soprano player.

I suppose it could be done in the time available but it could also be wishful thinking. If Hughie's lip was still swelled by the time we were to play then we could borrow the soprano player from the band that had just played before us but that depended if that particular player would play for us.

As it happened, we did not have a chance of the soprano player from the band before us, playing for us, he had been one of the bandsmen who had been battling with Hughie in the toilets and it seemed that Hughie had given as good as he had got. During the fracas Hughie had broken one of his front teeth and he could not play at all. The word was that Hughie had been reported to the contest committee so we were not all that sure that we would be allowed to play and even if we were allowed to play there was still the chance that we could be disqualified.

While we were still practising a message arrived for Adam and Hughie to go and see the contest secretary. After they had given their side of the argument the decision would be made as to what would happen to either both bands or just both players. In the meantime Ernie Benson took over the rehearsal, once more playing his cornet with one hand and conducting with the other.

About an hour later Adam and Hughie arrived back with the news that Hughie had not been disqualified from the contest, the whole band had. The band that had made the complaint had also been barred. The committee, after listening to both sides of the matter, could not decide who was really to blame, as the complaint had been that Hughie had been trying to 'nobble' the other band's soprano cornet player and Hughie's reply was that he had not known that the man had been a soprano cornet player, and the third man had not been found, so both the bands were disqualified. I, and the rest of the band were lost for words, all that practising for nothing.

Adam was not pleased. Not pleased at all and he let us know in no uncertain tones about how he felt. David Green came in for some flack as well, it had been him that suggested the band have a drink before the contest. All that was now finished, in future the band would not be given a choice, if a bandsman was found to have had a drink before a contest Adam would disqualify the player himself and if the band committee did not like it they could find someone else to conduct their band.

To make a rule like that against a band like ours was going a bit over the top. Banding was a way of getting out for a drink for most of them, at the same time doing what they liked best. The two just went together and I felt that some middle ground would have to be found if Adam was not going to lose some of the playing members. That also went for the players as well or we could be short of one conductor, but I had known some players walk for miles just on the off-chance of getting a drink so I doubted if Adam's warning would do much good, we would just have to wait and see.

Well, that was that. Even though we appealed to the organising committee, the decision stood. The only thing that we could do was bring it up at the next regional meeting. Today we were out of the contest. What a disappointment! What could we do with all this extra time on our hands? We sat and thought for a while, it must have been all of three seconds before, as though at a signal, we all rushed down the stairs to the bar. It was said that it would take quite a lot of ale to get over the disappointment of not being allowed to play in the contest. What a laugh! The only disappointment was when we could not catch the barmaids eye in order to get a drink.

We still could not believe it. All the rest of the day to sup in! The worry being would the cash last out? I think that Bert Rawlins and Tom Perkins getting into a card game provided the solution.

They were past masters at this sort of thing and played so well together. With those two playing as a team we should be able to rely on them to supplement our cash-flow problems. As if there were any question about it! The only question was would anyone cotton onto their shenanigans? If they were caught trying to pull any fast ones, they were for it. They did not need to, they had played together so often that they were unbeatable.

For the rest of the day we stayed at The Black Dog. Even when closing time came, Fred Dalton allowed us to stay, along with anyone else who wanted to. As long as there wasn't any trouble and the newcomers came in by the back door, Fred would continue to serve them all. Also, as long as there were newcomers coming in and supplementing the card game, Bert and Tom were ready and willing to accommodate them. The more the merrier.

By the end of our stay at Rempton the arguments were still being discussed whether both, or any one of the bands should have been disqualified. Maybe we would get some support through our band newspaper, I feel sure that there would be questions and answers and the controversy would continue for some time.

As for us, we were disappointed, but not for long and by the end of the day we had all had a great time, with, perhaps, the exception of Adam Bailey.

Songs had been sung and beer had been put away in great quantities and now it was time to leave. We really were sorry that we had been unable to play in the contest because we felt that we had a good chance of winning, which was nothing to go by, we always thought we had a good chance of winning, there was no point in going if we did not, but that was it for this year and there would be other times. We had had a great time at The Black Dog. Next week we were playing at Burley for their annual walking day parade. That was on a Sunday. The walk would be about four miles.

13

A Bobby's Job

The next week we were playing at Burley for their annual walking day parade. That was to be on Sunday. The walk would be about four miles.

We met at the band-room as usual, but today there was to be no argy-bargy about who would travel in whose vehicle, today we were to travel in what is laughingly described as a luxury coach. In fact it was the same coach that we had booked for that disastrous contest at Rempton. Well, beggars cannot be choosers and as long as it got us there and back, we did not mind one bit.

Burley, the town where we were to play was a reasonable sized town situated about ten miles from Burston. The industry was made up of many different factions. Cotton mills and various textiles, engineering works and a large factory making tyres, chemical works and many other types of factories which helped to mix the smoke and chemical filled air - the results being shown in the dirty brickwork all over the town.

We set off nearly on time and to the tune of crashing gears and smoke belching from the exhaust of our 'luxury coach' we climbed over the steep Pennine roads to Burley. Here was where the coach driver left us as he had to return to Burston in order to do another trip. He said that he would return for us at six o'clock as arranged. We took that promise with a pinch of salt. Drivers had promised to be back at a certain time and then had put in an extra trip somewhere else finishing up calling for us about two hours late. I do not know why they promise to come back at a certain time for, all we needed to do was to give them the address of a certain pub and wait there for them to come, it just gave us more drinking time.

The driver dropped us off at St Mary's church with all the paraphernalia we required for a walking day, he then shot off back to Burston.

The sun was shining and it looked like we were going to have a nice day. The time was eight-fifteen and we did not have to start until eight forty-five. It was not far to our first stop which was a large recreation ground in the centre of the town. Here all the churches met and held a religious service in which they all took part.

The start of the service was to be at nine-thirty, or as near as possible, and would take about two hours. During that time we would not be needed so we were free to wander. All we had to do was to be back before the service ended.

In all there would be eight bands taking part in the procession. Each band would lead their particular congregation through the town and onto the recreation ground. When the church service was over the bands would again lead the processions out of the ground and round a specified route through the town finishing up back at their own church.

As I said earlier, the morning was warm to start with and if the weather stayed as promised, by the time the church service was over it could be a very pleasing day. The trouble is that when you wear uniforms with tunics that button up to the neck, on a warm day it can become very uncomfortable. Of course that was only one of the possibilities, the British weather had a habit of proving the forecasters quite wrong. Even coming into early summer it was still possible to have hail showers, but surely not on a day like this, at least I hoped not.

Dead on time we set off for the walk to the 'rec' and with the double taps on the bass drum we moved off to the march *Slaidburn*.

The atmosphere was a happy one with the church banners flying, the children laughing and chattering with excitement, dressed in their Sunday best. Harassed church stewards fussed around the outskirts of the procession like worried sheepdogs and with the sun shining there was a real festive feel in the air.

The recreation ground was only about three quarters of a mile away but even at this time of the morning people were bustling along the streets trying to get to the best vantage points in time to see the processions as they passed by. The sounds of the bands approaching the recreation ground seemed to give the town a carnival atmosphere.

I did spare a thought for the police. Having different processions along various roads inside the town boundaries must have given them quite a headache, but from what I saw it did not seem to bother them. Great big strapping bobbies (stomach in, chest out), were grinning and waving back at the many children running along the pavement, one of their many jobs being to make sure that nothing would be allowed to hold up the processions.

Eventually we reached the 'rec'. We were the second church to arrive. There were stewards everywhere waiting to guide each congregation into place and once they were there they could relax and wait for the rest of the churches to arrive. Time also to give the basses a rest. They tended to get quite heavy after a while and there was still the long walk to come after the service was finished, so when the chance came for a rest we took it with grateful thanks.

We listened with interest to the other churches arriving, with at least three of them having managed to book one of the 'Top' bands of the day. After listening to them as they played on the approach to the 'rec' we realised that we would have to be on top form ourselves, they would certainly be listening to us.

At last the final congregation arrived and was shown into place. The service could now start. All the bands except one were marched to one side leaving more room for the church service and allowing the children to spread out. The one band chosen would stay and lead the hymns.

Some of the bandsmen left out would stay and listen to the hymns and we would get a report later on how well they had played, you can bet they would say that the band playing was not up to standard, the jealousy at not being chosen to stay and play would really creep in. Maybe they were right, who knows? Personally I preferred not to play, on a warm day like this it could become very sweaty crowded together on the 'rec'.

Pete Barton, our third trombone player, decided that he did not want to stay and listen to the hymns etc. and as it would take a couple of hours to get through the service he was going to have a look around the town and try to get the feel of things, perhaps he would find somewhere to get a drink. Some hope so early on Sunday morning, but at least it would pass the time away till the pubs were open.

That was it. Jim Robins, Ernie Benson, Dick Hardy and myself decided to go with him, then Bert Rawlins said that he would tag along just to keep an eye on us. He left with a reminder from David Green that we had to be back no later than an hour and a half from now. We thought that we would be back much sooner than that.

We wandered down a side street leading from the 'rec' hoping that it would lead to the main street. It did not and after a short argument in which Pete got called a few chosen names we changed direction down another street.

What a set of plonkers we were, it did not take us long to realise that after coming less than four hundred yards from the 'rec' we had got ourselves lost in the endless back streets that seemed more like a maze. Pete said that he would be able to find his way back when the time came and like idiots we believed him.

We carried on to the end of the street and Jim Robins, who was in the lead said, "Owd on lads there's a pub down here."

The magic words 'pub' filtered through our arguing and we looked in the direction he was pointing, not for a minute questioning the fact that it could not possibly be open at this time of the morning. Sure enough there was a pub, The Gamecock Inn. We gazed at it with something like rapture, if only?

The thoughts were obviously passing through everyone else's mind as well. Just then the door opened and a man's figure appeared. He was wearing an overcoat over his pyjamas and had obviously just come to pick up the milk from the doorstep.

"Er, excuse me." Jim was the first to recover from the initial surprise. "We've getten ourselves a bit lost, which way is it back to the 'rec'?"

The man looked up at Jim in surprise, he had not seen us come round the corner. He spluttered a bit and pulled his coat round him trying to hide his pyjamas.

"Tha ony needs tuh go tut bottom ut street, turn reight an it'll lead thee straight theer."

"Thanks," Jim replied and before the poor chap could say or do anything else, Jim got in, "by the way is there any chance of a pint?"

The bloke looked at Jim 'gone out', probably wondering if he was quite right in the head.

"Tha cheeky bugger," he burst out, "I 'aven't even 'ad me breakfast yet an' thy'are't askin' me tuh open the bloody bar?"

Not so easily put off, Jim said, "Well, it's like this, we're playin' in the procession an' it's thirsty work, when the pubs er open we'll be playin' an' when we've finished playin' tha'll be shut, but don't take it to 'eart I'm nobbut askin'."

Now this chap, who was obviously the landlord, looked at Jim for a minute in amazement but as he took in the cheeky grin on Jim's face he could not help but smile himself.

"All reight, yuh cheeky buggers, go round the back and I'll open the door for thee." With that he shut the door quickly. It sounded ominous and I thought he had closed it to shut Jim's grinning face out but true to his word by the time we had found our way round the back he had the door open and ushered us inside. He led the way into the bar.

"Reight, what'll it be. Tha con only 'ave bottles, I 'aven't got the pumps on yet."

We took our chances with both hands and asked for a couple of bottles each after which we went and sat down in the tap room. The landlord poked his head back into the room.

"I'll 'ave tu leave thee fer a minute while I go an' get dressed an' finish me breakfast. Don't worry I'll be back but I'll know better next time ther's a walking day, I'll not go tuh bloody bed, I'll sit on the bloody doorstep an' wait for thee tuh come round. Save thee knockin'."

He looked at us for a couple of seconds and then realising that his sarcasm was wasted on us, he disappeared and we heard him clumping up the stairs, probably to get dressed.

I do not know how it happens but if a pub is open during closing time, some bandsmen seem to be able to smell it out. It does not matter how many precautions you take and we made sure that no one was about to see us go into the pub. The street was completely empty, not a thing moved, but within two minutes there was a tentative knock on the back door. We did not make a sound. Then a tap on the window and there we were. We did not have a chance, once we opened the door in they came. How they found their way here was a mystery but here they were, more bandsmen, and we could not do a thing about it, in no time at all the tap room was going full blast. Cards, darts and dominoes.

When the landlord reappeared about five minutes later he could not believe his eyes, he just stood there for a few seconds unable to take it all in. He had only been gone for about five minutes, just to finish his breakfast and get dressed and when he returned the tap room was packed with bandsmen all clamouring for a drink. What could he do? He was totally outnumbered. The one good thing was that the bell on the till never stopped ringing, a sound that made up for all the work.

How was it known that this particular pub had opened its door (back door) to us, we had only been here about nine minutes? The explanation came later. It seems that a bandsman from another band had been out on the scrounge at the same time as we had and in his wanderings he had caught sight of us disappearing round the back of the pub, so he decided to wait a minute or so and then he followed us and, hearing voices, he had looked through the pub window and had seen the landlord opening some bottles for us, on deciding that he should also have some of this, he followed us round the corner towards the back door.

As he turned the corner into the back street, a policeman had walked into view at the other end of the back street and stopped there, possibly to bend his knees a time or two to rearrange his credentials. He decided that this was a bit chancy. He could not very well just walk straight down the back street and into the back door of the pub, one, because he would most likely be seen and two, because the pub was not supposed to be open yet.

The question then arose as to how he had overcome this difficulty? It seems that he waited to see if the bobby would move and as he did not show any signs of doing this he decided to risk it, so he crept from one back gate to another, as we had seen it done many times with the soldiers on the newsreels when they were shown fighting from house to house in the war.

He eventually reached the back door of the pub, luckily without being seen. Or, so he hoped, and then he had tried the back door handle, which some silly sod had left unlocked and here he was. It seemed a bit far fetched but he insisted that it was all true. Of course the same thing had happened to the rest of them, one having followed the other.

The pub was buzzing by now and the landlord begged us to keep the noise down. He said that if we wanted to confirm the story all we had to do was to go halfway up the stairs and look out of the stairs' window which overlooked the back street. As there were still a few bandsmen slipping quietly in through the back door we took him at his word.

When we looked out of the window we doubled up with laughter. It was just as the first bandsman had said because we could see the whole length of the back street. Obviously the policeman was still there because we could see figures dashing in and out of the doorways of the street until they arrived at the back door of the pub which had been left ajar.

We returned to the tap room and told them all what we had seen happening at the back of the pub and the antics of the bandsmen willing to try anything in order to get a drink.

After a short while one of the latest arrivals asked us what was tickling us and we told him all about them creeping down the street and of the bobby standing at the bottom, who had no idea what was going on behind his back.

"What bobby?" he asked. "I didn't see any bobby."

"Well, what were you doing dodging down the back street like the rest of them? You could have walked straight in the back door without all that messing about," Ernie Benson said.

"I wasn't messing about," he insisted. "I've been stood at the end of the street for about twenty minutes trying to think of a way to get a drink and I heard a noise behind me. I turned round just in time to catch sight of a bloke disappearing into the back door of this place so I followed him and here I am."

Those of the bandsmen who had heard him suddenly went quiet, then one of them said, "Does tha mean that we've bin doin' all that dodgin' about, an it were thee standin' at th' end of the street?"

"Aye, I suppose it musta been," he admitted. "I suppose the uniform does look a bit like a bobby's from the back."

The atmosphere in the room started to change. It was considered a crime in the band world to keep a bandsman from his pint and I thought for a minute that they were going to separate him from his breath but the landlord stepped in and defused the situation by telling them that if there was any trouble he would close the bar and throw the lot of us out.

156

"Come on lads," Jim Robins said. "It were an 'onest mistake an' we did get the landlord to open up for us."

With a few veiled threats they went back to their drinking. It would not be long before we were due back at the recreation ground so we did not have time for any bickering.

A few minutes later Ernie Benson looked at his watch and warned us to 'sup up'. If we did not start now we would be late getting back in time but one of the other bandsmen, who had been on this job before, said that we had plenty of time. Once the Vicars started spouting, and there were a few who wanted to get their penny-worth in, then they never knew when to stop. It was not every day that they had a captive audience.

We started back anyway. We had promised David Green that we would be back in time and we did not want him having a baby and prattling on about us losing a very lucrative job, one which we could not chance losing.

He arrived back at the recreation ground to find David anxiously looking at his watch. Some of the other lads who had wandered off were only now beginning to arrive back at the ground but he need not have worried when he realised that they were all accounted for and it was still another thirty minutes before the service was finished, thirty minutes that could have been spent much more effectively back at The Gamecock Inn.

At the end of the service all the bands assembled with their various congregations, the stewards fussing round them to get them into their correct positions ready for the march round town.

The morning sun was very warm now and the choking tight collars which had to be done up to the neck, did not help one bit. We were starting to sweat and we had not set off yet. The quantity of ale that had been consumed was effecting the same parts that we wished it could not reach.

We had visited the toilets before leaving the pub and returned the ale from whence it came. It all had not been able to go through the system in time, but it had to go somewhere and before this walking day was over there were going to be quite a lot of red faces as the pressure built up.

The crowds had gathered at every vantage point where only the police barriers held them back. In some places they were as much as seven or eight deep. These were the days of Sunday Schools turning out for the witness celebrations and the great thing about it was that as the processions walked past parents, relations and even just onlookers, they would dash out into the road and push a coin into a child's hand or pocket. I've seen this done as the band walked past and, with some bands having little more than children playing for them, complete strangers would dash out from the crowd and put a coin in a child's pocket.

We marched round the town and down so many streets and roads that had we not been in a procession we would very soon have been lost. The fact that we had our own church marshal leading us dispelled that anxiety and the reality that he was just following the congregation in front of him did not occur to us.

After the long walk round town we knew that we were nearing the turn-off to our own church. The stewards had done a magnificent job in their arrangement of the order of march of the churches in that they were able to turn off to their own church without any disruption of the rest of the procession.

When our turn came to turn off everything went just as smoothly, the steward gave the signal and as we were playing a march at the time we just followed him and suddenly we were outside our church playing the rest of our congregation into the schoolroom.

We had got ourselves organised as we knew that we would have to give a short concert in the school-room but that would not be for about an hour yet. There was tea, sandwiches and biscuits for everyone but best of all, right next door to the church was a pub, The Three Barrels. What a stroke of genius, once again we had landed on our feet. This was not just a one-off thing, it happened all over the country, a pub right next to a church. Luck or just good management, we could not say, but whatever it was it was all right with us.

As was to be expected with our band, we went into the pub for 'lunch'. What was totally unexpected was that the Vicar came in as well and had a noggin or two.

After we had had a good drink the Vicar remarked that he had heard that we could sing a bit, so we repaired to the singing room and Ernie Benson sat down at the piano and began to play. We had thought of trying to shock the Vicar with a few choice songs but when he joined in the chorus of *Four and Twenty Virgins Came Down From Inverness*, we decided that it was more possible that he could shock us if he really let himself go. I think that after he had told us that he had been an army chaplain we began to understand. He had us outgunned so instead we sang our favourite *Cwym Rhonda* which was great for harmonising. We moved on to *Deep Harmony* and many more. Before we had finished I am sure that we had gone right through the hymn book; and from the look on his face I felt that we had been completely out manoeuvred, the Vicar of this church was not as daft as he was cabbage looking and before we knew it, it was time to go back into the schoolroom to give the concert. We'd been in the pub for a good hour and in that time we had only had a couple of pints, with no chance of over doing the beer. What a crafty Vicar.

We returned to the schoolroom in good time for the concert. Everything was ready. Chairs set out and music stands set up with the music ready and waiting, we did not have to do a thing except play. The children had all finished their lunch, cleared all the lunch things away and were now sitting, waiting for us to start.

The concert we played was a selection, with children's favourites and a mixture of songs from 'Gilbert and Sullivan'. In these we had something for everyone to sing to. After the concert the Vicar gave a short speech of thanks to the band and the church organising committee plus everyone who had helped and an invitation for the band to come back next year. That was that and now we were free for the rest of the day, at least until six o'clock.

Playing the concert and packing things away afterwards had kept us busy until well after the pubs had closed, so we had to find some out of the way pub who would open its door to us, but where?

Burley was a medium sized town and we did not know our way around very well. Tom Perkins said he had his Working Man's Club affiliation card with him so if we shaped ourselves we could probably find a club that would let us in, all we had to do was to find a club.

First we raided the telephone kiosks for a directory. From that we got a list of Working Men's Clubs and their addresses and after a few wasted enquiries we arrived at the Burley Conservative Club. Tom Perkins tried to get in with his card but a member would have had to sign us all in and they were very reluctant to do so, especially since Tom's card was for a Working Men's Club.

Panic stations. Time was running out fast. We had not had a

drink for over two hours and some of us were getting withdrawal symptoms we could never hold our heads up again if we had to admit failure at getting a drink during closing time. The rest of the band had come to expect great things of our small group. We had bragged that we never failed to get a bevy somewhere during the hours that the pubs were closed and up till now we had always managed to uphold this dubious honour.

He were about to give up, fed up with tramping round trying to get a drink in an obviously dry town. We were foot-sore when we found that our aimless wanderings had brought us back to the recreation ground. Surely there had to be one club or pub where we could get a drink! Our reputation was about to be shredded and we only had just over an hour before we would have to admit defeat and return to the coach that would take us back to Burston. Suddenly Bert Rawlins said, "Hang about lads, what's that light across the rec?"

We all turned to look in the direction he was pointing. At first we could not see a thing but Bert insisted we looked again.

"Theer by the side o' them factories. See, theer it is again."

We looked but still could not see it so, Bert, in an exasperated voice said, "It's theer, an' I'm goin' tuh 'ave a look."

He set off across the 'rec' towards where he thought he'd seen the light. Like a lot of sheep we followed. Well, we had nothing else to do, so why not? As we got nearer to the factory we realised that Bert had been right. There was a light, only dim but it was there just the same. Dick Hardy said, "By gum Bert, I'd never 'ave believed it, tha must 'ave eyes like an 'awk tuh 'ave seen that light from o'er the other side o'the 'rec'."

"Aye," Jim Robins said. "It must a bin a bloody shite hawk, talk about luck, if he fell down a petty he'd come up with a bar o' bloody chocolate in 'is mouth."

Luck or not, there it was, a dim light shining onto a boarding proclaiming the magic words, The Railway Workers' Social Club. A sight for sore eyes.

As we stood there the door was thrown open and a shaft of light escaped as one of the members staggered out of the club and it was only then that we realised that it was not night that had fallen, it was much too soon for that, it was getting very foggy and that was the reason that the light outside the club had been switched on, otherwise we would not have found it. Foggy or not we now had a good idea just where we were so if we could get into this club we would have time for more than an odd pint. First we had to get in.

"Go on Bert," Jim Robins croaked, the fog catching his throat, "tha's gotten thy card, knock on the door an show 'em, they con nobbut say no."

"OK, but don't be so bloody pushy, gimme chance tuh get it out, mind you a must say, it's a scruffy bloody place. Still, I'll try owt once."

Somebody pushed the bell on the side of the door. I do not think they expected it to work but after a minute or so the door opened a few inches and a voice said, "What d'yu want, makin' all dat bloody racket. Keep it quiet." Bert stepped back a bit.

"We're bandsmen," he stuttered. "We've bin playin' in the procession an we're just lookin' fer a pint."

The door shut with a thump and we heard the sound of chains being removed from the door. The door opened about a foot and a big black arm, the size of a leg of mutton, shot out and grabbed hold of Bert's coat and dragged him in through the door into a dimly lit hallway. We followed quickly before the door could be shut on us and once inside we were confronted by a giant of a negro. I could only surmise that he was tall because the light was dim and the place was filled with cigarette smoke which hardly rose above the tables in the room we were directed to. Once inside the room the giant spoke.

"What'll it be den?"

"Six pints," Bert said quickly.

"Stay d'ere," the giant ordered. "I'll bring de drinks."

He returned a few minutes later with six pint glasses which were about three quarters full but one look at those thick black arms and any arguments that could have been forthcoming were frozen on our lips, we certainly were not going to protest to anyone the size of this chap. We paid for the drinks and sat down at the nearest table. The negro spoke again.

"If yo want any more de bar is down on de right." With that he padded off into the haze. We had said our thanks as he moved off but he did not acknowledge us and we were left to try to check on our surroundings.

As I said, none of the pint glasses were full pints but who were we relative pygmies going to complain to? It went against the grain to accept less that the full quota of beer paid for but in the circumstances the less we said the better.

"Well," Pete Barton said, "I've never been in a place like this before, I'll bet they still use spittoons here."

"Never mind," Bert said. "We've got a drink, of sorts, sup up an we'll 'appen get another one. Same again?"

We agreed, same again. Bert collected the glasses and disappeared into the smoke. I had a panicky thought as he disappeared down the room, the smoke left billowing in the spot where he had just been stood. I wondered if we would ever see him again. I had read about people disappearing from places and being sold into slave labour. Naw! Who the hell would pay good money for an old wrinkly like Bert Rawlins? He was way passed his 'sell by' date. He was turned fifty.

After about ten minutes waiting, Bert still had not reappeared, so we decided to go and look for him. Oh God, surely it could not be happening here? This was 'Burley' not the 'Middle East'.

We all started to make our way in the direction that Bert had taken, feeling, our way from table to table, the smoke still being pretty thick. If we bent down we could see reasonably well down the long narrow room.

On the left there were alcoves with just ordinary pub tables and chairs where we could see some figures huddled together talking. We could not make out it they were men or women the room was so darkened. The tables and chairs on the right were similar but being pushed further hack against a wall we could not see if there was anyone sitting there or not.

We carried on down the room until we came to the only thing that represented the bar. It did not seem much, more like a collection of boards covering a sort of solid desk. All around this 'bar' was thick wire netting broken only by a sliding board which represented a sort of window and was lifted about eight inches, this, apparently, was the only place where we could replenish our glasses.

As we approached this opening, six semi-filled pint glasses were waiting on the bar and a hand poked through the opening and motioned towards the glasses of beer, obviously these were our beers left by Bert, but how they knew that they were for us it was a question never to be answered because we could not see a damn thing for the smoke.

Opposite the bar were some benches covered in some sort of plush material. These seemed the most popular seats and were filled with men and women. As we peered under the smoke we could see hands everywhere. Up skirts, down trousers, the laughing and gasps with no one taking a blind bit of notice. Further back in the gloom there was movement as two or even three bodies were stretched out on the covered seats, but no one seemed to care what was happening. It seemed pretty obvious that these activities were not unusual.

We continued on down the room in search of Bert but what was going on in these seats were nobody's business. I suppose if he had been here my father would have called it a den of iniquity. Joe Sudders, being more experienced said that it was more like a brothel and it was not until much later we remembered to ask him how he knew it was more like a brothel, but Joe, who had spent some time in the Middle East during his army service, would not say and after muttering something about the 'Cazzbah' he clammed up saying nothing more.

On reaching the end of the room we were just in time to see Bert coming out of a room with a ram's head pictured on the door underneath which was printed 'Men's Toilet', this in turn having been crossed out and replaced with the word 'Heads', which again had been crossed out and the word 'Bog' painted in. It would have taken too long to read all the names written there but they all meant the same. We were not slow, we cottoned on that this was the toilet, it was written in all Languages.

I was relieved to see Bert coming out hurriedly and when I told him he said, "Aye lad, thart not half as relieved as I am. I needed that, but I wouldn't go in theer if I were you, ther's fellers in theer frey countries I cannot even pronounce. All colours they are an' if thart not careful they'll have the bloody shirt off they back. I only managed to get out because they started arguing o'er my jacket, who were goin' to 'ave it, an I were still wearin' it."

Bert then walked past us and back up to where we had been sitting he picked up his ale and with one gulp he downed the lot and made his way towards the door out of the club. We followed Bert's lead and drank up. It was generally agreed that none of us needed the toilets after Bert had told how they were feeling his jacket.

"It weren't just that," he said, his face going red. "One bloke tried to grab me family jewels, so I got out o' theer as quick as I could, nobody's safe in theer on ther own."

There was no time to argue. Things were getting a bit out of hand and although this was the only place where we could get a drink we were all of the same opinion, it was time that we got back to the coach.

We had been in some rather unpleasant places in our time for the sake of a pint but it was generally agreed that The Railway Workers' Social Club at Burley will always remain in our memory as the 'pits'. We would have to be gasping and totally off our blocks before we went in that club again. It makes me wonder sometimes though, if they were having a damn good laugh at us. Thank God I only have to wonder.

We caught the coach on time and the journey back to Burston went quietly except for the questions thrown at Bert about the club we had left but Bert just fobbed them off. He did not even want to talk about it and believe me it took something to quieten Bert Rawlins.

Our arrival back at Burston at about seven thirty did not cause any consternation amongst the populace so we put our gear back in our temporary band-room at 'The Duke' after which we were free to sample our own mixture of 'hops' and get the taste of that smelly club out of our mouths. It was agreed that only a very savage ale drought could get us back into that club again, or, of course, if there was nothing else open! Anyway we were back on home ground now, so to speak, and the evening was ours.

Playing with the band, from our point of view, meant that we were out for the day. There was no thought of going home. Out was what we were and until the pubs closed or we ran out of money, this was where we would stay.

The walking day at Burley had been very good, taking everything into consideration. A reasonable amount of ale had been consumed but that did not mean that the day was finished. It meant that we did not have to be at a certain place at a certain time. We always kept our instruments with us and if we ran out of money we could always go busking, be it in a pub or club or even outside, we never failed to raise enough money for ale.

14

Post-horn Gallop

Christmas 1949 and the New Year's Day 1950 celebrations passed in the usual drunken manner, except that this year we did not stay out all night on Christmas Eve. This year we could not raise enough players who were willing to forsake a warm bed. The amount of players were enough but the mixture would have been all wrong, so we decided to give it a miss. The farmers were told that much to our regret we would not be coming round this year. We got the expected moans but the news was generally taken with good grace.

Adam Bailey had been trying for some considerable time to get us to think about the sound we were making; not that we had any complaints but just blowing and hoping for the best would not be good enough to win contests. He harped on about us listening to one another when we were playing and trying to keep in tune.

Listening was all right when we were not playing but when I tried to listen and play at the same time I either lost my place on the music or miss counted the bars on the copy. I mentioned this to Hughie Mack one night but all he said was, "You'll just have to keep at it lad, we all have to concentrate to do it but when it all comes together and you've learned to listen you'll find that it's the difference between a good band and a bad un. Keep persevering, an' tha'll soon feel it come reight."

I thought about what he had said and I kept on trying to play and listen at the same time but the way I was going on I would never get into that class of player. Maybe it could come in time but I wished it would hurry up. It would not be long before a letter arrived from His Majesty inviting me to join his army or something.

Before I did that however, I would have to go for a medical, I supposed, to make sure that I was fit enough and I had not even been invited for that yet. My mother did not think it fair that I had to go into the army just when I was beginning to bring some much needed cash into the house and that she was going to write up to the War Office to complain. She maintained that her and Dad had kept me for eighteen years so she was not going to let me go until she had got her money's worth.

My father listened to her ranting on about the army. He uttered not a word, he just smiled and shook his head, happen it would do her good to get it out of her system. Later, when he got me on his own and after he had warmed me up with a few tales of how he won the war, he then told me that when the invitation came for me to go for a medical not even my mother could stop me going. If she tried they would send a couple of warm-hearted gentlemen with red bands round their hats to try to persuade me to go. I must admit that I did not take much notice of my mother's ranting, in fact I was quite looking forward to it. My only worry was that I would not pass the medical.

In the meantime Adam had decided that we would try to enter the Belle Vue contest in May. We had already sent off the entry forms in the hope that by sending them early our entry would be accepted. We had tried before to enter in the fourth section but we had been unsuccessful because there were already enough entries in our section and all entries to a Belle Vue contest were filled up very quickly. This happened every year, but we hoped that this year our luck would change.

'Belle Vue' was a Mecca for brass bands everywhere. The name alone was enough to conjure up memories of a by-gone age. Older brass bandsmen would go glassy eyed at the very sound of the name and would speak in awe of some of the great bands and bandsmen they had rubbed shoulders with in the 'Gardens', as they called it. Just to play there would be a privilege, but to be there and see some of the greats of the brass banding world like Irwell Springs from Bacup, Black Dyke from Yorkshire, or Fodens, Munn & Feltons, Brighouse, Besses 'o th' Barn and who knows how many more? What a day that would be, but let's not count our chickens, we had not been accepted yet.

However we still had one or two engagements to fulfil. A concert in the local Mechanics' Institute was the next job for the band. I asked one or two of the lads where the Mechanics' Institute had originated but as usual no one knew for certain. Jimmy Belfor said that he thought that they had been developed to teach budding motor engineers their trade but after a few more idiot answers I decided to go to the local library and find out for sure. I do not know why I felt that I had to know about it but it seemed to get right under my skin.

After a fruitless search through countless books in the library I decided to go straight to the top, and getting a grip of myself I knocked on the chief librarian's door. How I found the courage I do not know because it was not advised that you disturb the librarian himself, it was recommended that you make an appointment to see the great man. Well I, in my ignorance, did not, so here I was standing outside his door shaking in my shoes. I need not have worried, he found the relevant details while I sat in his office, in fact he was kindness itself.

It seems that the Mechanics' Institute was the brainchild of a Dr George Birkbeck from of all places the land of the dreaded Yorkshiremen, at that time it was not thought that Yorkshiremen could have ideas as good as this, but he did and his first 'Institute' was started in Scotland in 1823.

The idea of forming 'Institutes' was born of trying to find something for the workers to do instead of them going out and smashing up machinery brought in to the great mills which did the work of countless workers, throwing many of them out of work. It was to try to develop the educational and recreational pursuits of the working classes who, through lack of amusement had been driven into vice and criminal activities. This worried the ruling committees etc., who decided that if the working classes were to be saved and become contented workers, recreation was essential and this is where Dr Birkbeck's Mechanics' Institutes came in. Music was introduced into the 'Institutes' curriculum, amongst other things, the idea being to stop them having to expend all their energies in rioting and debauchery.

Well, that was the beginnings of Mechanics' Institutes and before very long there were over seven hundred and fifty of them throughout Great Britain. I decided that these must have been the very earliest night schools. The mind boggles. At a time when there were not many day schools, they invent night-schools. I read it over and over again and eventually came to realise that it all made sense, even in those times there must have been people who wanted to get on in life so they used the 'Institutes' to learn their trades. It must have been one hell of a time to learn about music and brass-banding and now our next concert would be in the local Mechanics' Institute where it all started. A thought did cross my mind. I wonder if Dr Birkbeck's parents came from Lancashire? It would make more sense if they did. It was not in a Yorkshireman's nature to 'do owt fer nowt'.

Then one practice night the good news came. We had received the test piece for Belle Vue and our admission to the contest. The contest piece was *Ernani* by Verdi. This was a piece that Adam said would stretch our abilities to the full. Cornets, baritones, flugelhorns and euphoniums all had hard parts. Flugel and baritone had a duet, the solo cornet had a cadenza as well as the euphonium. It was agreed that there would be some fur flying before this contest was over. Adam had his ideas and the band had theirs but there would be only one winner, unfortunately not before blood was spilt.

The test piece itself was considered to be beyond our capabilities by some of the older bandsmen. Well, we would see. We had the soloists who we thought to be good enough, but did we have the experience in the underpart players? I had the feeling that in the coming weeks there were going to be battles galore as frustrations crept in, there could only be one answer and that was home practice.

I had to practise the piece, my father made sure of that. The fact that at times it got very boring made no difference as over and over again I counted the rests and after-beats. Playing little tunes was OK, you could follow it, but when you had lots of after-beats without a tune to guide you that was when it became awkward and boring but with my father forever looking over my shoulder that is how it had to be. At times like these I felt that I would never make the grade as a musician.

Unlike any other piece of music this one was going to be special. We would be playing it in the hallowed halls of Belle Vue Gardens, to give it its proper title. It had been many years since the Burston Band had played there, with nothing in our records to suggest that we had anything to show for it.

This was only the beginning of weeks of practice that was to follow. In between we had to rehearse our concert music. This was our bread and butter.

The concert itself was to be held in our own Mechanics' Institute and would be an afternoon's concert, our chance to show the people of Burston that they had a band that perhaps someday they could be proud of, also, the concerts helped to fill the coffers of the band. If we made a good job of the contest at Belle Vue maybe we would be able to raise our fees next year.

At the concert we would not be the only artists there. They had a baritone singer called Tom Darby and a lady singer known locally as 'Madame Clara' who turned out to be a very large bosomed lady. When 'Madame Clara' sang it was as though the very rafters shook loose and when she tried to hit the very top notes and missed, which she frequently did, she would turn and glare at the pianist as though it was his fault. I felt that this lady's pianist had drawn the short straw when 'Madame Clara' had asked for an accompanist for the concert. It had been suggested to Tom Darby that he and 'Madame Clara' should sing a duet, but for some unknown reason he had developed a fit of coughing and, with a look of abject terror on his face, he had made a dash for the gent's toilet and could not be persuaded to return until the threat of singing a duet with 'Madame Clara' had been removed. These goings on caused Tom a great deal of ribbing when they were being related in the pub afterwards. It seems that more than once 'Madame Clara' had offered her services for the concert and this time there had been no one on the concert committee who dared to oppose her. I doubt that if the 'Mechanics' had burned down it would have stopped 'Madame Clara' from singing.

We stayed in the pub for about two hours, drinking and playing cards but this time lady luck had deserted us and we decided to move to another venue. Also we had run out of funds and this was one publican who just would not let us 'go on the slate'. The only way we knew to replace our funds was to find a pub where we could busk and get paid for doing so.

Once outside we pooled our cash and found that we could only afford half a pint of ale each, so we decided to go to one of our better appreciation pubs which was on the outskirts of Burston, the Dog and Partridge. We had called there one time in the past

h

and after livening the place up with a few well chosen tunes, had been invited back sometime. Well now was the time to return with the hope of getting free ale and as we opened the door of the pub we were welcomed with cry's of delight.

"Hello lads, 'as tha come tuh sup or are tha gonna give us a tune or two?"

That was Ted Taylor the landlord, a rather dour chap who liked everyone to think that he was a born and bred Lancashire man when in fact he originated from Derbyshire. It did not matter to us where he came from as long as he payed for the ale. After a bit of friendly argy-bargying they got the idea. We would play anything that they wanted and they would pay for a round of drinks. This was not too bad at first but at the time we arrived there were only about twenty people in the pub and it soon became obvious that they were not going to pay all night.

It was during one of our stops for a drink that someone spotted the post-horn hanging over the bar.

"Hey Ted, how long have you had that post-horn hanging up there?"

"Well, not long. Y'see, we've had it hanging up here behind the bar fer ages an' one of the lads said why not put it where everybody could see it, so we gave it a bit of a polish an' hung it theer. It can't be blown cause there is summat stuck in it, but it looks good."

"Has anybody tried tu blow the thing?"

"One or two o'the locals have had a try but couldn't manage it, mind yuh they weren't professional blowers like you lot." The last remark being delivered while at the same time giving a sly wink to the other occupants of the bar. Of course we fell for it.

"How about lettin' us have a try at it then? 'Appen we con clear it an' give thee a tune at the same time."

"Tha con try lads, by all means but I think it'll tak' more puff tuh do it than you lot 'ave."

Harry Rawlins lifted the long post-horn down from its mounting over the bar and gave it a shake. Then he lifted it up to his eye to see if there was any daylight showing through it.

"Tha's reight Ted, I can't see a damn thing through it. It's blocked all reight." Harry banged the post-horn against his hand to try to loosen the blockage and then raising the instrument to his mouth, he took a deep breath and blew into it as hard as he could.

170

After a few seconds his face started to go very red. His eyes looked as if they were about to pop out of their sockets at any time, but not a sound could he get out of it. At last he capitulated. Sweat streamed down his face from the effort he had made. In between gasping for breath he handed the post-horn to Dick Hardy.

" 'Ere Dick, see if tha con do owt we it, the ony thing I've moved is me bowels." He sat down to catch his breath and have a drink, feeling a bit foolish at having bragged about clearing the damn thing out.

"Go on Dick," someone shouted. "Give it some bloody stick. Tha con do it."

Dick did just the same as Harry as he puffed and spluttered trying to blow the horn but it was no go, all we heard was a loud expending of air as Dick parted with the pressure, unfortunately from the wrong end. At last Dick had to admit defeat and with a face as red as a beetroot he lowered the post-horn.

"By 'ell Dick," Ted said, grinning all over his face. "Tha were tryin' but pressure just got the better of thee. I did hear one note, pity it didn't come from't post-horn, I think that the only way we're goin't clear damn thing is tuh drill it out."

"What are tey talkin' about drillin' Ted, the post-horn or Dick's arse?"

The thought of it made Jim Bibby burst into laughter till tears ran down his cheeks. "I dern't know Dick, I knew tha were full o' hot air but I've never heard you prove it before." With that Jim clutched his stomach and sat down, still laughing fit to bust. It looked for a moment that Dick might take a swing at Jim but after a second or so he grinned and sat down, just for once having been bestead on breath power, and believe me Dick had been noted for the power he could put into his instrument when asked to do so.

We carried on like this for about an hour or so. I had a go but could not do a thing except make my eyes bulge. We had done everything we could to loosen the muck that must have been blocking the horn, even some of the regulars in the bar had tried but to no avail, the blocked post-horn would not give up its secret. Eventually we got to the point of giving up, perhaps Ted had been right when he had said that the only way to unblock it was to drill.

We thought that everyone who wanted a blow had had one, that is without our newest addition to this boozy group of ours, Jack

Nuttall. He had been stood at the other end of the bar watching the proceedings and getting quite a laugh each time we failed to blow the blocked instrument. His presence had been noted and he was not about to get away with that. If we were going to look foolish so was he.

"Come on Jack," Jim Tubbs shouted above the laughter. "There's only thee who 'asn't tried tu blow the bloody thing yet an' tha'rt not gettin' away with that. Tha's gett'n a lot o' ale out 've this lot an' you've let us all loosen it up fer thee so let's see if tha con do any better, or are tey all talk?"

Jack straightened up from his leaning position on the bar. "All reight," he said, taking hold of the post-horn in both hands, "let the dog see the rabbit, hell, I can fart harder than some o' you lot con blow."

He lifted the horn up to his lips and, taking a deep breath he concentrated all his efforts into his first try at blowing the post-horn but, although he blew as hard as he could, nothing happened. He looked round at the grinning faces in front of him and tried again. This time we thought he would burst a blood vessel, still no joy and with a triumphant shout from the rest of the crowd he lowered the post-horn and retired back to his place at the other end of the bar.

"Tha couldn't blow thy way out of a paper bag," Tom Bibby said, "but tha still goes around spoutin' at us fer not bein' able tuh do what tha can't do thyself, thy'art all wind an' piss, tha mouthy pillock." He turned back to the bar grinning at the landlord.

Once more Jack took the bait and came round the bar. "Give us that bloody horn," he shouted. Obviously he was getting mad at being baited. He grabbed it up from the bar. "I'll show you bloody lot how tu blow." With that he lifted the horn up to his lips once again.

"Make way you lot," Joe Sudders shouted. "Give 'im room, tha mouth's goin' tuh do it this time, I can feel it in me water."

Having Joe mouthing off at him like that only seemed to get Jack's back up and as he lifted it up in the air we all scattered. As Jack put all his effort into blowing it just so happened that the horn was pointed at the landlord who was laughing his socks off. He stood with his hands on the pumps, safe in the knowledge that Jack had no chance of blowing the post-horn.

Because it was Sunday night the landlord was dressed in a

white shirt, black bow tie and dark trousers, and with his hair combed back he looked very neat and tidy. One thing he should not have done though, was to laugh in Jack's face. It was like a red rag to a bull. Jack's face reddened and he gave a great big thrutch and blew into the post-horn as hard as he could. As the pressure filled the inside of the horn there came a whooshing sound and a big clod of tightly packed dust flew out of the end and hit the landlord squarely in the chest, bursting into millions of particles and spreading over everything in the bar. We could hardly see one another as we coughed and choked.

When the dust cleared and the coughing had subsided we turned to look at the landlord who was definitely in shock. I thought for a minute that he was going to explode. He was covered in dirt and his eyes were glazed. His once white shirt looked as though it had been worn by a chimney sweep. Then the glazed look turned to one of horror as he surveyed the disaster area that the bar had turned into. The customers were trying to brush themselves down but every time they did so a cloud of dust rose again. On the bar there had been about twenty pints of ale in various stages of emptiness, now they all had a film of dust floating on the top.

It was obvious that it was going to take them a while to get this mess cleared up but just for now the landlord was struggling to regain the use of his vocal cords. Jack, who, with the help of the rest of us, had caused this commotion, just stood there like a statue, his face as white as a sheet.

The room had gone very quiet and then slowly the chatter started and got louder by the second. It started with a chuckle from someone. We looked around, this certainly was not the time for laughing. There it was again. After a wander round the room our eyes focused on Jack himself, the one and only who had managed to breach the blockage in the post-horn. He was turned away from us at the time but we could see his shoulders shaking. We did not think that it was that bad and wondered why he should be so upset. He turned towards us with tears streaming down his face but he was not upset he was laughing fit to bust. It did not take the laughter long to spread and suddenly we were all laughing, that is everyone except the landlord, Ted Taylor. He was livid.

"Who's goin' tuh clear up this mess then?" he almost

screamed. "An' look at me bloody shirt, I'll have to go and get changed all over again an' it's all your bloody fault you numb buggers, if you 'adn't wanted to piss about wi' that bloody post-horn, this wouldn't have happened. I'm goin' upstairs tuh get changed an' when I come down you'd better not be here." For a moment he seemed to struggle with his emotions, we thought that he would calm down seeing as he had egged us on with the post-horn, but no, when he did speak it came out like a death knell. "You're bloody barred, the lot of you, you're bloody barred for life." With that he turned and barged out of the bar and slammed the stairs' door behind him.

The noise in the bar, which had gone quiet now rose again as everyone tried to speak at once. After about five minutes it once again went quiet as Ted made his reappearance, changed and smartened up. His eyes blazed when he saw that we were still in the bar, he got mad all over again and shouted.

"I thought that I told you bloody lot to bugger off? If you're not out of here in ten seconds I'll molycrush the damn lot of you."

"Hang on a minute Ted," Jim Tubbs said. "You were just as much to blame as we were. You were egging us on all the time so don't try to put it all on to us. We didn't know that all that shit in the post-horn was goin' t' cause all this trouble but we'll help tuh clear it all up an' any way yuh owe us some ale, this lot's covered in dust an' muck."

Well, I think that really did it. Ted had given the ale free in the first place and he certainly did not look in the mood to give us another one. He just stood there for what seemed ages, the pressure rising and looking as though he was going to burst a blood vessel. Then one of the regulars gave a nervous laugh. This was too much for Ted as he pointed a shaking finger at the door.

"Out," he shouted. "I mean it, out you bloody go an' don't bloody well come back, and I meant what I said, you're all barred, barred for bloody life."

It was like something out of a silent movie when the heroine is thrown out into the street by the baddy. Dramatic! One of the regulars ushered us towards the door.

"Leave it for now lads," he said. "He'll be all right when he's calmed down, we'll sort it out, it weren't your fault. When he's settled down he'll realise that. Call in another time."

We walked out of the door a bit shamefaced and I think that

174

Ted was feeling a bit sorry for loosing his temper like he did but he could not very well back down in front of his regulars and the other people in the bar.

One of the lads, I think it was Jim Tubbs, called some time later and the pub had a new landlord. It seemed that Ted had moved to another pub somewhere in the Manchester area. Well, never mind, perhaps we would come across him when we went to the contest at Belle Vue.

We stood outside the Dog and Partridge, wondering where to go now? Ted had disowned us, thrown us out in the street and not much brass. Suddenly it happened, Harry Rawlins had a brain-wave. He suggested that we call in on the Riverside Inn up on Torside.

The Riverside Inn is a place that we do not frequent too often, mainly because it is where the toffs tend to go. On Sunday night they arrive in their big cars, dressed in their penguin suits with their women or wives, you could never tell which was which, who would arrive like 'mutton dressed as lamb'.

To get to the Riverside Inn it was either walk or have transport. It was situated about three miles outside Burston on the moorland road. Some Sundays there would be music provided and, as the place was 'plush', scruffs were not encouraged to go there but, as we had long had an open invitation and were still wearing our band uniforms, the chances were that we could still get in even though the 'Inn' had recently changed hands. If we pulled it off then the evening could prove to be very lucrative indeed so, it was unanimous, the Riverside Inn it was.

Travelling in the back of a fifteen hundred-weight truck is not all it is cracked up to be. It can be very uncomfortable. I feel that it is only after a few pints, which helps to dull the pain, that we can even begin to feel something like easy. We were just about that stage now. Just as well because the road to the 'Inn' was anything but smooth.

Eventually we arrived and turned into the car-park. Jim backed into an open space and we all got out. What a place! To start with Jim had parked right next to a Rolls Bentley, all shiny and new looking. When Jim realised where he had parked his face turned a shade green, even in the glow of the dim car-park lights.

"Oh God," he groaned. "Keep away from that damn thing. If you so much as look at the bloody thing it could cost us a bomb."

We moved quickly away to a safe distance as Jim restarted his truck and moved right away to the other side of the car-park. It did not come over that he was scared, it was purely self defence. If that Bentley got so much as a scratch, Jim wanted his truck to be as far away from it as possible.

Still taking quick glances back at his truck in apprehension, chance it might move of its own accord, Jim led us into the well lit porch of the Riverside Inn. The building had once been a large country house before the war but anyone seeing it now after it had been renovated would never have recognised it.

The entrance to the Inn was so large we could easily have driven the truck straight in with plenty of room either side. We entered the large open doors into a hallway that stank of luxury. Everywhere we looked it had wall to wall carpeting. I must admit I felt quite out of place in these luxurious surroundings. I just was not used to this sort of place but, making sure that the rest of the lads were in front of me, I followed them inside. I hoped that there was no one inside who would recognise me. Who was I trying to kid? I did not know anyone with this sort of money or even a car and what did it matter if someone did recognise me, what then? I began to wish that I had never come.

Still leading the way, Jim opened the door which led into a very large room. At the far end was a small stage on which stood a grand piano. This did not look the place that would welcome a brass band, let alone just part of one.

On looking around the room, which was packed with people drinking around various tables, we noticed that they were dressed for the occasion. Men in penguin suits and the women in various fancy clothes. In our local Working Men's Club this would be classed as the 'singing room'. In this place it was a music room.

As we opened the door and entered the room there was a buzz of noise as they all talked in lowered tones, which quickly stopped as everyone seemed to look at us. Their eyes seemed to burn right into us. I felt as much at home as a nun in a brothel.

I turned back towards the door, ready to make a break for it when I heard Tom Bibby say, "Oh hell! That's torn it." I turned back just in time to see Jack Nuttall striding straight down the middle of the room, just as though he was on parade. Cap straight, his uniform buttoned up to the neck and looking neither left or right. The low murmur of conversation that had started up again now stopped as all eyes turned to see who it was and what was going to happen. Jack did not bat an eye-lid as he ascended the steps leading up onto the stage and over to the grand piano.

We all knew that Jack had been drinking steadily since teatime, but now he seemed to be in a trance. We also knew that another of Jack's attributes was that he could always guarantee to knock out a tune of some sorts on a piano.

It was like a bad dream that we could not wake up from. We watched with bated breath as he stopped in front of the piano. He lifted the lid and propped it up then, pulling the stool forward he flicked out the back of his jacket, just as though he had coat tails on and then sat down ready to play. We had all followed Jack's progress in the hope that we could get near enough to grab him and 'exit stage left' but we were too late. He lifted up the piano lid and turning towards the audience he bowed and placing his hands on the keys he began to play.

We held our breath. It was not all that bad either, I had heard the tune on the wireless, it sounded like *The Warsaw Concerto*. We watched in silence as Jack's fingers fluttered out to his right to the top notes of the piano. We breathed again, this was very good. When Jack finished playing we would be in. What an ace.

Oh damn! We had relaxed too early. As Jack's fingers fluttered up towards the top notes of the piano, his fingers did not stop. It was like a 'Keystone Cops' film. His fingers fluttered up and over the edge of the keyboard to Jack's right and as they did so he overbalanced to his right off the stool; as he fell his left foot caught round the leg of the piano and as his momentum carried him off the stage the leg of the piano was pulled away from under it. There was a thunderous crash as the piano tilted over onto the floor where the leg was now missing and Jack landed on his back on the floor of the 'music room'.

He lay there for a moment not moving as we all tried to distance ourselves from him then, rolling over on his side, he got hold of the steps leading to the stage and struggled to his feet. The room was deathly quiet now as everyone just waited to see what was going to happen next. So were we, this had not been part of the plan.

Suddenly we realised that we were standing near the front of the room gawping at Jack like a lot of country yokels. We tried to

177

move back out of the way as unobtrusively as possible, but then it started. At first it was only a titter and then quickly gathering momentum it turned into a full blooded roar of laughter which echoed round and round the room.

It seemed that it had only been seconds since we had entered the place and now it was in an uproar with the grand piano leaning over on its end a probable wreck. How the hell were we going to get out of this one? Once again lady luck was on our side.

At first I expected that we would either be arrested or thrown bodily out of the place because a rather large gentleman was making a bee-line straight for Jack. We moved quickly to Jack's side hoping somehow that there would be a miracle and we would be spirited out of the place but unfortunately the large gentleman arrived and as we turned shamefaced to him hoping to appeal to his better nature, we realised that we were in deep trouble.

We had tried to make ourselves invisible but it was of no avail, we were cornered. As we turned appealingly to him we suddenly realised that there were tears streaming down his cheeks as he grabbed hold of Jack's arm.

"Hold on lad," he said with a sort of a giggle. "That's the funniest thing I've ever seen, I've never laughed so much for years. You could be a better turn than Tommy Handly. By the way who let on to you that the piano was dropping in bits. I have been meaning to get rid of it for some time, it's full of woodworm. That leg was the only thing that kept it upright."

It was with great relief that we agreed with him that Jack was a laugh a minute and much too good for us, but that he would be OK when he was better.

"Why, is he ill?" the gent enquired.

"No, not yet," Bert replied, clenching his big fist.

After a bit of coaxing - we really wanted to get out of this place as soon as possible - we agreed to give them a couple of tunes. We played a few marches and a couple of hymn tunes which were very well received, then we said that we had to go. We did not want Jack doing any more of his impromtu comic displays.

We said our good-byes and and left the music room as quickly as possible but as we got outside in the reception area the same man from the music room was waiting for us. What now? He grabbed Ernie Benson's hand and I thought now that we were out of sight of the patrons he was going to give us a right going over.

Nothing could be father from the truth. As he gripped Ernie's hand he beamed at us all and just could not thank us enough.

"Thank you gentlemen. It's been quite a night and I've enjoyed every minute of it. I hope that you will come again and bring the full band with you."

This was something else, he called us gentlemen and we had just wrecked his grand piano, even if it had just been there for show. Ernie muttered something about him having to write to our secretary and we made a bee-line for the outer doors. He shook hands with Ernie once again and opened the door for us to leave.

When we got outside Ernie called us together and said, "Do you know who that was?"

We just stared at him.

"He just happens to be part owner of this place and he's willing to pay the band for a concert sometime soon."

"I'm not coming back here fer at least twelve months," Tom Bibby said. "Ah dern't dare show me face in theer agin' after that load o' cods." He turned away in disgust.

"Well, tha weren't want owt' tuh do wi' this then?" Ernie's cheery voice said.

As one we all turned to look. There in Ernie's hand was a white fiver.

"Wheer the 'ell did yuh get that frey?" Joe Sudders exclaimed. "I 'aven't seen one o' them fer bloody years."

"That bloke who owns the 'Riverside' pushed it in me 'and as we were leavin' the place, said to buy us all a drink we' it cause 'e 'adn't laughed so much fer years." Ernie chortled. "Yuh see, yuh never know what'll 'appen next do you? Anyway, let's get movin', it's gettin' late but if we 'urry ourselves we can still catch the Grey Mare open."

"What about Jack?" I said. "He's knackered."

"Throw 'im int' back o'the truck," Jim Tubbs replied. " 'Appen t' fresh air'll bring 'im round, if it doesn't we'll sup 'is share fer 'im an' serve 'im bloody right too fer puttin't fear o' God into us, the useless pillock."

"Steady on Jim," Ernie said. "If it 'adn't been fer Jack we wouldn't have owt tuh sup wi'."

Jim just scowled and turned away. He would never admit it but Ernie was right even if it had been an accident.

A fiver! That would keep us in ale for a week or two, so

179

grabbing the drunken Jack we literally threw him into the back of the truck and piled in after him after which Jim, driving very erratically, set off for the Grey Mare, another pub off the main thoroughfare but on the way back to Burston.

The Grey Mare stood well back from the main road just this side of Littleton village. It was a well known country pub said to be over three hundred years old. It had been the stopping place for the old Leeds to Manchester coaches long before these new-fangled roads were built. In those days people had been able to stop overnight in one of the many old rooms and even though the pub had been virtually rebuilt you could still get a room for the night if need be.

We arrived at the pub at about ten fifteen. Jim Tubbs turned into the driveway so suddenly that we were caught unprepared and finished up in a tangle with the instruments in a great heap. Jim did not bother one bit as he drove straight into a space near the wall, pulling up with a screech of brakes, thank God they worked, but it did not help us one little bit. What language, and all directed against the hapless Jim.

"Tha great puddin'. If any o' the instruments are damaged I'll bloody damage thee, thy 'art a bloody maniac, if it were up tuh me I wouldn't let thee drive a bloody wheel-barrow."

The voice coming out of the darkness was unmistakenly Tom Perkins'.

The threats against Jim Tubbs life were coming thick and fast as we tried to sort ourselves out in the dark. Instruments and bodies littered the back of the truck, but though the ride had been hairy and fraught with danger, here we were outside the Grey Mare with nothing more than a few bruises.

Jim had been tipsy when we set off, and the way he had driven to get us here had done nothing to endear himself to any of us, the thing that we all conveniently forgot was that without Jim Tubbs and his old truck we would not be here at all. Perhaps playing all those hymns was paying off because somebody up there was surely watching over us.

When we walked in the door of the pub, a great shout went up. We had been there before and they had been expecting us for over an hour, I do not know why, I did not know of any arrangements made earlier.

"At bloody last," a voice shouted. "Where the hell have you

180

been?"

I just could not understand it. How could they have known that we would be coming? We had only decided ourselves twenty minutes ago. The answer came a second or so later as Ernie Benson said, "Sorry but we got held up."

"What with a bloody barrel of ale?" A voice laughingly enquired.

"It's the only thing that would stop you bloody lot gettin' here."

It seems that Ernie had phoned the landlord of the Grey Mare, who was a friend of his, earlier in the week and said that we would most likely be coming this Sunday evening. Of course Mary and Jack Thompson, mine hosts of the pub, had spread the word and as a result the place was packed, the only thing was, where the hell were we going to play? There was hardly room to swing a cat.

"Don't worry lads," Mary said at the look on our faces. "We've reserved a good place for you lot. Come with me."

We followed her as she pushed her way through the crowded bar. At the far end of the room was a very large oval table. Mary pointed to it.

"Will this do?" she asked. "You can rest your music on the table propped up against your ale glass and you're right out of the way. Don't look so worried I'll make sure that you get enough ale."

Would it do? It was the biggest table that I had ever seen. Hell, we could have sat all the band round it. Well, nearly. Just then a waiter pushed his way through the crowded bar-room and put nine pints of beer down on the table, compliments of the landlord. Phew! This is the life. Sat down and being waited on. Free ale. What more could a chap want?

After we had finished our drinks Ernie said that we had better make a start and give them a tune or two, so we upped with our instruments and started off with *The Wearing of the Green* followed by the *Thin Red Line* and *The Voice of the Guns*, then it was time for another drink which was on the table waiting. We had five minutes rest and then someone in the crowd asked for a special tune.

Jack Nuttall, still a bit woozy from the last debacle said, "Ask away. We'll play owt tha wants but the price is a round o' drinks

181

fer the band."

A well dressed bloke stepped away from the bar. "Right get these lads some ale in," he said. "But if I'm paying for the ale and the tune then I should be the one to conduct the band."

He turned and smirked at his companions by the bar who were egging him on. This was something that we had not bargained for, a stranger and obvious nutter wanting to conduct us? We did not even know if he could conduct and if he could not there would be a right palaver.

" 'As tha conducted a band before?" Joe Sudders asked, just a bit too politely.

What was he up to?

"Well no," the bloke replied, grinning at his pals, "but it can't be that hard can it? It's only a matter of waving your hands in time to the music." He turned to his friends at the bar, obviously showing what a clever dick he was. It was quite clear he had called at the fountain many times and he was going to show this lot that money had its advantages. He could take the micky out of anyone or anything. He had paid for the privilege so he was now ready to show them. We waited. We would just see what he could do.

"Reight lads," Ernie said, giving us a sly wink. "Keep one eye on the baton and the other on me."

The special tune that the bloke had asked us to play was *Colonel Bogey*. He was ready and he laughingly took a pen from his pocket to use as a baton. The game was on.

Ernie smiled up at the bloke disarmingly and said, "Ready when you are."

The bloke lifted his baton and started to wave his arms about. Nothing happened except a few weird sounds from various instruments. The bloke went red in the face.

"Count two aloud and then start," Ernie said helpfully.

The bloke nodded at Ernie, his supercilious smile having now vanished. He counted two and then started to wave his arms about, this time in something like a march time. The bloke turned to his friends in triumph, the grin now back on his face. This was the moment that Ernie tipped us the wink. Ever so slightly Ernie slowed the tempo down. The idiot did not even notice that the beat had slowed. Half a dozen bars later the tune had slowed to a dirge. The people started to laugh and suddenly the bloke realised that we were going too slow. He tried to quicken the beat so we quickened our playing and then his beat was much too fast. He then tried to slow us down but he did not know how. He made efforts to cut the band off by making wild slicing motions with his arms, the band was playing in different tempos and the audience were in hysterics.

We could see by the look on his face that the bloke was getting very exasperated, his collar suddenly seemed much too tight and he was starting to panic. He looked round at his cronies but obviously no help would come from there, they were laughing with the rest of the room. Now other people from around the room were beginning to take notice and were enjoying it as well. We could see by their faces that they were enjoying this man being taken down a peg or two.

We were told afterwards that for some weeks he had been treating the place as though he owned it, flashing his money about and treating the waiters, and everyone else, like a load of rubbish. He had missed going into the forces for some unknown reason and he had made his money, some say, selling meat on the black market. How they knew this I could only guess at, but he certainly was not liked around here and they were all enjoying his embarrassment. He was making a right fool out of himself. Of course at the time he was not aware of this, he was just a twit trying to make a fool of us, and that he just could not be allowed to get away with.

At last we took pity on him and let him seem to have made some sort of recovery and finish his stint of conducting with a flourish. The people round the room gave a great cheer and the now chastened bloke turned and bowed to the audience as though he had been in on the fun all the time. He turned back towards us and if looks could have killed we would have been struck dead on the spot. I think that if he could, he would have taken back the ale he had bought for us but it was too late for that, we had drunk it before he had started to conduct.

One thing that the man had done was to set a precedent. Anyone who wanted to conduct the band, such as it was, could do so but first they had to buy a round of drinks for the band.

So it went on until at last the landlord called 'time' and even then the customers did not want us to stop playing, even though we had gone through our full repertoire twice since we had started to play. The bloke who had started it all had long since disappeared.

Well, as they say, all good things must come to an end and we were given a rest. It was then that we looked round the table at all the ale still left there that we had to sup. We had been playing so much that by the time we had finished playing the big oval table was packed with pints of ale. If we stopped here all night we would not be able to drink this lot. If that bloke was here now he would laugh his socks off. The table had been well and truly turned and now we were stuck.

We looked at one another in consternation, how were we going to be able to drink all this ale? We were still sober, it was one of those traits of blowing a brass instrument. When you have been blowing for some time it seems to stop any inebriation happening, what did that matter now though? We still had all this ale to sup and not long in which to do it? This just was not fair. We had always been able to stand our corner when it came to drinking but getting rid of all this ale was something else.

The more we looked at it the more it became obvious that some would have to be got rid of on the quiet, even if it meant pouring it down the drain. We could not bottle it, more's the pity. Here we were for the first time in our lives with more ale than we could drink. It was a catastrophe!

It did not help to keep looking at it, we had to get started. As some of us started drinking Joe Sudders started to pour some of it into the bell-end of his euphonium until it was nearly full and then with ale dripping from every crack and crevice he carried it to the toilet. As he reached the toilet Dick Hardy opened the door to come out and Joe passed him and with tears in his eyes poured the contents down the toilet. Dick grabbed his arm.

"What the 'ell are tey doin' Joe? Surely yer not throwin' good ale down t' privy? We've played all bloody night fer that."

"Piss off, yuh stupid pillock, d'yuh think I like doin' this? It's the worst moment of my life. I sharn't be able tuh look the lads in the eye again." He gave a sob. "We'll never be able tuh live this down so dern't say another bloody word, just go in theer an' tak' a look at all that bloody ale on t' table, I'm ony glad that the folks as bought th'ale fer us 'as all gone 'ome. If they saw this calamity they'd never buy us another drink as long as they live."

Dick gave a quick shufty at the ale laden table and returning to the woebegone figure of Dick standing in the toilet doorway, he said, "Aye, I see what tha means lad but carn't we sup as much as possible first an' then get rid o'the rest, if ther's any left over?"

Joe looked at Dick in astonishment. " 'As tay ony idea just how long it'd tak' nine men tuh sup that bloody lot yuh great 'gobbin'. Even wi' our drinkin' capacity we couldn't get rid o' that lot in a month o' bloody Sundays."

Dick took a step back at Joe's outburst. "Steady on lad, I were on'y tryin' tuh 'elp, mind yuh, I did wonder why Tom Bibby were droppin' them pints quick like an' then rushin' outside an' spewin' 'is ring up."

"Aye, I know abeat that," Joe said wryly. " 'E's bin out theer three time up tuh now an't last time we found 'im slumped o'er the wall on the car-park. 'E didn't know what bloody day it were never mind where 'e were, an' even then 'e didn't recognise us, so we grabbed 'im an' dumped 'im int' back o'the truck, but by the time we'd got back int' bar 'e were already theer suppin' some more. A bloody glutton fer punishment that lad. I wouldn't mind but I've spilt more down the front o' me bloody tie than 'e were gettin' in 'is gob. Anyway I'm goin' back tuh try tuh clear some of it out o' t' way afore Arthur sees me. Yuh realise dern't yuh that if this ever gets out we'll never live it down so, shap thyself an' get back in theer, tha's a bit o' suppin' tuh do afore we get cobbed out. I on'y 'ope that Jim Tubbs isn't swillin' it down or 'e'll never be able tuh drive us 'ome an' that's the last thing we want, Jim Tubbs pissed as ars'oles an' tryin' tuh keep that broken down truck on't bloody road. It's bad enough bowt that sort o' complication." Sermon finished, he weaved his way back into the bar where we were all downing the ale as though it was going out of fashion. How we eventually cleared that table is still a mystery but Ernie Benson swears that before he left the bar to come out to the truck, the table was clear of all ale.

Things were a bit hazy for a while but the next thing I remember was coming too in the back of the truck and trying not to think about what it was that was swilling about on its floor. As the truck lurched once again I found myself pushed up against a very glassy eyed Bert Rawlins.

In between Bert and Joe Sudders was a double bass which they were both trying to keep upright, bell-end to the top. Dick Hardy stood at the front of it doing his best to steady if as though his very life depended on it, which it did. Every time Jim drove over a pothole they cursed him with a venom I never knew that they possessed.

I sat there trying to get my eyes in focus and wondering what the hell they were doing trying to keep the bass upright for. It would be much easier to lay it down. A minute or so later all was revealed. As the truck hit another bump the bass shook and some liquid spilt over the edge. It fascinated me. An idea did cross my befuddled mind about what the liquid was but I dismissed it, it was too daft to even think about, they could do that over the edge of the truck without having to save it. I sat there in silence hoping that someone would come up with an explanation, but they did not and it was only when the truck pulled up at the side of the road that I eventually got my answer.

"Where the bloody 'ell are we?" A slurred voice asked from the darkness, sounded a bit like Jack Nuttall.

"We're on't road tuh Burston." Came back the reply.

"What've we stopped fer?" I asked, the fresh air now blowing in my face.

"Well," This time I recognised Ernie's voice. "We poured the last o' the ale into Bert's bass an' loaded it onto the back o' the truck. I don't think that Arthur saw us. We were goin' t' pour it away when we got down 't road but it seems a pity tuh waste it an' I'm in need of a wet, that's why we've stopped, fer a drink." He gurgled as he got out of the truck.

As they had borrowed a few glasses from the pub we now started to sample the illicit ale. I must say it was very awkward trying to pour ale from the bell-end of a double bass into a pint glass, more went on the floor than went in the glass.

I tasted the ale as it was thrust at me. Surely it was not the same ale we had been drinking all night? This ale was foul, even to my inexperienced palate. I had no sooner taken a good drink than my stomach seemed to fill my mouth and I only just made it over the back of the tail-board before the lot came up. I dived into the grass by the side of the road feeling a bit ashamed that the lads should see that I could not hold my ale. As I leaned over emptying the contents of my stomach I realised that I was not alone, someone else was doing the same thing just a short distance away. Seconds later another figure arrived wretching all over the place, then another. This was fast becoming a popular spot. They

186

were all at it. That is all except Jim Tubbs who, because he was driving had not had any more ale, especially this horrible mixture out of Bert's bass.

We bent over wretching and feeling very stupid at doing such a foolish thing. There must have been millions of germs in Bert's instrument. Madame Curie would have had a field day, if only she had known where to look. I wretched again just thinking about all the muck that must have accumulated in the bass, it must have been there for umpteen years. Jim Tubbs! He just sat there in the driving seat laughing his head off. He had cottoned on to what was happening. It was obvious to him that the bass, not having been cleared out for ages, had soured the ale.

It's a wonder that we had not poisoned ourselves, and we were not sure about that either, but, as Jim put it:

"I've seen everythin' now, I alus knew that thad sup ale fro' a sweaty clog but tha's beaten lot of em wi' this do." He chortled. "What a set o' daft pillocks thy art, fancy suppin'ale frey an instrument that's on'y 'ad other people's bad breath and spit goin' through it fer o'er fifty yers er so, it serves tha reight the bloody lot of yer fer bein' bloody greedy, didn't tha 'ave enough back at the pub bowt tryin' tuh bring some of it out on tut moor? Come on tha drunken buggers, get back into the truck tha's emptied they stomachs now, let's get they back whome."

We eventually got back into the truck feeling even more foolish now. What a night. I was not feeling at all well. The sooner I got home and into bed, the better.

I was all right now that I had my own house key, so all I had to do was to keep the noise down and I would be OK. Ah well, roll on Belle Vue. That was our next big job and only a short time in which to save up.

15

The Drum

Being a public subscription band is a very personal way of brass banding. The band is run by a committee elected at a general meeting by band and public members and the first thing on any agenda is cash. As a subscription band the cash has to be earned or collected from the public.

Collecting from the public is always a very disagreeable job as this means once a year collecting from door to door throughout the town. No one liked doing this because it always felt like begging, but without cash there would be no instruments or repairs, no uniforms music or all the other paraphernalia connected with brass banding, so if the town wanted a brass band then it would have to pay for it, and although collecting money this way did not pay for everything, it helped.

Another way of collecting was to play round the town in full uniform collecting as we went. We could also approach the people of the town and ask them to sponsor the band at say so much per mile over a given route. Then there was accepting donations from people who wished to become Vice-presidents.

On a 'sponsored march' we would specify the route round town which would take us about twelve miles, making sure that the route took us where we would be seen the most and taking in the town centre. To be seen by our public walking and playing over a marked twelve miles was far better and we were allowed to collect at the same time. The one rule was that we had to play at least three different tunes per mile.

In this particular case the 'sponsored march' had been arranged for the following Saturday. Full uniform was the order of the day and this, Adam said, meant that we should all wear black or navy socks and black shoes. He would be checking everyone before we set off to make sure that we had on the correct dress, though what he would have done if one of the soloists had come in coloured socks I do not know. Well, he could not very well bar him from the parade because he needed him.

We met as usual at the Duke of Wellington and Alf, the landlord, was persuaded to give us a 'livener' before we set off. Jim Baxter our librarian, had once more condescended to play the bass drum, as long as he got some help carrying it when we were not playing. This was agreed because he was getting on and as he was a cranky old sod he would probably tell us to get someone else if we did not help and that would cost money. After having finished our bevy and Alf refusing to to let us have another one, we ranked outside the 'Duke' and we were ready.

Jim Baxter looked quite out of place because it was felt that getting a uniform for him would cost too much as he only played when we couldn't get anyone else, so he had to play in his dark suit. His only suit, he said, but as the sheen was beginning to show through, he must have had it since 'Adam were a lad'. (And I don't mean Adam Bailey.) So, there was old Jim, shiny black suit, bowler hat and a leopard skin wrapped round him and tied with straps and buckled in such a way as to have the hook at the front with which to hook the drum on to.

Although it was very good of Jim to help us out on these occasions by playing the bass drum, I do wish that we could have found a uniform to fit him, but the fact that he had a belly on him like a brewer's 'goitre' meant that we could only just get the leopard skin to fit over half of his enormous stomach. I must say, he looked a right tat-ta. Still, it did not matter what he looked like today, even in his 'burial' suit, as long as he kept that drum beat going whilst we were on the march.

It was just turned ten o'clock when we set off. Joe Sudders young son Tom, who was ten years old, walking in front with a placard proclaiming that this was Burston Band's Sponsored March. There were many more people who accompanied us both young and old, when it came to collecting we accepted anyone who was willing to help.

The march started off in a very spirited fashion. We had enjoyed a beer before we set off and this had perked us up no end. The only time we stopped playing was when there were no houses and when this happened we stopped playing and marched in a very relaxed style. Having a few jokers in the band helped a lot and a joke at a time when we were just walking helped to pass the time. As we approached the houses Adam would give the signal and the band would smarten up and our part-time drummer would take up the beat and away we would go again.

We carried on like this until we came to our first stop, which was of course a pub, this one was called The Magpie. The landlord had been warned over a week ago that we would be coming this way and so he had everything ready. We were quickly served with our usual refreshments and were soon back on the road again.

Adam decided that we would not stop too long. For one thing we did not have time and another was that if we got settled he would have one hell of a time getting us going again. This next bit was the hardest. We were at the beginning of the council estate and once we started round, there would be no pubs for at least an hour. Once we left the estate we would call at The Fighting Cocks just on the main road.

Going round the estate was a bit like going out at Christmas time. The kids would wait for us to pass and then they would throw all sorts of things at us. Bits of grass and mud, in fact anything that they could lay their hands on. Unfortunately some of these projectiles contained bits of stones and if they hit the instruments they could mark them (we didn't count bandsmen), and chasing them only made it worse, so we tried to get round in the shortest possible time.

Eventually we arrived at The Fighting Cocks, foot-sore and weary. It was like the light at the end of the tunnel. We were gasping for a pint and there it was just waiting for us. The only thing was, it did not touch the side as it went down. We did not even taste the first one and it was only by a bit of deviousness that we managed to get a second. Jim Belfor laid his euphonium down and stretched his shoulders.

"Thank God that part of it's over, my bloody euphonium's gettin' 'eavier by the minute."

"Cut it out," Bert Rawlins whispered to a sweating Jim. Dern't

190

let 'em 'ere you, they'll all be moanin' an' they've another three hours to go, try to get 'em laughin' er summat, what wi' that an' a few beers we might even finish the march all together and in one piece."

Bert wandered off to see how old Jim was doing on the drum. He had done well up to now but he was getting on in years. He found Jim sat in a corner holding a bottle of Guinness in his hand, seeing an empty bottle on the table he surmised that Jim was a drink in front.

"How are tha copin' wi' the drum Jim?"

"Oh, al'reight," Jim replied wearily. "Dern't thee worry abeat me. I'll outlast some o' these young buggers."

"I weren't worryin' whether tha'd finish, thar't too damn cantankerous t' know when thar't licked, but if tha feels it gettin' too much fer thee, give me a shout an' I'll get one ut youngsters to tak' o'er."

He left Jim muttering to himself, something about, "How no young smart Alec were going to have to help him carry his drum, hell, he'd been doin' this before they were born an' if it came to 'hey lads hey' he could conduct, play ther bloody instruments, aye, even better that he'd heard some on 'em play. He sorted their music out for 'em didn't he? Did they want him tu wipe ther bloody arses for 'em, hell, he could play the soddin' drum an' still be able to collect as 'e went along. What were they tryin' to do, teach ther mothers tuh suck eggs?"

With all these thoughts going round in his head, he went to the bar and ordered another two bottles of Guinness. He had got a fair sweat up carrying that drum this morning but 'he'd show 'em'. He had been brought up in a far harder school than they would ever see. He would not be the one to quit. There were still life in the old dog yet.

Bert wandered round the pub while he was drinking, trying to keep an eye on everything that was going on. He did not want them to drink too much or getting settled in, but it was like having eyes in the back of his head and he did not have a chance. The only thing he could do was to see that the younger end of the band did not get too much of anything. Thirty minutes later Bert decided that if he did not get them moving now he might never get them out.

His decision was greeted with the usual moans and groans but after a bit of argy bargy he got them on their feet and outside set up ready for off. Quite a few of them did not want to move but Bert, being a big chap and a good band sergeant, smothered their protests with a smart word and at the same time helped them none too gently through the door and into the ranks of the band.

During our stay at The Fighting Cocks the weather had deteriorated and, unnoticed by us, the clouds had gathered portending a possibility of rain and no sooner had we got away from the pub when the heavens opened up. Luckily we were able to shelter under a railway bridge where we stayed for about fifteen minutes but as we set off once again water was draining off the side walks and running down the gutters nearly swamping the drain grates in the channels of the road. It was not raining at present but the dark clouds were looking very ominous.

The band lads, with one eye on the dark clouds and the other on their music, quickened their pace, completely forgetting that we had one or two members that were getting on in years, especially old Jim Baxter.

The band continued playing and marching completely unaware of the distress of Jim at the rear of the band who was getting quite breathless. It was not until they noticed that the drumbeat had stopped that things came to a head. The band slowed eventually coming to a halt. It was Tom Perkins who lashed them with his tongue. He fair cursed them for the pace that they were setting and then David Green looked round just as he exploded.

"What the bloody 'ells 'appening 'ere," he gasped. "We're not at bloody 'Brands Hatch' racing down the road, if yuh dern't slow down a bit I'll shuv this bloody slutch pump up some bugger's arse an 'e con try rushin' down the road trailin' the soddin' thing behind 'im. If we keep this rate up I'll be too knackered to lift me glass when we get tut next pub."

The band was now stopped and everyone trying to speak at once as the grumbling went on. It was very unusual for Tom to explode into the verbals like that when we were on the march, he had been brought up in an extremely disciplined manner as far as brass banding was concerned.

He stood gasping, with his hand on his knee resting the other hand, with his trombone in it, on the grass verge by the side of the road. His face was white as he tried to get his breath back. He could not really blame anyone else because he had been one of the four instruments on the front row and he had let them push him along. He looked at the four bass players who had now taken their instruments off while they got their breath back. Two of them, Bert Rawlins and Jim Hogan were two of the oldest instrumentalists in the band, with, of course the exception of Tom himself and Jim Baxter.

It was David Green who spotted it first as he looked round the band and became aware that someone was missing. We all looked round and realised that in our gallop down the road there had been none of that solid drum beat to accompany us. Old Jim and the drum were nowhere to be seen.

"You lot hang on here," David said. "I'll nip back up the road and see where he's got too, I'll bet the silly old bugger's sat on a wall somewhere having a rest. Too bloody obstinate to ask us to slow down."

He quickly walked back up the road for about three hundred yards and coming to some houses with gardens at the front he heard a groan. He followed the sound and as he looked over the garden wall he saw old Jim flat out on his back in a flower bed, the drum having unhooked and rolled down to the bottom of the garden. Jim's face was covered in mud and the water from the rain covered bushes was running down his face leaving white streaky lines through the dirt. He did not look at all well.

"Quick," Adam said as he ran up and saw what had happened. "Get him up onto the wall. He'll drown if we leave him there much longer and it's just like these people to charge us for ruining their damn flower beds."

We heaved Jim up out of the garden and onto the wall. He was just starting to come round. At that moment it started to rain again.

"Damn it," Adam growled in frustration, though whether he meant old Jim or the weather I do not know. We had managed to keep ahead of most of the rain and now that we were only a short way from finishing we were going to get soaked.

"Reight, who's goin' tuh play the drum for the rest of the march?" he asked. "It's only a short walk and then we're finished."

He should not have asked. Everyone wanted to play the drum, if only to try something different. He suddenly found himself

j

having to intervene when the arguing got to the point of battle.

"All right you lot, cut it out. Hells bells, here's Jim shagged out an' nearly dyin' on 'is feet an' all you lot can do is feight o'er the damn drum, I wish I'd never asked now but as we haven't far to go I'll stop all the arguing, I'll play the damn thing myself." The thought had crossed his mind before but going from leading the band at the front to playing the base drum at the rear did not appeal at all.

"By the way, how's Jim gettin' on? Is he OK?"

In the argument over the drum we had forgotten about Jim. We looked around, but he had disappeared again, we had to find him he had the leopard skin and all the straps on him and we needed them. There came another groan from over the garden wall.

"Oh damn," Adam was in a right mood now. "Pete! Harry! You two were seeing to him weren't you?" He glared at the two trombone players.

"He were here a minute ago," Harry said. "I left him with Pete whilst I went to get the drum."

"You lyin' bugger," Pete interrupted. "You were supposed to be seein' to him."

Another moan, this time louder. Again we looked over the wall and there was Jim plastered back in the mud, the rainwater now running down his neck and into his collar and he just could not move.

As soon as Adam had mentioned playing the drum our two idiot trombone players had rushed to get in their claim to play it, each thinking that the other would have kept hold of the hapless Jim. The state that Jim was in, he had just tumbled back over the wall and into the soft mud of the garden. Luckily he had landed on his head, otherwise he could have been hurt.

Again we pulled Jim back into a sitting position on the wall and this time held tight on to him. He was coming round and he seemed to be more like himself again, cantankerous as ever.

"What happened?" he growled. "I've bin laid in that damn garden lookin' up at t' sky it seemed fer ever. I couldn't move neither one way or t' other an' all I could 'ere were you lot argifyin' about who 'ad tu play t' bloody drum. Well, yu con all play the bloody thing from now on, tha's 'ad it. Find thyself another silly sod tuh carry the bloody thing an' dern't think tha con buy me off wi' a few measly drinks when we get tut pub.

194

Next time tha wants a drummer tuh keep thee in step, dern't come fer me, cause tha con kiss my arse."

Adam stepped in to try to defuse the situation. He should have trained as a politician the way he started to con old Jim and that is not easy when the rain is starting to run down your neck with still a mile to go to the finish.

How he did it I do not know but after a minute or two Jim said that he would finish the march as long as they kept to a proper step. He knew that one way or another he was going on to the pub so he might as well carry the damn drum, he was soaked through anyway, so what the hell!

The thing was that Adam did not want old Jim going on about being left behind and forgotten in that garden any more than he had to. He needed Jim as the base drummer until he could get another.

They arrived at the pub without further mishap and feeling a bit sheepish for not sending anyone back for him, the band lads made sure that the drinks that Jim got were paid for him out of their own pockets, if only to get Jim drunk enough to agree to carry on playing the drum until we had a replacement. The only thing now was to get the sponsor money in and counted.

The band lads were feeling better as the evening wore on. It was showing in the way that they relaxed, in some cases they were too relaxed.

Peter Davidson, one of our front row cornet players, was looking decidedly the worse for wear and it was still only nine o'clock, pm, that is. Bert decided that we had better get him home. He had not been married long, only about eighteen months, and his wife Anne wasn't exactly in harmony with his constant band outings. The only time that she saw him at home he was mostly the worse for wear after drinking with the band, so we had to get him out of the pub and pointed in the general direction of his house where we hoped his zig-zag course would lead him.

We did not dare go all the way with him, if Anne caught us staggering up the street with him she would wake the whole neighbourhood with her caustic remarks as to the integrity of the Burston Bandsmen, the reputation of which was all ready too well known. It was not until the following day that the full story came to light.

On Sunday lunch-time we were supposed to be playing a short

195

concert at The Malt Shovel public house. It was not a big pub so, when the band had got themselves sorted out ready to play, there was not that much room left for the customers. A small donation from the landlord and a collection round the pub totalled six pounds nine and three-pence, not bad for a Sunday lunch-time. One player who was missing was of course Peter Davidson and it was not until after the concert had finished that he put in an appearance.

Peter walked in as though he was going to a funeral. Dressed in his best Sunday suit, no uniform, no cornet in sight. As he came up to the bar we naturally, in our best social voices, asked him, "Where the hell he'd been?" While we were playing an awkward concert? After he had had a couple of pints he plucked up the courage to tell us the sordid details of the night before.

The story, as far as he could remember it, was that when eventually he had arrived home, Anne had been waiting for him. While he had been out with the band on the sponsored march, the new suite, that they had ordered from the Co-op in town, had arrived. The delighted Anne had spent her time setting it out until she was satisfied and had then waited for him to arrive home, which he had promised would be about tea-time.

It had been nine-thirty when he had tried to unlock the front door and Anne, hearing the noise of his key in the lock, had pulled the door open just as he was leaning on it, the result being that he had fallen through the doorway into the hallway drunk as a mop.

Anne looked down at him struggling to get to his feet and had dragged him into the house so that she could shut the door and stop any nosy neighbours seeing him. This was the last straw for her and as he staggered up the hallway and into the living-room Anne gave him such a clout that he lost what little balance he had left and fell over onto the new settee. Being in the state that he was and with his head reeling from the clout that Anne had given him, the churning in his stomach suddenly erupted and he was violently sick over the new furniture. He proceeded to make matters worse by rolling over into the steaming vomit in a drunken stupor. I suppose it was about that time that Anne really blew her top. While he was laid there unable to help himself, Anne dragged him off the settee and onto the floor. Looking at the mess on her new settee and Peter laid on the floor covered in sick was more than she could stand and she burst out weeping. After a while the weeping stopped and she dried her eyes and set about cleaning the sorry mess off her beloved furniture and carpet, even to the extent of cleaning some of the mess off his band uniform.

When she had done what she could with the uniform and cleaned up everything off the floor she again burst into tears and had another good cry. Some time later she stopped feeling sorry for herself and it must have been at this time that she decided to teach him and his blasted band a lesson that they would not forget.

Once her mind had been made up there was no going back on it. She got out her sewing box where she kept her scissors and starting with his band jacket she proceeded to cut it into long strips even while it was still on his back. She kept all the strips still joined together. When she had finished with the jacket she started on his trousers. Minutes later she stood up and looked at the results of her handiwork, when she was satisfied with the results she put her scissors away. Then, taking his cornet out of the case she put the downstairs light out and retired upstairs. She was not quite finished yet though, she still had his cornet to sort out so, opening the bedroom window she threw it as far as she could out into the main road. She listened with complete satisfaction as she heard it land on the road with a clatter and then she closed the curtains and with a sigh of satisfaction, went to bed.

Peter eventually woke up with a splitting headache and a feeling of nausea. He did not feel at all well and it was some time before he realised that something was wrong. He stood in a strange living-room, where had he seen that settee before? Suddenly it came to him. That looked like the new suite he and Anne had ordered at the Co-op but why was it wet? His head was buzzing and the draught round his knees was disconcerting. Oh God what had happened last night? He knew that he had been drunk but what daft, he stopped in mid thought as he became aware of his tattered uniform. He looked at himself in the mirror. Hell, he looked like a scarecrow. He took his jacket off, if he could call it that now, and stood there looking at it wondering what he should do next? Eventually he recovered from the first shock of the night's happening and went upstairs to remove the tattered uniform, have a bath and get into some clean clothes. Who could have done this stupid thing? Surely not Anne. Try as he might the happenings of last night would not return.

197

Unfortunately the shocks of the day were not over yet. When he got to the top of the stairs he found that most of his clothes and things had been thrown out of the bedroom onto the upstairs landing. What a mess. He realised that Anne must have been the one who had trashed his uniform, oh hell, he was in trouble now.

From the pile of clothes he sorted out a pair of trousers and a clean shirt, changing them for the rags he had just removed. With a burst of self preservation he decided that now would not be the best time to ask Anne for an explanation, but something must have upset her to make her act like this.

He quietly returned downstairs and made himself some breakfast. He had to think. Bit by bit it all came back to him. He remembered being at 'The Duke' and having a few drinks with the lads but she had never objected to that before, not after the hard days playing they had had. He knew that he would have to wait until Anne woke to answer that one and he was not going to be the one to waken her. Happen if he took her up a cup of tea he might get some explanation.

He brewed up and then had to collect the milk from the front doorstep but as he bent down to pick up the milk something caught his eye. Something shiny. He looked away for a second but when he looked back it was there again, he couldn't believe his eyes. Surely she would not do that, not to his cornet. He darted out into the middle of the road and picked up the nearly flattened object. It was his cornet. He nearly wept to see it in this condition, but why? She must have thrown it out of the bedroom window straight into the road below.

He looked again at the remains of his beloved cornet. Last night it had been a fine precision instrument and now it was just a handful of twisted metal. There were tears in his eyes as he turned to the kitchen. He muttered to himself. "Think man think."

Whatever had happened last night must have been something terrible to make Anne lose her marbles like this. Oh God what will they say at the band? How could he explain it? Instruments and uniforms cost money! Peter tried to think, which was not easy when there was a little man inside your head banging away with a sledge-hammer. He sat there gazing in bewilderment at his battered cornet. How was he going to tell them? What possible explanation could he give to the band? Either way they would have to know this morning, he was supposed to be playing with them at The Malt Shovel at lunch-time.

When eventually Anne came downstairs she did not say a word, she just made herself a cup of tea and then putting on her coat she went to the front door.

"Going somewhere luv?" he asked tentatively.

She stopped, stared at him for a moment then picked up her suitcase that she had just left at the bottom of the stairs and said, "Mother's."

"Why? Has something upset you? Can I help? Please tell me!"

Anne stopped her momentum through the already open door and turned to face him. The look on her face told him that his time could be up. He backed slowly into the kitchen as Anne came menacingly towards him. She put on her 'do not dare interrupt' look and proceeded to regale him of the events of the night before. She left out no details and in language he did not even think she knew she castigated him left right and centre. When she had finished, which was about an hour later, she said, "Well, what have you to say for yourself, what's the excuse now?"

"I'm sorry luv I just don't remember but it won't happen again," replied a distraught Peter. "It were just that after the march I couldn't walk another step. I only 'ad a couple of pints."

"A couple of pints," Anne screamed at him. "There were a couple of gallons spewed all over my new settee last night and it took me most of the night to clean the stinking mess off. I will tell you this though, it will not happen again, at least not while I am in the house. It is all the fault of that idiot band of yours but that is it. I am standing no more. If you want me I will be at mother's. One thing though, be careful before you call because when you do, make sure that you have thought it through. There is going to be some changes around here, starting with that soddin' band." The broadside firmly delivered, she grabbed her case and flounced out of the house, slamming the door behind her.

"So, that's it!" David said, taking another gulp of his pint. "I've no cornet, no uniform and no wife at present. I've really buggered it up this time. I'll be lucky if she lets me come to a band concert after this never mind a practice, but now I've a wife to collect and bring home. I can't begin to think what I'm going to say to her, but I think that for now banding had better be out. I don't know how I'm going to pay for it all but I'll come to the next meeting and sort it all out."

Looking at his face and seeing that he was nearly in tears kept us from saying anything to him and there was a very awkward silence, so he just turned and without another word he walked out of the pub.

True to his word, he did pay for all the damage to his uniform and cornet but he was a changed man after that day and, although he did play for us again, he was not the man we had known. He was a tiger tamed.

16

Bonfire Night

It was about this time that we acquired a new bandsman, his name was Jim Barker and he had just finished his National Service. (This being a two year period of service in the armed forces which men eighteen and over had to serve. The only ones who did not have to go were, for example, miners, students, apprentices to trades who had to finish their seven year period of training and a few more, some of which were objectors, conscientious and otherwise.)

Jim had served in the Royal Air Force and while he had been in the RAF he had served in Germany. It was during those two years that Jack had learned to play the trumpet. On his demob he had returned to Burston where he had applied to join the Burston Band. This was a stroke of luck with us just having lost the services of Peter Davidson. The fact that the mouthpiece of the trumpet was not unlike the cornet mouthpiece would help Jim to settle in. As it happened we were in dire need of a flugelhorn player and Jim had no objection to filling that position, once again the mouthpiece being compatible with the trumpets.

At the time that we accepted Jim into the band we did not know just what we were letting ourselves in for. He turned out to be a man of many facets and a real 'nutter'. Not in a bad sense but more of a likable sod-pot. He was not the sort that you would leave with your wife because he was sure to try something on with her.

The one thing that we soon got to know about Jim was that he would bet on anything at all, a couple of dogs chasing a cat, a card or football game, it did not matter, if you said that black was white he would be sure to put a bet on it. Sometimes he won and sometimes he lost, it did not seem to make any difference to him, he just enjoyed a bet. One thing is for sure, he was an asset to the band and soon fitted in.

Jim's great strength lay in the fact that he was a 'jack of all trades'. He could turn his hand to anything. Whilst he had been in the RAF he had trained as a motor mechanic and on his return home he had bought a clapped out 'SS Jaguar car'. This car was one of the most sought after cars just after the war and, although it had seen better days, Jim had snapped it up with the intention of rebuilding it. At first we thought that it was just wishful thinking on Jim's part but we had not allowed for the determination of a man in love. That is just what it was, love, only time would tell and, as there were only a few viable scrap yards around Burston, the difficulties in getting spare parts for such a wanted car were immense.

As time went on, getting these spare parts proved a much harder task than any of us could possibly have imagined, not that this put Jim off at all, all his spare time was spent travelling round the district. Should anyone mention of any 'Jaguar' being dismantled, Jim would be off like a shot, no matter where it was.

One thing you could say for Jim Barker was that he was lucky. He hadn't been back home more than a couple of months when our one and only garage came up for sale. The garage had only two petrol pumps, one of which was a bit 'dicky', but what it did have was a very large building which had two pits and a broken chain driven ramp.

Once Jim had looked over the garage we knew that he would pull out all the stops to get it, even if it meant robbing a bank to do it. He did get the garage and how he managed it he never said, but as we had not heard of any banks being robbed we heaved a sigh of relief and it was only a month later that the garage was opened under Jim's name.

After the garage had been opened for a few months Jim's 'Jag' made its first appearance. It was bright yellow and you could see it from miles away. When it was started up the engine did not sound too well but Jim said that he would get it right in time, he had rebuilt it with spares which were not too dependable and although his explanation did not give us any great confidence in his ability as a mechanic, we did give him full marks for perseverance.

In the band-room Jim's ability on the flugelhorn was not as good as we had hoped for but his bubbling enthusiasm made him very popular. Come to that our playing was not anything to write home about so he was in good company.

The nights were drawing in and going much colder as autumn came around. This was the time when we had to start getting ready for contesting and as the contests were not qualifying contests we were still allowed to make our own choice of music. Adam had again decided to do these contests with Meyerbeer's *L'African*, his argument being that with all the time that we had practised it, we should be getting better.

Before the contests though we had an engagement of a different sort. A chap that Joe Sudders knew over in Merthorpe had started a business making fancy wrought iron designs for indoor staircases or round the garden etc.

At the beginning of the war, all wrought iron and metal things had been collected and taken to the foundry to be melted down for the war effort. It had been great fun at the time going round the streets collecting the scrap. Sometimes the railings round the garden of one of the big houses belonging to a councillor or mill owner, would have to be cut off for scrap and what a song and dance they made about it, they thought that they would be considered too important to be disturbed. It did not make an 'ape'orth (halfpenny worth) of difference, into the pot it all went. I think that we got more enjoyment watching the workmen cut down their precious railings than anything else. That would teach them for trying to be too superior. We were all in this thing together.

Now that the war was over and the iron and metals were becoming more available the small business people once more turned to private enterprise. The big-nobs wanted their railings back and there was once again a market for wrought iron fixings and that is just what Joe's friend had done.

His name was Edward Walton, Ted for short, and he had built a small foundry near to his house on the outskirts of Merthorpe. He had been in business for about two years and according to Joe, he was doing quite well. As it was getting near bonfire night, Ted had decided to put on a bonfire party for some of his friends and customers.

With the help of the local kids he had collected the wood from miles around and set it up on some spare ground near his foundry. What he wanted Joe to do was to invite as many of the band as possible and for them to bring their instruments in order to add a little music to the festivities, a sort of 'Tommy Kelly' do. The payment for this small service would be free ale and plenty of eats. This was right up our street, but as this was an unofficial band engagement we were told not to wear our uniforms, a bonfire could be a very dirty place at times.

When November 5th night arrived we found that most of the band had decided to come along and that Joe had booked an old motor coach for us to travel in. The coach had cost ten pounds to hire, the cost being shared by everyone who travelled in it.

Ted Walton had told Joe that he could invite the bandsmen and friends, enough to fill the coach, the cost being worked out at five shillings each and a few bob over for the driver.

As we got on the coach we began to think that the Gods were against us, it started to rain and by the time we reached the foundry it had turned into a steady drizzle. We had set off for Merthorpe at six o'clock in the evening and as it was only a twenty-five minute drive, we were at Ted's foundry before six thirty.

When we arrived Ted was waiting to greet us and after some quick introductions took us all inside his house. It was packed but after a bit of pushing and shoving we found our way to the bar. Ted introduced us to the barman friend of his and then left us to get some drinks. This was more like it. One more surprise though, Ted had not mentioned it before. He brewed his own beer. What a first drink that was, like drinking a pint of bitter with a double whisky in it.

After drinking one pint I decided not to have any more of Ted's home brewed ale, another pint like the last one and I would be on all fours. As for the rest of the lads, they took to it like a duck to water. Tom Perkins was heard to remark that he had not had a pint like that since before the war, he did not say which war he was talking about though.

After a while the party started to liven up. Ted somehow got the rain soaked bonfire going and as I looked around, it seemed that Ted had invited all the village. The busiest place being around the bar. A traffic policeman would not have been out of place here.

What an easy job this was, all we did was to drink. I wondered when Ted expected us to play? It would be awkward because there were not many lights about and if he did not get us playing soon we would all be too sloshed.

After we had been drinking for about an hour, Ted's wife asked us if we wanted something to eat, of course we all said yes, If there was going to be all this ale around then we needed something inside us to soak it up. It was a well known fact that the second rule of drinking was to try to get some food inside you, the first rule being of course to get someone else to buy the drinks.

We followed Ted's wife into the dining-room. What a spread! On a table that seemed to cover the whole length of one wall was a banquet. This much food would have fed most of Burston for a week. There were chicken legs, breasts, wings, beef, meat pies and a large baking tin, about two feet by three feet. In it was a meat and onion pie cut up into squares. There were sandwiches, hot black puddings and in the middle of the table was a very large salmon, cooked but still in its shape. It seemed a pity to cut into it, also there was a long pork pie with egg in the middle and dishes with all sorts of relish.

I couldn't believe my eyes. I had never seen so much food even in a shop. I am sure that if anyone had looked at me just then they would have seen me slavering. Thank goodness the plates were only small, it was just as well because we would have gluttoned ourselves, which was a waste because we could always come back if we wanted any more.

Stomachs satisfied we then went to find Ted. By now the bonfire was going great and everyone seemed to be enjoying themselves. Ted seemed to be here, there and everywhere, bustling about, laughing and joking with everyone he met. At last he saw us standing there and came over and asked us if we were ready to play? Joe said, "Yes, what would you like us to play?"

"Suit yourselves," he said. "Get 'em singing if you can."

With that he bustled off and we did not see him for another hour or so.

Not being an official band engagement we had not been allowed to bring our concert music with us, we had managed to smuggle out some sing-along music though and our march-books so we would have to make do with those.

We positioned ourselves on the rear veranda of Ted's house where he had a light. We were not in any concert formation because getting in a position to see the music by the one light was awkward enough.

At last we got ourselves sorted out and were ready to play. We started with a few lively marches, a couple of good brass band pieces, finishing off with some popular tunes from the 'Black and White Minstrels' shows. This really got them singing and when we finished we were greeted with a great roar of approval. After that drinks were pressed on us from all angles, this was obviously going to be a great night, even though it was still raining. From the humour of the guests, the rain was not putting anyone off the festivities, probably the effects of the home-brewed ale.

It was now getting quite late and the families with younger children were quietly leaving to get their children to bed. No doubt some of the parents would be back shortly to finish off the evening. The spirit of the night had surely taken over.

At twelve o'clock the party was still in full swing. Our coach driver was getting impatient but, as he had also had a few drinks, it did not take much to persuade him to stay a bit longer.

A few drinks later a guest suggested that we should play the march *Colonel Bogey*. We did not have it with us but that did not matter because we could not see the music in the dark anyhow so we decided that we could 'busk' it. The idea was that as we played they would march behind us singing the words written by some unknown soldier, the saucy version of course. We marched round and round the fire forgetting that all the rain had softened the ground to a fine sludge and by the time we had finished we were covered with the stuff.

Of course the party had been a great success from our point of view. The ale was good, especially being free, and the success of the party made Joe heave a sigh of relief. The lads, who had taken a chance on coming to the party, had threatened to throw Joe into the canal on the way back home if it had not been good. Mind you I do not think that it would have been possible the state they were in, the only thing they wanted to do on the way home was sleep.

Drinking engagements was one of the things we were very good at even without practice and it was obvious that the evening had been a very enjoyable one for them all. Tomorrow we were out again and this time it was a Mayor's swearing in so it would not be a long job. I think that Harry Rawlins said that he would give Carla Mason a ring at the Golden Bobbin so that it would give her time to lay some food on, then we could eat and drink during closing time.

The following morning we assembled as usual at the 'Duke' and, as quite a few of the band now had transport of some sort, we would travel in theirs. The band committee had offered each driver petrol money, hoping, of course, that the offer would be turned down. It was common knowledge that the band funds were in the red.

The main thing was that Jim Tubbs was there with his faithful truck so that after the procession we would have transport to go down to the Golden Bobbin.

As it turned out we had no cause to worry. Jim was there ready and waiting. The morning weather, after a brief rain shower, had now warmed up and the procession went off very smoothly, so that by twelve thirty we had finished for the day and for once we arrived at the Golden Bobbin during opening time. We did not like this very much because it just was not in our nature to have to enter a pub by the front door, the thrill was only there when we were able to drink after hours.

When we walked through the doors of the pub, Ben Mason greeted us with open arms. Our drinks were quickly pulled and within a short time we were relaxing in an atmosphere of cigarette smoke and booze.

The Golden Bobbin was a great pub and we quickly got to know the regulars. Cards, darts, dominoes and I even saw a game of crown and anchor being played in the tap-room. This was great. No rush. We could now calmly settle down for the rest of the day. There was none of that grabbing a quick pint and then having to dash out, hardly having had time to blow your nose before we were off again, today we could take it easy. We had enough money for dinner-time drinking and we had already settled up with Carla for the food, so all we had to think about now, although there was a distinct possibility that we might have to do a bit of busking later on, was booze and gambling.

As it turned out that afternoon, things took a turn for the better. At the gambling we won a few bob between us, mainly from playing cards. 'Nine card don' was the favourite game of cards in this pub and as we regularly played it back at the 'Duke', we were all very conversant with the game.

Very soon we began to show a decent profit and that without having to resort to cheating. Maybe it was the luck of the cards, it does happen sometimes, and maybe it was playing a wrong card at the right time, who knows? Whatever it was, we accepted it gratefully, whichever way the cards dropped they seemed to be in our favour and by closing time we had made enough money to see us OK later on. We did promise the regulars that we would be around later on and they could try to get their money back then, but the way we were playing I could only see them losing more to us.

When closing time was called and the rest of the clientele had left, we carried on playing until the call came from Carla that the food was ready. Now we like our indoor sports as well as the next man but when it comes to food and drink everything else went by the board. When food was around we were like gannets, food being the foundation of a good drinking session. So, this was the time to get something inside us before we started our evening's binge.

We spent the next hour clearing away all the food that Carla had prepared for us and there was only one way to do that, we cleared the lot. I did, however, manage to smuggle a couple of meat pies from the room. I cut them into pieces and wrapped them in paper, then I packed them carefully into my horn case. It was a bit of a squeeze but that would not matter when I became hungry later on.

The bar reopened at about seven-thirty officially, but of course we had had a few drinks before then and by the time the regulars had begun to arrive we were well on the way to getting tanked up, what we needed just now was to start playing something, just what did not matter because it was the blowing that we needed to take away the effects of the booze that we had already drunk.

The idea was OK but first we had to give our dinner-time opponents the chance to retrieve their lost cash. It just was not their day. Lady luck was still on our side and the only thing that they did was to add to our lunch-time winnings, so it was not long before they suggested that we gave them a tune. This suited us down to the ground. It was now eight-thirty and if we played for about an hour we would be ready for another bout of quaffing of the hops.

The unfortunate thing was that we only had our march and hymn-books with us, mind you, if we played everything in both the books it would take us all night to finish the impromptu concert. So, what we did was to mix some marches with hymns and a little bit of busking and by the time we had finished the room was packed, with hands banging on the table in time with the music and ale flowing in our direction, free and with a regularity that delighted us.

When we were playing, time seemed to pass very quickly and before we knew it Ben was calling time. It took him all of an hour to get the place emptied and we used this time to finish off all the free ale bought for us. This did not help our equilibrium at all.

Pete Barton, our third trombone player, must have had a beano. As we were saying goodnight to our hosts, someone asked where Pete had got to? We knew that he would not have gone home without telling us and anyway it was quite a way to where he lived on the outskirts of Burston.

Back into the pub we went in search of Pete, eventually finding him fast asleep in the gent's toilet. We shook and pummelled him without avail, we just could not wake him up, he was in a real drunken stupor. If we returned him to his mother in this state she would have our guts for garters, somehow we had sober him up. I do not quite know how we did it but we managed to load him into the back of Jim's truck, it was like trying to lift a bag of oil with his lolloping arms and legs seeming to have a mind of their own, but at last we did it and then set off back to Burston.

On the way back we tried to hang him over the tail-board to be sick but the state we were in it is a wonder that we did not lose him over the tail-board all together. The fact that Jim seemed to hit every bump and hole in the road eventually did the job as Pete, with his head hanging and banging over the side in the fresh air, emptied the contents of his stomach all over the road back to Burston.

When we arrived back in the town we decided that the best thing to do was to get him back home and leave him leaning on the back door of his mother's house. Pete was not married and as his father had died some years ago, there was only him and his mother left. The house that they lived in was out on the edge of town. It was old and dilapidated with weathered paint-work that had not seen a brush in many years, but the rent was low and it was all that they could afford.

We leaned Pete against the back doorpost and knocked on the door. It was at this point that Pete decided to go to sleep again and as soon as we left go of him he started to slide down the doorpost and finished up sitting on the ground, his head supported by the wall. Even as we watched his head lolled over to one side followed by the rest of his body. Just as we were trying to lift him up again the door opened and there stood the dragon.

What a sight! Mrs Barton in all her glory. She had an old overcoat on in place of a dressing-gown and curler ribbons dangling from her hair. She was only a small woman but stout with it and not a pleasant sight at all. Stood there without her teeth she looked to have a grievous defect in the facial department and the scowl on her face could have stopped a bus.

"What the bloody 'ell do yer think yer doin' bringin' 'im 'ome in that state?" She growled in a semi-whisper. "I've a damn good mind tuh banjo the bloody lot o' yuh, an' dern't think tha's gonna leave 'im theer fer me tuh fettle wi', tha con carry 'im upstairs an' dump 'im on't' bed."

We bent down and picked him up without another word being spoken, we were not about to argue with Pete's mam. We were still half cut but it would not have mattered if we had been stone cold sober, she was a hell-cat when she was mad and she would have set about the lot of us if it had not been for the fact that she needed our help to get Pete upstairs, mind you there was still time if we were not careful.

I cannot help feeling that it was a good job that Pete was too drunk to have any feeling, he would not have enjoyed the struggle we had getting him upstairs. It was only a narrow staircase and with us being kettled he had a very bumpy ride up the stone steps. The fact that his head banged on every step meant that in the morning he was going to have an ache like the anvils of hell, well that was his worry, ours was to get him to bed and get out in one piece, if that was at all possible.

Eventually, with big shoves and little shoves, we got him to the top of the stairs, it had not helped a lot with his mother coming up behind us cursing us, every word being punctuated with a clout with the sweeping brush, she was a real tartar and she had not even got into second gear yet.

After a struggle we got him into the bedroom and timidly asked if we should undress him.

"Just sling 'im ont' bed," she roared, getting some steam up, "an' then tha con bugger off, the drunken sod con stay theer as 'e is, I'll sort 'im out int' mornin'."

We did not need telling twice. We swung together and then let go of him as we would a sack of coal. He landed smack in the middle of the bed, arms and legs all over the place. Suddenly there was a crack and one of the bed legs disappeared and the bed tilted over to one side, then another crack and another leg went, we did not know what was happening because there was not any lights upstairs only the one spluttering candle in an old fashioned candlestick held in Mrs Barton's hand. She put the candle down and hurried downstairs, all we could see was that the bed was down at one end and in our state we could not figure out why. After a few moments there came a yell from downstairs where Pete's mother had gone.

"Yuh great dozy useless buggers, look what you've done tuh me ceilin', yuh drunken sots."

We rushed downstairs so fast that I think that Jim Tubbs fell down the last three steps in his haste to see what had happened. The sight that met our eyes would have done justice to any comedy film. There was Pete's mother stood in the middle of the living-room covered in dust and bits of plaster, her fists shaking up at the ceiling as though pleading with the almighty.

The place was a mess. Dust and ceiling plaster everywhere and as our eyes were drawn to the ceiling we could see why. Two bed legs had poked straight through the plaster and brought most of the ceiling down with it, it is a wonder that the whole house had not collapsed bed and all, what a mess.

That was it. We just could not hold it back any longer, we burst out laughing and once started we just could not stop. There was Pete's mother covered in plaster with tears of rage and frustration running in lines down her face and all we could do in the circumstances was laugh.

"I'll kill yer fer this," she screamed. "Yer knockin' me 'ome down round me ears, look at the mess yuh dozy useless swine, it'll tak' me all night tuh clean it up. Get out of me 'ouse, go on, bugger off before I do summat I'll be sorry for, but you'd better

211

be back 'ere in the mornin' wi' the rest of yer stupid crew tuh sort it all out."

Although I hate to say it, we ran out of there as though the devil himself was after us. If we had stayed there to help, things could have got really nasty. As we staggered down the road we realised that we were in 'Dicky's meadow' now, Mrs Barton was not the sort of woman to let us get away with a thing like this.

After work the following day we waited for Pete at the bottom of the street and when he saw us he came over and asked us what had happened, he said that he had been wakened up this morning with a splitting headache and the room covered in dust, his bed all out of balance and when he had got downstairs he saw that the bed legs were showing through the ceiling of which more had fallen some time during the night. His mother had been out when he had got up so he had been down to the brewery, who owned the house, to try to get something done about the mess.

We then told him how he had passed out in the Golden Bobbin and how we had to take him home and carry him up to bed. We left out the part about him bumping his head on the stairs' steps. We explained about the ceiling coming down and how his mother had cursed us. He groaned aloud at the thought.

"By 'ell," he said. "We must 'ave supped some stuff last night, I dern't remember a damn thing, I wakened up ont' floor this morning an' then found the bed legs were through the ceiling, I'll bet me mother were mad as 'ell when she went out this morning cause she just left a note sayin' that you lot'd caused all the mess an' it were all your fault, I can't think why an' I've an almighty headache."

We stood and listened to him, never saying a word until he had finished, then we told him our side of the story. After we had finished telling him he said, "I dern't know why me mother's so mad then if th'art tellin' it straight, I'll bet them floorboards were rotten before that. They've bin squeakin' fer a while now, anyway let the brewery sort it out, it'll serve 'em right, they've spent bugger all on them broken down 'ouses, I can't ever remember 'em doin' owt fer us, not even a lick of paint tuh brighten the place up, well, now they'll 'ave tuh do summat."

We agreed with him wholeheartedly, the people who owned these houses and had rented them out all these years should be the ones to pay. They were the ones who took the rent money and never did anything about repairs, they did not get their money in the bank by spending it, we knew from bitter experience that people with brass took some parting from it. Their attitude seemed to be that they had done their part in allowing us to rent the dilapidated places, the rest was left up to us. What they would do in Pete's case was anybody's guess.

Being interested parties and fearing that we might have to pay something towards it ourselves, we collared Pete on practice night and asked him what was happening about his house, he told us that it had all been sorted out. The men sent to assess the repairs had found that all the rest of the floorboards were badly infected with woodworm and they had decided to replace them all because if anybody had been hurt they could have sued the brewery and that could not be allowed to happen under any circumstances.

Once again we heaved a sigh of relief, it could have turned out very nasty for us, but it did not and I still do not think that it was our fault that the bed went through the ceiling. Still, that was not the point, it was Pete's mother who still blamed us saying that if we had not been there it would not have happened and the fact that the brewery were repairing everything did not excuse us. It was her candid opinion that her son should keep better company, he should not bother with us from the band because we were a bad lot. I do not know why she complained about us, it had been her that said throw him on the bed and we had done it, so why should she complain? Anyway she was a right scruffy old bat and we said so but not until she was well out of hearing, she did not need any excuse at all to catch us one round the ear-hole. Our opinion was that she should thank us for helping to bring all those faulty floorboards to light. Without us it might never have happened.

17

Whit-Friday Quicksteps

Whit-Friday! The time of the year that is branded on the mind of all bandsmen. We were lucky enough to have been engaged to play for a church called St Chads. After the walk round the town with all the other churches we would play for an hour or so for an afternoon concert and then at about three forty-five we would pack up and get ready for the evening's 'quickstep contests' (march contests).

The day started for me at five o'clock in the morning. Up to then, apart from the paper round I used to do, I would never have realised that there was a five o'clock in the morning. We had to be at the band-room ready to depart at six-thirty with everything packed in the coach. Our destination was one of the villages round Saddleworth near Oldham called Tupper Hills.

Our arrival at Tupper Hills did not cause any undue excitement, although there were quite a lot of people about, even at the unearthly hour of quarter to eight. The coach pulled up outside a pub at the top of the main street called The Fox and Pheasant where we were bundled out of the coach and formed up in marching order.

I knew that every band that played for a church at Tupper Hills on Whit-Friday started off at this pub. From here we would play the same hymn that every other band played, *Hail Smiling Morn*. This was the first time that I had played here and I did not quite know what to expect.

The morning had started off very cool with a clammy mist but with the sun trying to push its way through I felt sure that the day was going to warm up.

I had been told that we were going to play in a procession with other churches later in the morning but the great news was that this particular village liked to have the big name bands of the day playing for them, we would just have to wait and see which ones.

Playing at Tupper Hills was really something special, especially on Whit-Friday. First of all we did not go direct to St Chads on the coach, we had to march down to the church playing the hymn.

After we had formed up outside The Fox and Pheasant with Adam Bailey fussing around us like a mother hen making sure that everything was buttoned up and smart looking. Nothing was left to chance as he checked round us all and we really got the word that this walk down to our church was the most important part of our day. Bands were judged on the way they carried themselves and how they played as they marched to their different appointments.

The usual double taps from our bass drummer and we were off with Adam leading the way smartly, walking about four yards in front of the band and done just as though he was still in the army. He had impressed on us the importance of our marching and playing and as we stepped out playing *Hail Smiling Morn* we held ourselves in the best tradition of any band there.

It was just eight o'clock and there were thousands of people lining the streets and from listening to each band as they passed they would decide which band was on form and which was not. When we at last arrived at our church and had been dismissed we all rushed back to the main road to listen to the other bands arriving and listening to a couple of old timers talking was like listening to the two wise men.

"Hey! That's Brighouse isn't it?"

"Aye, they don't sound too bad do they? I'll bet they give 'Dyke' a run for their money today."

"I think that's 'Dyke' forming up now so we'll soon see."

We waited for a few moments, all straining our ears for the sound of the next band to come.

"Aye, it's 'Dyke', you can tell that sound anywhere."

Everyone strained to catch a glimpse of the great Black Dyke Mills Band as they marched down the road. Onward they came and one lordly voice likened them to a steamroller as they seemed to fill the whole street with there presence and sound.

"How about that for a sound then? Have you ever heard anything as good as that?"

"Aye," the retort. "Last year when the Irwell Springs band from Bacup played here. They were the best on the day an' best on the neet as well."

These sort of arguments would go on all through the day as each set of supporters spied their own particular bands. Hammonds Sauce Works, Yorkshire Imperial Metals, Manchester CWS, Fairy Aviation Works, the list went on and these were only the ones who would be playing for the local churches, at the contests tonight there would be one of the greatest galaxy of bands seen at one time as each one rushed in, played their contest march and then rushed off to the next village for another contest.

The contest tonight showed names of many bands who had won fame over a hundred years ago but would go unrecognised by the ordinary public as they still tried to regain some of their lost honours by beating the best in the world, and tonight was the only night of the year where they could possibly do it. Maybe tonight one of the great bands would have their beards trimmed by the minnows, who knows? It could be us.

We joined the procession precisely at nine o'clock and it wound its way round the centre of the town prior to starting the climb up the very steep hill that led to the church where the congregational service was to be held. Once again near to the church was the inevitable pub, The Bantam Cock. What I wouldn't have given to have been there when the decision was taken to build a pub right next to the church. That man or men should have been put forward as saints because the same thing seemed to have happened a great many times throughout at least the North of England.

I was not aware at the time but today was the day when I was to come of age as to what a great brass sound was all about. Up till now I had thought that we, in the Burston band, produced a very good sound but to hear those great bands playing on the march, in tune and with a tone that I would have killed for, taught me that we were only in the learners' class. The sound of 'Dyke' playing BB & CF produced an ambience all of its own and, as these great bands marched in procession, I could not help but feel that this must be the pinnacle of any bandsman's career.

It was not a loud blasting sound but more of a correct sound that carried, no matter what they were playing, in tune and played correctly. Such an impact was made on me that day that no matter where they played in the procession the relaxed well played sound could always be picked out.

As we played round the town I was unaware of what was to come but when the procession started to wend its way up the hill to the church and the road became steeper by the yard, the step, especially of the bandsmen, was cut so short that at one time the procession seemed to be stopped. Short as the steps were it was not long before the bandsmen with the larger instruments were puffing and panting. This did not stop the bands from playing and we had to stand our stint at the wheel. As the band in front finished their tune we started up with ours.

"Watch out behind!" A shout went up and almost like the downstroke of a baton the procession parted like the Red Sea must have done as an escaped bass drum came bouncing and banging down the hill, closing again immediately it had passed, luckily missing everyone in its passing. We were playing at the time and later in the pub a bandsman was heard to praise us as he said:

"I don't know how you did it, you must have been practising. It was pure poetry as the band opened and closed as the drum went through and you didn't miss a note."

Praise indeed coming from an opposing bandsman wearing the uniform of one of the top bands. It was not often that Burston Band came in for praise of any kind but it had been duly noted that the marching and discipline of the band had been up to scratch. The comment overheard at the bar of The Bantam Cock where we bandsmen finished up, the congregations having gone straight into church for the service.

After the church service the procession was once more assembled and we moved off down the hill, round the village once again and then back to our respective churches where we were given a light lunch before going out onto the playing fields, where the afternoon games for the children were held to the accompaniment of the band playing a light concert.

After the concert we had a cup of tea and then we were ready to sign in for the first contest of the evening which would be here

k

at Tupper Hills. We were lucky being the second band to sign in, from now on it would be mainly luck as to how many contests we could enter during this madcap evening.

On leaving our coach we had to march up to the contest field, stopping playing in the middle of a tune by the bandmaster raising his arm, this had to be done so that the adjudicator would not be able to recognise the signature tune of any band approaching. We then marched in silence onto the contest stand.

Once more there was a variation in the type of contest stands. Some would be set up as in concert formation, half moon fashion, others still set up as they had been for the last hundred years, in a square with the band stood around it and the conductor in the middle, others with modern stands that you could set up in any order you liked. There were also a few contests that did not provide stands at all and you had to play with the music held in your hands or in the music lyres on your instrument.

At the side of contest area were a number of beer crates, I immediately thought of all the bottles of ale that they had held and wondered why they had been left there. The answer came as I watched the next band go on on to play. There were two small boys playing with this band and as they could not quite reach the old stands the beer crates were used as steps to stand on. I noticed all this as we were leaving the field, that is until I heard Bert Rawlins shout:

"Come on Joe, you dozy bugger. Move your damned self."

He then set off running for the coach which was parked with its engine running ready to go. He jumped on and turned and hooked his arm under mine dragging me bodily onto the coach which had set off.

"What's the big hurry?" I gasped breathlessly.

"Come on Joe don't let it show that you're as thick as you look, keep 'em wondering," Jim Robins said. "Haven't you been listenin' to anything we've said? We've a lot more contests to try to get to tonight, so that means that we've to get a move on. No hanging about. Watch my lips! Move yer bloody self. As you know Bill Jackson, landlord of the Golden Ball is goin' in front in Jim's truck, he'll try to book us in just as we're comin' in to each contest an' if there's too many bands waiting he'll tell us to carry on to the next contest on the map, so you've got to be ready to move quick."

From then on I was in a complete daze. We would be driving first one way and then the next, stop at a contest, march, play and then run like hell back to the coach, drive like mad to the next one and so on.

I had been looking forward to a good night's playing and supping. Well, I was wrong. We visited places I had never heard of and probably would not hear of until next Whit-Friday, I cannot remember most of them but I heard names like Saddleworth, Greenfield, Ticcleford, Lower and Higher Tosside and a little village called Dobcross, all small villages whose names became famous once again each Whit-Friday.

It was at Dobcross Band Club where we got our first pint. The place was packed, with the boozers inside and a lot of their families outside watching and listening to the bands. The trouble with playing is that you do not get chance to listen to the top bands play because you have to be off again as soon as you have finished playing.

There were many more contests being held around the district in villages with names like Stalybridge, Millbrook, Lees and another that sounded like Delph.

The evening came to an end with us playing up the main street at Stalybridge in the dark and as we got onto the field the secretary of that contest tried to stop us marching onto the playing area, but after Bert whispered something in his ear, he seemed to turn quite pale. Maybe it was the light but I do not think so, I felt sure that it was something that he would sooner be kept a secret because he abruptly changed his mind and nearly pushed us onto the contest area. Whatever it was that Bert said to him had done the trick and as we were leaving the contest he gave Bert such a look that should have turned him immediately to stone.

That was it. Finished for the night. My lips felt like they were dangling down to my knees and at that moment all I could think of was a pint.

It was late and all the pubs were closed but we were waiting for David Green to return. He had promised us that he had made arrangements for us to be let in at a club at Higher Brompton but he had to ring to make sure that the arrangements were still on. Two minutes later he was back.

"Right!" he said, "we're in luck. If we get to Higher Brompton Labour Club before half past ten they'll let us in, so let's get a move on."

The news was greeted with great enthusiasm and the coach sped off in the direction of the aforesaid club.

We arrived at the Labour Club just in time, another couple of minutes and the door would have been closed and these lads would not have opened them for anyone, especially to a coach-load of beer starved bandsmen, booked in or not.

When we got inside the club it was packed to the seams. There were waiters doing a stirring job, but trying to get beer to all these bandsmen, most of whom had not been able to have a drink all night, was asking too much from too few waiters. We fought our way to the bar, elbows digging, drawing snarls from other such patrons wanting just the same thing and eventually managed to slide quickly into a space vacated by a bandsman with a tray totally overloaded with drinks. What chance he had of getting that lot back to his friends intact I certainly would not have liked to bet on.

After what seemed a lifetime Pete Barton, who was the one who had managed to squeeze in to the bar, started passing pints over the heads of the men packing the bar. He passed us the pints and we passed him the cash. One or two scuffles broke out as our pints were nearly waylaid but at last we were all satisfied that we had enough beer to last us for a short while. In the meantime Bert Rawlins had managed to purloin a table and some chairs in the corner of the room.

Time was getting on and the only thing we had managed to accomplish was drinks and a table, in between crossing insults with some of the bandsmen that we knew. We had just settled down when there was a call for 'order' from the clubs concert secretary, who was sat on a raised chair to the right of the stage about three feet above the clubroom floor.

In front of him was a table with his drink on and in his hand he had a rather large gavel. Every now and then, when the noise of the drinkers rose above the different artistes who were called up to sing or 'do a turn', he would pound the table until he could be heard, threatening them that the concert would be terminated if 'order' wasn't given. Everyone knew that if the concert was stopped the beer would also be stopped so it did not take him long to get the 'order' he required.

"Order lads, order. If I don't get order I'll have to close the bar."

"You'd better not close it yet," Hughie Mack shouted. "We've only just got here and you said that you would keep the bar open longer if we got here in time, well we got here so get them waiters round double quick or you'll have more than a bloody concert on your hands."

There was a loud cheer as Hughie sat down.

"Now come on lads we're doin' our best you'll all get served in time but if we don't get 'order' you won't be able to hear the artiste."

The booing that followed his speech seemed to shake him and for the moment he disappeared, the call of nature he said but he was right to give it a rest for the moment, obviously the sound of his own voice was what he enjoyed the most. He returned a short time later to cat calls and boos and climbed back in the chair.

"It's all right you sitting there supping but you said that you would give us a song if we kept the bar open for you so, if you can sing better than tha can shout, get up here and give us a song."

A bout of clapping accompanied his words and he immediately ordered another pint before the noise or the singing, whichever was worse, got out of hand.

What had started off as a rush had now settled down and what followed was one of the best, off the cuff, concerts they had ever heard in this club, this the secretary remarked afterwards.

The first one up was our ace in the hole, Tom Perkins with his wonderfully resonant voice, and as he opened with *The Old House* the words cut through the noise in the room.

"Slowly I wandered through streets of my childhood." His glorious baritone voice filling the club, the chatter subsided and the silence only disturbed by the chink of the waiters collecting the empty glasses, at which there were shushes all round the room and these not from the secretary but from a very surprised audience as they suddenly realised that this singing was quality.

At the end of the song Tom received a tremendous ovation from the packed clubroom who made it obvious that he would not be allowed to regain his seat until he had sung another one. He allowed himself a quick drink that emptied his glass then making it obvious that he expected it to be filled again when he had finished singing, he launched himself into the beautiful song *The Rose Of Tralee*. Once again the crowd roared its appreciation, shouting and clapping for more, but Tom had done his bit so thanking them he sat down.

It did not take us long to realise how good a job Tom had done for us. His singing had brought the house down and that appreciation came in the form of paid for drinks, far too many for Tom to drink on his own, but then what are friends for? Ale did not stay in the glass too long when there were gannets like us around.

After a while 'order' was restored and the secretary persuaded someone else to get up and give a song, how he did it I do not know. Anyone who had to get up and follow Tom Perkins sing had a struggle on. It was certainly a hard act to follow.

It seemed that another band in the club were not going to be outdone by Burston Band and volunteered one of their members to get up, not that he was a very good singer but the worry was that if there were not enough singers the bar would close.

After that things seemed to go with a swing and when our second horn player, Andrew Makin, mounted the stage with Ernie Benson to accompany him, the crowd were in the mood for anything and anyone. Andrew surprised us by giving a very jaunty version of *Paddy McGinty's Goat* and although cheered on by the audience he quickly jumped off the stage and, grinning all over his young face, admitted that it was the only tune that he knew.

"Right, come on now, give us some order," said the voice of the concert secretary crackling over the now faulty microphone. Well, what instrument would not go faulty with someone spitting in it all night. "Who's next?" he said with a silly grin on his face. The question was irrelevant. He would not have cared whether anyone was singing or not. His eyes started to glaze and one of the committee members darted forward and made a futile grab as he slid slowly to the floor, out to the world.

Another 'chairman' was quickly found and it was the lads from Burston who provided another song. Andy Carlton, Brian Dale and Hughie Mack jumped up onto the stage and Ernie once more cranked up the piano to give a very funny rendering of *The Bold Gendarmes* after which Pete Barton gave us the old tongue twister *Barley Mow*.

The chairman again asked for singers, as he tried to keep the concert flowing, then Bert Rawlins jumped to his feet and for a minute I thought he was going to give a song.

"Hold on a bit," he shouted above the din. "Are we the only ones who can sing as well as play? I know we're the best singers here but surely somebody else con give us a lift?"

"Aye," came a voice from the corner of the room. "We'll give you a song or two, nobody's gonna say that Wadehock Band can't hold their corner when it comes to singing."

With that a bandsman with Wadehock written on his uniform pocket emptied his glass and strode up onto the stage. That was the start of another great song spot. There were duets and even a barber's shop quartet and to top it all they finished off with a very good choir. Burston Band had performed extremely well and now the players of Wadehock Band had more than equalled us with their wide variety of talent.

Although there were many more singers who we enjoyed listening to, the main talking point that night were the Burston and Wadehock bands. Not many people outside of our towns had heard of us before but we would be remembered in these parts for many a year, if not for our playing then at least for our singing.

At last the bar was closed for the night and we all made our way back to our respective coaches. Tom Perkins was just getting into our coach when a figure rushed up to him.

'Oh hell,' I thought, 'not another punch-up, and after a great night like this.' Then I heaved a sigh of relief. It was no punch-up. It was just one of Wadehock's bandsmen telling Tom how much he had enjoyed his singing and maybe we could get together sometime and have some sort of singing concert and contest. Tom thanked him and said that it was something that they should think about. We all said goodnight and amidst good humoured insults, got into our coach. It would not happen right away. It would be some years before it actually came about but the seed had been sown.

When the coach arrived back at Burston it had started to rain so we dropped the instruments off at the 'Duke' and after cadging a quick late pint we started to make our way home. It had been quite a day, and whether we had won any prizes along the way would not be known for a few days, but for some of us it was not quite over yet.

Jim Hogan, our E flat player had partaken of more of the hops that he should have done and as he stepped off the coach he tripped and fell flat on his face. Luckily because of the state he was in, he was beyond all earthly help or feeling so he just picked himself up and set off on the long walk home.

Jim lived with his wife Peggy in a house at the top of a very steep hill just outside town. The house was just one of the many council houses built for the first world war soldiers to come home to, something about 'somewhere fit for heroes to live', better than some but worse than others. Jim did not give a hoot why they had been built, he just liked his house with the small garden at the front sloping down from the pavement to the front door, with the grass growing just a bit longer beneath the windows where his bit of lawn was cultivated. Round his garden Jim had built a small fence, about twelve inches high. The fence was painted white because Peggy said that it would make it look tidier and Jim always liked to keep Peggy happy chance she cut off his band nights. All this seemed irrelevant, but Peggy told us the story later on that week, much to Jim's disgust.

It seemed that Jim, arriving at last at the top of the hill, staggered towards his house and turned left into what he thought was his garden path. He was a little bit previous though and tripped over the small garden fence. Before he could stop himself he had rolled down the garden being brought to a sharp halt, face upturned, jammed beneath his front window, the rain running from a cracked guttering and falling straight down onto Jim's upturned face.

Jim Hogan was not a very tall man. He stood about five feet five inches in his stocking feet and about the same around the middle, at least it looked like that when he rolled down the garden, his large waist and the angle of the garden trapping him immovably beneath the window-sill.

Because of the state he was in it took some time before Jim realised his predicament, the water soaking through everything that he was wearing. He struggled to free himself without avail. The more he struggled the tighter he became stuck. After struggling for some time and not making any headway he started to panic. How the hell was he going to get out of this? He could not stay here all night, he would most likely get pneumonia or something, he might even drown and in water at that. Oh, damn and blast, he realised it would be hard to live down if this got out. Then he had a brain-wave. If he could just reach the window and attract Peggy's attention, she could then come outside and release him and then no one would have to know about him getting stuck. The trouble was, how could he get Peggy to hear him? She had made it quite plain that she did not agree with all his drinking. She did not mind him having the odd pint but lately he had abused the privilege. He shuddered at the thought. Peggy was caustic enough at the best of times about the band and its drunken crew, as she liked to put it. But for the band he could be home in bed with her instead of being stuck here beneath the window. It was all the band's fault, the useless pillocks, they kept getting him into these situations. While this train of thought was about him he vowed to himself that he would spend less time with all those useless drunks. But for the band he might have been home at a decent time instead of staggering home in the early hours of the morning drunk as a mop. He tried once more to free himself. No use, he had to get Peggy's help.

By squirming round a bit he found that he could just manage to reach up and touch the window. He knocked lightly. He did not want Peggy complaining that the neighbours had seen him coming home drunk again. He waited for a moment but there was just silence. He knocked again just a bit louder. Still no Peggy. By now Jim was tired, soaked with rain and muddied up to the eyebrows and still no nearer to getting himself free. He gathered himself. This had to be it. Neighbours or not he had to get help. He felt that he had been laid there for hours. He was just reaching up for the final big bang when he heard the door open and out stepped his wife Peggy.

"Thank God, Peg love, I'm here stuck under the window," he wailed. He had not meant for it to come out just like that, all soft and whimpery, it just happened. Peggy just stood there looking in his direction pretending that she could not see him.

"Oh come on love get me out of here, please," he grovelled. "I'm soaked through to the skin," he pleaded.

Peggy stood there for a while hoping that the neighbours had not heard him. She knew that if she gave in too quickly this glorious moment would be lost forever. What she would not give for a camera. She knew that she would have to give in eventually but she needed to savour the moment, besides she had heard it all before when Jim came home drunk, he could be a right little pleader when he wanted to be. At last Peggy relented and her ample figure loomed over the hapless Jim.

"Jim Hogan," she said menacingly, "if it wasn't for the neighbours I'd let you stay there forever. You're sloshed again, filthy and disgusting. You make me sick. You can't even find your way down the garden path when you're drunk and when you fall over with the drink you come whimpering to me for help." She stood there not wishing to relinquish these moments but knowing that she would soon have to free him. Then Jim did a foolish thing. He interrupted Peg when she was in full flow.

"Help me up Peg love, please," he pleaded once again. "I've been stuck here for ages. I'm frozen through."

Peggy looked down at him with a straight face, though she really wanted to laugh. He shivered because he knew what she was thinking and he did not like it one bit. When Peggy looked at him like that and with no teeth in he was in for trouble.

"I know you've been here a long time," she said with a leer. "I looked out of the window half an hour ago and saw you wriggling like a fat slug. I was determined to leave you there all night hoping that the rain would sober you up but I've got my good name to think of, so think yourself very lucky. When I looked out of the window to see what all the shenanigans were and saw you lying there I felt that all the people on the estate could hear you but I decided to leave you there and went back to bed. Unfortunately you were making so much noise that I knew that I would have to come down and get you inside, but believe me you haven't heard the last of this, not for a long time." With that she grabbed him by the leg and dragged him none too gently out into the garden. She thrust his leg away from her in disgust and, giving him a look that would have shamed the Devil himself she stalked into the house.

Jim lay there for a while oblivious to the rain that was running down his neck. He was feeling very sorry for himself. Not for a second did it enter his head that Peggy was mad at him for coming home drunk with his clothes filthy and wet, no, all that bothered her was what would the neighbours say when they found out, if they had not done so already. Well, bugger the neighbours he thought, I am master of my own house he reassured himself. Just the same he made sure that when he went through the door into the house that Peggy was not waiting behind it to clobber him with something hard. Ah well, never mind, tomorrow was another day, she would get over it, she always did. The point was would he? Mind you things would be a bit tight for a day or two, he thought as he got out of the wet clothes, but she would come round eventually. Until then it would be silent meals. "What I go through for this band!"

18

Belle Vue

This was it! The final week of practice before we took the stage for the contest. 'Belle Vue Zoological Gardens'. The name itself sounded so grand. The thrill at the thought of playing there was giving me dreams of grandeur. It was a hallowed name when talking about brass band contests and although it was only about twenty-five miles away, I had never even been there.

The morning seemed to go past with such speed and before we knew it our coach was passing through the City of Manchester and on through Longsight to Belle Vue. We were to stay with the coach until we got to know what number we were to play. From our coach we could see into the great amusement park which was an integral part of the Zoological Gardens.

We looked round the sights, or at least the ones we could see, and we waited. Half an hour later David Green arrived back with the news that we had been drawn number ten and that the contest would not be starting for another hour yet. I groaned quietly to myself. We had promised Adam that we would not have too much to drink before the contest and, as the contest would not be starting for another hour yet and the rate of playing would be about five to the hour, that meant that we could not get to grips with any ale for at least three hours. What a blow! How were we going to spend the next three hours? Cash was too short to be wasted on rides or amusements. The money we had saved was only for serious drinking.

As usual Adam had things well in hand. This situation had

been foreseen and catered for. We were to go to the Red Lion public house which was about half a mile away. It had been provisionally booked by David on the chance that we could have a blow before the actual contest. Tea and biscuits had been laid on after our rehearsal. I had the feeling that we would not even get those if the rehearsal did not go well. One of the things that Adam had feared was that we would have time to indulge in our boozy sports, well, this was one time that the 'hops' would have to take second place.

Adam felt pleased with himself at the outcome of his scheming. He was quite sane. He knew that somehow we would get a pint or two before we left the pub, but the way he saw it was that he would be able to keep the intake of booze down to a very minimum. That was his plan, but a lot depended on the landlord of the Red Lion, he was the unknown factor, it left a question mark against his well planned idea.

We arrived at the Red Lion about ten minutes later and our first look at the dirty red bricked pub filled us with optimism. Just our sort of place. The windows didn't look as though they had been cleaned since before the war and though we tried, we could not see through them into the pub.

As it was still not opening time yet the doors were locked and David had to bang on them with his shoe before we heard sounds of a bolt being drawn.

"All right, hold your bloody horses will yah? Tha doesn't need to wreck the bloody place. I saw you comin' but I couldn't get down here in time to put the red carpet out."

The sarcasm from the scruffy man who opened the door was a bit uncalled for, anyway it was totally lost on us, we had been spoken to sarcastically by professionals so it did not worry us one bit.

The landlord was not a very tall man. He stood about five foot six in his tacky slippers, he had the shape of a barrel but gave the impression that it was not all fat. He seemed to have no neck, his head set down squat onto his shoulders and his rolled up sleeves showed massive forearms covered with various tattoos. His quite ugly face was bent out of shape and mostly covered by a large squashed nose. He did not look like a man you would want as an enemy and even as a friend. I knew that I would not walk down a dark alley with him. He looked a brute and it was not until I got to the bar that I realised where his misshapen face had come from.

On the wall were various pictures of wrestlers in the ring. When someone dared to broach the subject he laughed, showing broken teeth and told us that they had been taken when he had been a fairground wrestler.

It seems that in the early thirties he had travelled with a fair, setting up his booth and taking on anyone who wanted to try to earn a 'florin'. All they had to do was to put him on his back on the canvas, something which, according to him, they never did. I looked at him and his massive arms, his barrel chest and his bull-like head and even though he was now getting on in years, I felt that it would still be like tangling with a bull. A thought crossed my mind of me and him in the wrestling ring. Me, with all of my nine stone wet through. I shuddered at the thought of what I could look like when he had finished with me.

The mirror across the bar was facing me. I grimaced and pulled my mouth to one side and pressed my nose in, the picture was not a nice one. What a sight. It did not bare thinking of.

First things first. Were we going to get a drink before the practice or not? Once again Adam supplied the answer.

"No drinks until after the practice," he said. "That is even if the landlord will give you one. I don't think that it'll be opening time even when we've finished the practice so, don't get your hopes up."

We set the stands up and squeezed into the small room, but by pushes and shoves we managed to get into something like concert formation.

"Right, get your hymn books out and we'll have a warm up." Adam's voice was businesslike. "We'll start off with *Diadem*, then *Abide With Me* and that should have got you warmed up and while your instruments are still warm we'll see about the tuning."

Once again we were down to basics. The long warm notes of the hymn music, first played at double forte and then with feeling at double piano. It fair made the lip tremble trying to keep the music down to a whisper but it did the trick and after about twenty minutes of this we were well and truly warmed up. While Adam tuned up one section of the band we had to wait and while we were waiting we had to keep our instruments warmed up by gently blowing into the mouthpiece.

It took Adam the best part of an hour to get the band tuned up to his satisfaction, or as near as possible at the present time, though I cannot remember his being really satisfied. We thought that he had gone about it quite wrong. We felt that having a pint or two would loosen us up a little but he would not have it and when he had finished the tuning we could hear him, "I suppose that'll be the best I'm going to get you. If you could blow the same note twice on the run I'd be able to do something with you. The point is, if you don't hold your tuning when we play in the contest I'm afraid that there's nothing for us, we're all over the place and that's down to home practice, I mean the fact is that some of you obviously don't do any."

We carried on with the rehearsal of the contest piece, going over bits here and there as Adam tried to draw a bit more feeling from the music. Before we knew it an hour had flown by and at last Adam gave up the unequal struggle.

"Well, as you can't go much worse, the chances are that a pint will do you more good than harm. We'll just have to hope that your best performance has yet to come. You've got fifteen minutes and not a minute more."

The resulting rush to the bar jammed the door of our practice room until someone with a sharp elbow cleared the way. We need not have worried though as it was obvious that someone had had a word with the landlord, because though opening time was still some time off there were pints being pulled for us as we went into the bar, all we had to do was to pay for them.

Although we only had fifteen minutes, we used them well. The barman said he had not worked so fast for a long while. The ale went down as if there would be no tomorrow and it would have continued like that but for David Green putting a stop to it.

"Right lads," he shouted above the din. "Sup up and get your-selves on the coach. In exactly one minute we set off and whoever isn't on by then gets left here."

When we saw his face we realised that he meant it, but what he would have done if we had been late getting on I do not know; he downed his pint in one gulp and left the room. The landlord immediately closed the bar amidst dire threats against his life and that was that. We drank up and followed David onto the coach, all mutinous thoughts expelled by the closing of the bar.

That was it. No more ale for at least an hour. To some of the lads that was a lifetime and only the fact that one of them had a livener in his pocket flask kept them from storming the 'Bastille', but what were we going to do in the time left?

We arrived back at Belle Vue in good time to sign on. Too early in fact. Time enough for one or two of the hard drinkers to slope off for a quick one. With all the bandsmen from different bands milling round their disappearance was not immediately noticed. After a short while Adam started to gather the rest of us together, prior to going in to the signing on room and it was then that Hughie Mack was found to be missing. Adam went spare.

"Who knew that he had gone?" he grated, looking quite dangerous. "Someone must have seen him creeping away." He scrutinised each one of us as we said that we had not seen him go.

"Where is the stupid pillock? I'll swing for the Celtic twit if I get my hands on him."

We all started to look around for Hughie. Here we all were waiting to sign in at the Ballroom and our soprano cornet player missing. Adam grabbed David Green's arm.

"Look, go and see if you can spot him. If he isn't here in two minutes we'll have to get the 'sop' player from the band that plays before us and ask him if he'll play for us if Hughie doesn't get back in time."

A minute or so later a breathless David arrived back saying that he had asked the 'sop' player from the other band who had refused saying that he did not want to play for any other band than his own. Well, that was his prerogative. We were allowed to ask but he was not forced to accept. Adam listened to David and then let out a string of oaths that would have brought pride to a sergeant major's heart. I listened to him in total awe. I had never heard anyone put together a string of swear words in quite the same manner as these and he did not even repeat himself once. Suddenly he stopped swearing as Andy Carlton nudged him in the ribs.

"Owd on Adam here he comes now."

We all looked in the direction he was indicating and there was Hughie weaving his way through the crowded entrance hall towards us. A big smile lit up his face when he caught sight of us. Adam turned away in disgust. He could not bring himself to speak to Hughie, at least not until after the contest. I think that if Hughie had said anything to Adam just then, Adam would have gleefully strangled him. On the other hand Hughie was totally oblivious to the trouble he had caused, even though it was obvious that he had used the waiting time to slip off for a pint. He was in a very relaxed frame of mind to say the least, it just remained for us to see if he was sober enough to play his part when we got onto the stage. In the meantime David took Hughie aside and started to talk to him, I don't know what David said to him but Hughie just kept nodding his head.

Meanwhile Adam motioned for us to go on into the signing room and we forgot all about Hughie.

This was it. In no time we had passed through the signing on room and then onto the stage. We quickly found our seats and after a bit of shuffling around we settled down and quietly waited for the adjudicator's whistle which told us that he was ready for us. We warmed our instruments, anything to try not to let the nerves take over. The only one who was really relaxed was Hughie. He showed us the way. He just sat there breathing gently into his mouthpiece and moving the valves about keeping them nicely warmed up.

I will never forget that first time that I played at Belle Vue. Sure, it was not in the top section which played in the Kings Hall, but it was at Belle Vue just the same and you never can tell, we just might be playing in the mighty Kings Hall some day.

Unfortunately for us this dream would not be realised in the near future. Our playing was terrible, at least I thought so, but as we left the stage the applause was deafening so perhaps I did not know as much as I thought I did. Hughie played magnificently. He did not put a note wrong. From the rest of the band I heard one or two slips but even without them I felt that we were not playing together with odd intonation slips here and there. We had played it far better than this in rehearsal but on the stage we had let ourselves down still, we would just have to wait and see. The hopes that the adjudicator had not heard the slips were a bit forlorn but that did not matter now, for us the contest was over, we would just have to wait and see. We were now free until the results were announced at the end of the contest. So, what now?

We put our instruments away and regrouped outside the Ballroom and tried to decide where to go. I cannot be sure who led the way but we all seemed to be moving in the same direction. There was no rush, we had at least a couple of hours yet. We sauntered on past the merry-go-rounds. The speeding cars on the

'Bobs' whizzing past overhead to accompanying shrieks of delight from the passengers. The noise was tremendous. Everywhere we went there was noise and any amount of places in which to spend your money. I thought of going on the rifle range but as the others carried on walking, and I did not want to lose sight of them, I decided against it.

"Where the 'ell are we goin'? Brian Dale said turning round to face us. "I'm after some ale not buggering about on some stupid roundabouts."

"Stick wi' us lad an' you'll not on'y get yer ale but you'll be rubbin' shoulders wi' some o' the top bandsmen in the world, people you've on'y heard about on't wireless. We're goin' tuh the bandsmen's 'Mecca'. It's a bar just round here an' it's called 'Caesar's Palace'."

I just had to be stupid and show them my inexperience. "What's Caesar's Palace when you're at 'ome? It sounds like a gambling joint tuh me. I've heard of places like that on the wireless and, apart from me dad goin' spare if he ever heard about it, I 'aven't the brass tuh loose if it's gambling."

"Now Joe, don't be a pillock all yer life, tak' a day off." This from Jim Hogan, he had frequented the place before and he knew his way around. "Caesar's Palace is only one of many bars around Belle Vue and it's 'THE' bar as far as bandsmen are concerned. It's a bar where all the bandsmen converge when they are not playin', where they meet old friends from other bands and swop memories or news of other bandsmen and, if we're lucky we might 'ere one of 'em givin' a solo or even a few of 'em'll get together an' 'ave a buskin' session. Yuh never know yer luck." With that he turned and strode off in the direction he had indicated Caesar's Palace to be.

As Jim was not one to go into long sentences about something, I shut my trap and followed him. If he was correct, I would not want to miss this for the world.

As we walked towards the bar I was not sure what to expect. Were they having me on? If they were telling the truth would it be a big place with flashing lights? This was the city and they did things in the city with a lot more style than we were used to in Burston, so I was expecting something flashy. What a disappointment! It did not look anything outstanding, just a building that looked like any other around Belle Vue except it looked like part of it was a restaurant. The place seemed to be all windows and above the doorway was a sign proclaiming it to be Caesar's Palace. Not much to look at from the outside but as long as the ale was good it was OK by us.

We all trouped in through the door and the atmosphere seemed to change. Outside the bar the noise was of loud cheery music mixed with shrieks of excitement and pleasure from the people riding on the various roundabouts but as soon as the doors closed behind us the mood changed and we were in the world of brass bands.

Amongst this assemblage of bandsmen were the names of some of the greatest bandsmen in the world both past and present. Uniforms of every colour and design, most of them edged with some sort of braid, either gold or silver. The bandsmen sat relaxed with buttons undone and most of them with a pint in their hands animatedly discussing the likes and dislikes of one band or another.

After making sure of the most important aspect of our visit to the 'Palace', which was of course to get a pint or two down us, we managed to grab a table as it became vacant and sat down to soak in the atmosphere and relax.

I still could not believe it. Here we were sitting in the most famous bar in the brass band world. Around us some of the great bandsmen from some well known bands, the names of which were emblazoned on either the shoulder or the breast pocket of their uniforms. Arguments could be heard above the noisy talk in the room. Who was the best soloist in certain bands and which band had the best sound. Certain names kept coming up in the conversation, Sullivan, Lang, Mortimer and many others. It was not just the talk, these players were really here in Belle Vue. Obviously I would not recognise any of them if I saw them but they were here somewhere and that thought alone was enough even though the only blot on their characters was that they could possibly be adjudicating.

Why was it that some of the people I admired most in the brass band world went over to the enemy and became adjudicators, referees and suchlike? I suppose that the fact that someone had to give a judgement on the bands made it better that it should come from ex-bandsmen of some repute, but why had it to be some of the good ones? Up till now all the others that we had come in contact with had been wrong in their judgements, we had won nothing. Still, when you are at the bottom of the pack you can only go upwards! Maybe things were beginning to get better, it always looked that way when you were at Belle Vue.

When we had finished playing we could relax and enjoy the atmosphere. I noticed Bert Rawlins and Jim Hogan move away and talk to other bandsman who were sitting around the room and when they came back I was very disappointed when they told me that they hadn't spoken to anyone famous.

We had been in the bar for some time now and the ale was beginning to take effect as Harry Rawlins said, "Let's liven the place up."

"Don't talk daft," Pete Barton growled. "We can't outplay this lot, they'd have us for breakfast."

"I don't mean that you daft pillock," Harry replied. "I mean let's get 'em singin'."

"I don't think that it'd go down reight well just now," Pete came back. "They'd sooner just sit there and waffle. You know what these owd fettlers er like when they get together. Th'ale seems tuh be goin' down nice an' steady, seems a pity tuh disturb 'em."

Joe Sudders leaned over the table conspiratorially. "I know what'll waken 'em all up! Remember last year when we got rained off on that park job. Didn't we get suppin' in that pub at Delton before we went to the Dog and Partridge? Remember? We had a suppin' contest an' we didn't let 'em know that Andy didn't have any clack in his gullet."

"Aye." Pete's eyes lit up as he remembered. "An' we made a bomb with the bettin' an' if we go on suppin' like we are doin' we'll soon be out of ale brass so we'd better do summat."

"Ere,'ang on a minute," Andy Carlton said. "Don't I have any say in this? I've already had four pints. Give us a chance!"

"Tha talks like a wart," Jimmy Belfor said, warming to the thought of a bit of fun. "I'll bet this lot couldn't sup their way out of a paper bag. They do more talkin' than suppin'."

"I dern't know," Andy replied, wavering a little. Harry immediately settled it by climbing up on the table and shouting for some hush. He waited patiently for them to quieten down and said.

"If anybody's interested, we're goin' tuh 'ave a suppin'

236

contest, so if tha's got anybody who think that they con sup, they 'ave the chance tuh put there money where their mouth is, 'cos we've got a top gargler with us who's never bin beat."

The room that had been reasonably noisy before Harry had jumped on the table, quietened down for a moment and then the clamouring started as first one and then the another bandsman put forward his champion and it was not long before we had a list of so-called champion drinkers lined up.

"Reight then," Harry said, rubbing his hands together in anticipation. "First thing first. What are we suppin' for? What's the prize?"

After a bit of thought someone suggested that all the contestants should put a 'tanner' (six-pence, old money) in the 'kitty' with the winner takes all. Each contestant would pay for their own ale. Well, at that stipulation one or two of the so-called champion suppers stood down, they had thought of it as an easy way of getting a free pint. That still left sixteen contestants. Two teams. The winner of each team would sup off for the jackpot and champion supper of Belle Vue.

We pushed four tables together and the first eight contestants stood up on the table where everyone could see them. The rules were simple. At the word go, the first one to drink his pint and sit down with his empty glass was to be the winner. Anyone taking an early sup, to start before the off, was to be disqualified.

Everyone crowded round the tables, this was not a show they wanted to miss. The first start was stopped when someone pushed the table, maybe to give their champion a better chance. Who knows? One good shove on the table when someone other than their own champion was performing well could quite easily overbalance all the others and they were then sat down in order to prepare themselves again and to top up their glasses. This could become very unpopular and costly so everyone was made to stand off from the table. We knew about all these tricks. We had used them ourselves in the past.

Once more a start was made, this time with what should have been the second eight suppers, and this was won by a lad from Yorkshire. He won it hands down. He jumped down from the table waving his arms as though he had won the final and for a short time he had us worried. He moved away from the table accompanied by cheers from his supporters and backers. One wag, who obviously was not one of his supporters shouted, "It's a bloody fiddle. He can't possibly lose. Wi' a gob like he's got, 'e could 'ave supped a bucket full an' still bin off the table afore all the others."

A round of jeers followed his statement and the arguments were still going on when we set up the second round. Andy Carlton was our man and he was in this round. As there had been quite a bit of betting going on in the background things were getting a bit het-up.

On the word go, the second eight contestants went into action. Up went the glasses and the contest was on. A gasp went out from the audience as Andy and another lad supped up and sat down almost together, but the other lad was disqualified when it was pointed out that he still had some beer left in his glass. Numb bugger. You would not have caught Andy with any left in his glass, he would have found some way of getting rid of it before his bum had hit that seat. As it happened Andy did not need to fiddle. When it came to downing a pint of ale, Andy just could not be beat. The lack of a 'clack' had something to do with it, he just tipped his head back and down it went. Shouts went round the room like 'fiddle' and 'cheat' but they could not do anything about it. Andy did offer to take him on again after the contest but he would not accept, even if Andy had supped a few more pints he would still have licked him and he knew it, he had seen the ale disappear down Andy's throat like pouring it into a bucket and he had been an idiot leaving that inch of ale in the glass. He was miffed. His supporters had washed their hands of him and walked away in a huff. It was his own fault. He should have got rid of the evidence, we would.

That left Andy and the lad from Yorkshire, Ben something or other, I did not catch his full name with all the row going on but boy, he could sup? Andy needed all his supping powers to be in first class working order, we were not sure whether Andy had at last met his match. Well, after they had had a short rest we would see!

All the room had seen how these two lads could down a pint and the betting was getting quite silly, I feel sure that more than one gambler in this room was squeezing his wallet. To show willing I put my 'tanner' on Andy, although I was not all that sure that I had bet on the winner, but as we had done all the shouting we had to stick by our man.

This was the grand final and I feel sure that should any one of the betters have been due to play in the contest there would have been a strong possibility of them being late. Harry jumped up on the table and once more introduced the two contestants.

There were upwards of two hundred bandsmen and followers in that room and nearly all of them had a bet on of some sort. The odds were about even. Some shouting for one man and some for the other. Suddenly Jack Nuttall jumped up on a chair, how he got up there I do not know, he was obviously a bit kettled, but he waved his arms and shouted above the noise, "My bet's on Andy, and if he doesn't win, I'll show my arse on the stage an' stand you all a drink as well." Then he swayed sideways and fell off the chair.

The room had gone all quiet when Jack had stood up on the chair and shouted the odds, but sensing the chance of a free drink they gave him a great cheer which, unfortunately, he did not hear because he was sparked out on the floor under the table.

As the contest showed signs of starting the crowd started to voice their support.

"Come on Ben loosen they clack, get it down an show these braggin' buggers how tuh sup."

"Give 'em some fettle Andy. Show 'em who's the boss. The beer they sup in Yorkshire isn't fit tuh be called good beer."

The insults were rife as the two drinkers climbed up onto the table and sides were taken as brass bands answer to the battle of the roses began in earnest.

"Reight lads," Harry said in his best English. "Tha both know the rules. Yuh both start wi't full glass tuh thy lips. No drinkin' till I say go. OK?"

They both nodded in agreement and then turned to face each other. Faces serious. Eyes watching for any slip of the rules. Glasses filled to the brim, no slopping allowed. Suddenly a shout went up as Ben, unable to stand the strain, took a sip. He should have been disqualified straight away but Andy seeing that Ben had made a start, lifted his glass and down it went in one gulp, he then jumped off the table and sat down. Meanwhile Ben, who had tried to steal a march on Andy was flabbergasted at the speed that Andy had dropped his pint and he was still only halfway down his glass. At the last hurdle his supping powers had failed him and although he did manage to finish his pint, he was well and truly beaten and it was another ten seconds before he got down from the table, completely demoralised, so much so that as he got down from the table, he slipped and rolled off onto the floor and passed out.

We were still laughing and cheering as his pals carted him off to the toilets. Of Jack Nuttall there was nothing to be seen. After making his famous offer he had seemed to pass out under the table but since then, as no one seemed to be watching him, he must have crept out. There was no way that Jack Nuttall had been going to pay for a round of free drinks. After a brief search he was found fast asleep under one of the bench seats bordering the room.

Harry Rawlins had of course come up trumps, he had lashed out five shillings on Andy and collected his winnings and as we had all bet on Andy and won, we were all in the money. Not much, but enough for today. Mind you we had to make ourselves scarce for the time being just to let the dust settle, so to speak.

After a short meeting we decided to go to the Kings Hall where all the top bands were playing and try to absorb some of the atmosphere. There was something about the Kings Hall which could excite any bandsman.

The hall itself was arranged like an amphitheatre. High backed benches around the whole of the hall with the stage arranged in the centre and standing about four feet off the floor. It was used for various functions, boxing and wrestling etc., but mostly for the famous Belle Vue Circus. I suppose it was used for many more functions which did not interest us. The only thing that I was interested in was the May and September contests.

The feeling of anticipation as each band walked out onto the stage is hard to describe. Bandsmen who we knew and had been talking to only a few minutes ago were now going out onto the stage to compete for the British Championship. I wondered how long it would be before our band would be good enough to compete here? The mind boggles. This hall was for top section bands only, and only the best of them.

Our band was still only a fourth section band, but although only in the fourth section some of our players could certainly have fitted in well with any of the top bands. It was the band as a whole that was not good enough. Never mind, time would tell!

We only had an hour to listen to them and then we had to leave. We had arranged to meet everyone else back at the coach park, prior to leaving for Burston. If we got there on time we might be able to persuade David Green to have a word with the coach driver to postpone our departure time, maybe a whip-round could persuade him to stay.

We arrived back at the coach park in plenty of time and it was there that we learned that we had got into the prizes. It was only the third prize but you would have thought that we had won the championship. We were over the moon. Although the thought of prizes was always on our minds, we had never been really confident of winning anything but, as Adam was quick to point out, you can never be sure of anything at a contest. He followed up by giving us a lecture on just what was wrong with our playing and the probable reason why the prize hadn't been the first.

"Just think about it?" he said. "I know that you played well below your capabilities but imagine if you had played the way I know you can play. Remember, we were only three points behind the winner, which means that we had the ability to win. I only thought so before and now I'm sure so, you'd all better watch out, next time I'll be out to win."

David approached our coach driver and asked him if we could make Burston before closing time. We could have stayed but it would have meant making our own way back home and what that could have meant would have been scandalous, we were much better off going home on the coach free and then spending the rest of the evening on our own midden. At least from there we could easily walk home, drunk or not.

So that was the great Belle Vue? What an experience. Maybe it was my first visit to the famous 'Gardens' but it was not going to be the last if I could help it. It had been the best day in my short banding life and I had hopes for many more, unfortunately it seemed that we would have to wait for a while.

When I arrived home there was a letter waiting for me marked OHMS. There was only one reason why his Majesty would write to me and that was to invite me to join his forces. I did not quite know what to expect but whatever it was I was ready to try it. What branch of the services would I be in? The Army, Navy or the Air Force? The possibilities were endless. I might even finish up in a military band. Now, that would be something!

19

The Medical

The day of the medical arrived. I was up early, trying hard to hide my excitement. I had not been able to sleep and had tossed and turned all night long, at least it seemed that way. I washed, shaved off the odd whisker that turned out to be a small mark on my chin. My father had advised me not to shave because if I waited till after breakfast the cat would have licked it off. I had taken my yearly bath the night before and my mother had sighed with relief when she saw that I had unclogged the drain.

Breakfast had to be pushed down even though I was too elated to eat. Mother had made it and that was that. I did get away with putting two bacon butties in a bag.

As I had got myself ready in plenty of time, due mainly to my mother's chiding and hustling me along, I decided to walk the mile to Burston Railway Station. I had enjoyed what breakfast I had been able to get down and felt that the walk would do me good, maybe get rid of the butterflies I was beginning to feel now that the day of the medical had finally arrived. My sleepless night had been filled with thoughts of what today would bring, but the tiredness had not quite left me, so perhaps the walk to the station would waken me up and also save me twopence on the bus.

I walked towards the station with my mother's tearful farewell still ringing in my ears. Why, I do not know. I was only going for a medical and would probably be back in time for tea. From all the fuss you would think that I was emigrating to Australia.

My arrival at the station was in good time, and for once the steam train to Manchester arrived on the dot. After a lot of shouting and whistling, the crashing of doors and the hiss of released steam, we were off. I was not sure what to expect from that train ride, everyone else in that compartment seemed to nod off, not me, I was too full of excitement to sleep. Can you imagine it? Here I was, a young chap in the prime of life at eighteen and getting excited over a train ride to Manchester.

The train pulled into Victoria Station some two hours later and once more the crashing of doors heralded the exit of the passengers to their city jobs. The fact that I was in Manchester at the invitation of 'His Majesty', did not seem to concern them one bit. Back in Burston everyone seemed to know everyone else and if I walked down the town centre I usually met a few people that I knew or recognised. Here in the city, if they noticed me at all, I must have been just another country gawp.

I stood outside the station just trying to get my bearings and my mind went back to the bombing I had experienced when we visited relatives near Barton Docks one time during the war. We had got caught in an air-raid and it had been quite frightening. On our way back through Manchester we had seen the devastation in the centre caused by the bombing and at the time wondered how the people could show such disdain to the mighty German air force.

The hole in the roof of the station where a stray bomb had fallen through, had long since been repaired and, as I looked up Deansgate, as it was called in my small printed map, all signs of damage had been removed from the tall buildings which had been the scene of such frantic activity during my families departure from Manchester in those turbulent war years. It was as though nothing had happened here and now the only thing that seemed to matter was the making of money.

I bought a paper from a woman running a newsagent stand, not because I wanted the paper but so that I could check my map behind it. While I was there I decided to bury my pride and ask her for directions, at least it would save me being caught reading a map of Manchester, I felt that it would make me look a right twit. She glared up at me.

"Great Ducie Street is it? Don't the bloody War Office give you any bloody directions then?" She warmed to what was obviously one of her favourite topics and seemed to speak to no one in general except the few customers that had gathered round her stand. She motioned towards me with her head.

"Bloody civil servants! They think we've nowt better to do than stand here directing snotty nosed kids to their bloody Medical Centre. I wouldn't mind but they're hardly out of their nappies yet. Next thing they'll be asking us to wipe their arses." The waited for laugh came on cue and I laughed with them as though enjoying the joke. I tried to back away but I was not about to be let off that easily. It was apparent that I was not the first to ask for directions at her kiosk and the fact that I had only bought a paper had not helped. She carried on for what seemed an eternity and at last I tried to counteract her tirade of abuse by asking for five woodbines, even though I did not smoke.

"Five woodbines is it? Are you sure you're old enough to smoke?" She laughed uproariously at her own small joke, her dirty teeth showing yellow in her over-lipsticked mouth. The laugh cut off as though by a knife and a frown returned to her weather-beaten face. "I don't know what's going to happen to all you kids when they get you in the forces, but I can tell you this son, you won't be going into the intelligence corps, if you just opened you're eyes a bit instead of you're bloody gob, you'd be able to see that great big bloody sign up there on the wall. Gawd, if there's another bloody war and we've only you lot to rely on!" She left the sentence unfinished as she turned to serve a more important customer. One with money. I took the chance of moving away before she could scream at me again, wondering if army instructors could be any worse than her.

I walked shamefaced down the road towards the viaduct with the sign fastened to it. What an idiot! There it was in large letters, I should have seen it from half a mile away, National Service Medical Centre and an arrow pointing out the direction. I cursed myself for not reading the directions correctly, but then I would not have met the vivacious news vendor. The charmer of the city.

I followed the directions and found myself outside a collection of Nissen huts, one of which had a sign 'Reception' fastened to the door. I entered and followed another sign which brought me into a waiting room edged with wooden benches and a window with an arrow pointing to the window. I suppose I could have been there days just trying to find that window. I knocked on the window and waited, no reply. I knocked again and this time a bit

244

harder. A voice snarled from beyond the glass, "Wait yer bloody 'urry."

The window was jerked open and a spotty red face peered through. On the face was a pair of glasses that had lenses like jam-jar bottoms they were so thick. The face came closer in order to get me in focus.

"Well, give us yer bloody papers, we 'aven't got all day!"

I searched through my pockets for my papers, coming up with them in the last one, it would have to be the last one. I had held them in and out of my hands ever since I had left home this morning and just when I needed them they had to be in the last pocket.

"Come on! 'Ave yuh got any papers or not? If yuh 'ave let's 'ave em. Yer'll 'ave tuh be quicker than that if you're comin' in the army, we're too bloody busy tuh wait fer a dozy pillock still wet be'ind the ears."

My face crimson, I handed my papers through the small window, too shamefaced to give him any back chat. He rummaged through the papers, picked one out and then threw the rest of them back to me.

"Through that door on yer left and then left again."

With that he slammed the window to. What a reception for a would-be hero, and the day had only just started.

I followed 'Pimples' instructions and found myself in a long room. On the left were wooden benches above which were double hooks fastened to the wall. To my right was a partition. Behind the partition I could see lots of white coated figures looking bored to tears and sitting in their own little cubicles like spiders waiting for a fly.

On my side of the partition the room was crowded with young men all trying to find a place to hang their clothes and it took me some time to find an empty hook for myself. What a joke. Before the day was out I would be lucky if I could find my clothes again never mind an empty hook.

Not knowing just what to expect, I had set off this morning in my only suit. It was a bit on the large side because my uncle Tommy had been bigger than me and when he died and it had been passed on to me, my mother had accepted it on my behalf with the traditional verbals, "Aye, it'll do thanks Martha (Martha was late uncle Tommy's wife), it is a bit on the large side but he'll grow into it."

It was considered a waste of money buying new suits when there were so many good second hand ones to be had, you only had to look. My mother's philosophy being 'waste not, want not.' Not that it mattered, when I looked round the room it was obvious that many other mothers thought the same and I blended in very well with most of the other lads in there.

As I looked round the people who seemed to stand out in the crowd were three young men dressed in coloured jackets and wearing what were called 'drain pipe trousers' which were thought to have been put on when the men were smaller, I could not think how they could have got them on any other way, they were so tight. On their feet they were all wearing crepe soled shoes, known as 'brothel creepers'. Their hair styles were popular ones at that time, brushed from the sides to the middle with a parting straight down the middle, this was called 'a Tony Curtis style' and it cost a lot of money to get it cut and set just right. The shirt was a fancy stitched one and topped off with a pencil-thin tie. These were the Saturday night strutters called 'Teddy boys' and they certainly fancied themselves? It was going to be interesting to see how they got out of those drain pipe trousers.

After the colourful display by the 'Teddy boys' there were others who looked like they had slept in their clothes all night they were so scruffy. Looking round the room I came to the conclusion that this was the oddest assortment of young men I had ever come across and, like me, they were all here for a medical.

The day was Thursday and as I was later to find out, in the armed forces everything of any consequence happened on a Thursday. If Thursday had been taken out of the calendar I feel sure that there would have been no wars and we would never have had National Service.

I had just found a place to undress and sat myself down when a shout went up.

"Right you dozy lot, get stripped and that means everything, we're all boys here so don't be shy, grab a towel and get into line in alphabetical order."

It was the pimply youth with the bit of bird lime on the sleeve of his army blouse, in the army they called it a stripe and in the forces the only difference between God and man. He could not have been much older than any of us but he strutted about like King Dick. We looked at one another self-consciously. Where were the dressing rooms?

"Come on move yer dozy selves, nobody's watching, we're not going to steal yer family jewels and looking at some of you lot there isn't much worth stealing. Put yer coats on the hook and pile the rest of yer clothes underneath 'em on the bench. Gawd, look at yer, England's last defence."

Surely he did not mean us did he? The room was freezing cold and there were no dressing-gowns in sight. He stood there eyeing us all up and down and making it very plain that his patience was fast running out.

Slowly we started to strip off. Some rather self-consciously and others with a could not care less attitude. I managed to grab a towel and cover up my embarrassment, what they did not see would not hurt them and you never knew what sort of men these were.

It did not make much difference in the long run as towels were soon dispensed with and we were pushed and shoved into some sort of line by 'Pimples', all in alphabetical order. Then the show started. In the next few hours we did not know whether we were on our arse or our elbow. It was like being on a conveyer belt as we were called out and pushed into the first partitioned cubical which stood only about four foot high. The only thing that could be seen were the upper parts of our bodies and the top of the examiners head, as we moved from one doctor to the next.

"Right, drop 'em." This meaning the towels. "Step on those scales, off, bend over, straighten up, look above my head, right cough."

The touch of his hands on my goolies made me jump. Why is it that doctors always have cold hands? Do they do it on purpose? And why do they ask the daftest questions?

"Read this list. Have you had any of these illnesses? I looked at the list but you would have had to have had a university degree to understand some of the illnesses on the list. I cannot remember what I replied but before I could read them all he grabbed the list from me and not waiting for an answer he said, "Right, next."

Corporal Pimple then grabbed my arm and pushed me into the next cubical.

"Can you read this?" A card was held about a foot from my

face with letters six inches high on it. I would have had to have been blind not to be able to read it.

"Yes," I said and then at his insistence I rattled of the letters.

"Right, next."

I was once again moved on to the next doctor.

"Can you hear my voice?" he shouted in my ear. The answer 'yes' came from the other end of the room from a bloke with a hearing aid.

"Open your mouth." He poked about in my mouth, pulling my cheeks this way and that. Then he stuck a wooden spatula down my throat and told me to say 'ah' and by the time he had finished with my nose I felt that I knew what it was like going ten rounds with Joe Lewis the World Boxing Champion.

"Right, ear, nose, and throat OK," and it was all written down on a form by his assistant who had two stripes on his sleeve. He motioned me on to the next cubical.

Here, I was pinched, pummelled, and punched all over and checked with the coldest of stethoscopes as he listened to my chest and back, it must have come straight out of the ice box. "Breath in, hold it. Breath out, cough, up on your toes, down, right next."

Off we went again. Although we never seemed to stop I do not think that there was any part of my body that had not been looked into, poked or pummelled. My knees had been knocked and my ankles twisted until I was sore all over. I felt sure that in the morning I would be black and blue.

After the examinations we were told to get dressed and stay where we were and wait. Although 'Pimples' had screamed for quiet many times there was still a low buzz around the room and of course there had to be a funny man.

"Hey corporal, when are we getting our uniforms?"

"Pipe down, we 'aven't decided to accept you yet. We're very particular who comes in the forces," he said to the funny man.

"Sorry corporal, I thought we'd just finished basic training."

The reply raised a laugh but the corporal was not pleased as he retired to his private cubby-hole, returning moments later with another list in his hand. Once more he glared at us over the top of his 'jam-jars'.

"As I call your names go through that door marked 'B', we'll see if this'll wipe the smile off yer bloody faces."

The first names were called and we sat waiting our turn. Sitting there doing nothing we soon got talking. The lads here today had come from all over the North-West of England. Some, like myself, were looking forward to National Service, while others considered it a complete waste of time. Two years to be taken out of your life was no a joke. One surly bloke said that he would be a 'conscientious objector' but no one seemed to believe him. Others said that they were trying to get deferred in order to finish an apprenticeship. Perhaps they would, who knows?

All that was in the future though. Our next port of call was to be through the door marked 'B' and, although we tried to get the corporal to tell us what was in there, all we could get from the little prat was.

"Don't worry, you'll soon find out." He then leered at us over the top of his 'jam-jars'. I bet he was a real little crawler.

At last I heard my name called out.

"Clayton, J."

"Right," I answered.

"In you go and good luck, you'll bloody well need it."

Again the clever sod gave the knowing leer as I entered the door Marked 'B'.

I closed the door behind me and turned to face what turned out to be a very pleasant faced man seated at a desk. He smiled and pointing to a chair opposite him said, "Sit down Mr Clayton."

This was very good. I'd half expected something traumatic to happen and here I was being called mister. Thinking back I can only think of that saying, 'come into my parlour, said the spider to the fly'. It turned out that this man was the psychiatrist and it was his job to decide what branch of the service I would best be suited to if, of course, I had passed my medical.

He questioned me about what branch of the service my father had served in and then which branch I would prefer. This was a good start. I had a choice? I was told to write down my choices in order of preference. I did so, little knowing that this was one of the force's little charades. They always asked you what you wanted, therefore giving the impression that the choice was available but knowing full well that you would be put just where they sent you, depending on your medical.

After the questions came the tests. A series of cards with idiotic ink blots on them were shown to me and I had to tell him what I thought they looked like. Being all shapes and sizes I could only guess. What ink blots would tell them about me I will never know, they say you have to be quite crazy to become a psychiatrist, anyway some of my answers brought a smile to his face.

Next came the card games with squares, rings, triangles and oblong shapes on them. It was like a mind reading act. First he showed me the cards then he shuffled them and looking at them out of my sight I had to guess which one he was looking at. One thing's for sure I would not play cards with this chap. The problem was, if by chance a lot of my guesses turned out correct, I could have been in the Secret Service as a mind reader. So much for psychology.

Finally, the questions about my childhood, school, exams and my job in the factory. All the answers that I gave him he wrote down and when he ended the interview he just said, "Thank you Mr Clayton, go out by that other door."

I suppose that he did not want me telling anyone about what was going on in his room before he had time to question them, though why, I do not know.

As I closed the door behind me I felt like strangling that pimple-faced corporal, getting us all worked up about seeing that psychiatrist. Mind you the thought of anyone knowing you had seen a psychiatrist did tend to make you feel embarrassed, make anyone think that you could be a nut case. I suppose it had been the corporal's way of getting back at us for giving him a hard time and maybe he was a bit put out at having to be here at a medical centre instead of being in a proper unit. Possibly the thick jam-jar glasses he wore had something to do with it, and all those spots. Ugh!

By the time they had finished with me at the centre it was mid afternoon and I found myself outside with my collar turned up against the usual Manchester weather which was the wind and rain that had descended on the city whilst I had been inside. I turned and headed back towards the railway station, duty done. Now all I had to do was wait and see just what medical grade I was given.

As I sat in the train on my return journey home, reflecting over the days events, I had lost that initial excitement that had been my companion since I had first read the letter inviting me to join the forces. Were they all twits like the pimply faced corporal? Surely not. There must be some normal people running our forces. 'Blessed are the pure in thought'. What a lot I had to learn and as the train passed through Bury on my way home I could only reflect on how soon I would get that letter. Would I be grade one, two or three? I tried to put all thoughts of armed forces out of my mind but it was impossible and with the sound of the train wheels constantly churning out its rhythm I dropped off to sleep to be rudely awakened by a voice shouting in my ear, "End of the line young feller, time to get off, we're here. Last stop Burston."

I walked up the platform and it came back to me. Grade one, two or three, just like the eggs and meat. I suppose that is all we were really, so much meat for the grinder. They had demobbed so many men after the war that there were none left to peel the spuds.

Up to this morning I had looked forward to my two years in the services, especially if it meant that I would have the chance of travelling round the world. What if I did not pass the medical? I tried to reject any thought about that, I just hoped that it would not happen to me. I was reasonably fit but that did not help any, the doubts still remained. I suppose they would still do so until my call-up papers arrived.

Before then however, the band still had a few engagements left to do. Mostly local and as they were all concerts we would have to get down to some serious rehearsing.

The first one went down very well and Adam seemed satisfied, but on the second one, Pete Barton, our second trombone player turned up late just as we had started the concert and, although he crept onto the stage as unobtrusively as possible, he was seen by the audience. This raised a titter which blossomed into a round of applause making Pete's face turn from its usual sickly pale to a deep shade of red. Adam's words of wisdom at the interval did not help his colouring one bit.

On another of the concerts, when playing at a Working Men's Club, a pint of ale was seen being shoved under the curtain to one of the bass players. Again Adam voiced his dissatisfaction with the way the band was displaying itself on stage and the advice he gave the recipient of the said pint, one Tom Bibby, made Tom fit to explode, never-the-less, he got the message.

Apart from those lapses of stage etiquette the concerts seemed to have gone down without too much fuss, probably the choice of music had more to do with it than the playing.

It was the Thursday after the last concert that my big moment arrived. I was up at my usual time, getting ready for work, when the post arrived and a buff coloured envelope was pushed through the letter box, addressed to me. In bold capitals across the top, OHMS. I stared at it for a moment hoping that it would tell me that I had passed my medical but also knowing that there was a possibility that for some unknown reason I could have failed it. If that was the case then I do not quite know what I would have done. This was my one big chance to get out from under and I hoped that it would be a definite yes.

At last I just could wait no longer and grabbing the envelope I ripped it open and read His Majesty's personal message, 'You have been graded 2 by the National Service Medical Board.' I had done it. I was in. It went on to say that the lower grade was due to my having 'Hammer Toes'. I took my socks off and examined my toes. What were 'Hammer Toes' I checked them again but could not see anything remotely like 'Hammer Toes'. Anyway, what did it matter, I had passed the medical and that is all that mattered. I carried on reading the rest of the letter which said that I was to report to No 7 Training Regiment, Royal Signals, Catterick, Yorkshire, in two weeks time. There it was again, 'once more into the breach', but why always bloody Yorkshire?

Before I had to report to Catterick however, we had one more concert to do. This had been a late booking and it was in a park in Oldham. It was only an afternoon concert thank goodness, but one which we were very grateful for. It seems that a rather well known band had got their engagements mixed up and we had been asked to stand in for them. The payment for the job was a little more than we were used to getting, so we had agreed to do it.

When we arrived at the park it was nice and sunny. The place was packed. This was not the usual thing for us. The fact that we were not a well known band meant that we did not attract any large crowds to our concerts. It was not as if our playing was not as good, if not better than some of the better known bands, but they had made their good names before the war and were just cashing in on their memories. At least those were our thoughts.

It was Tom Perkins who supplied the answer to the larger than normal crowds. The posters advertising the concert had not been altered and only a few people recognised the fact that the band giving the concert (us) was not the band advertised. Perhaps this was our chance to show them that we could give as good a concert as any top section band, maybe even better. Having played quite a few concerts recently and rehearsed mainly concert music, we now had the chance to show them just what we could do.

Brass band enthusiasts are a well discerning group. If the music they are listening to is not good enough they just get up and leave, they will not sit and listen to rubbish. Sometimes they leave quietly in disgust and other times they are quite vocal, and then everyone hears their complaints.

We started the concert with *Colonel Bogey* which was well received, probably because there were many old soldiers in the audience who remembered the army version of this well known march, anyway the applause certainly gave us confidence and we followed it with *The William Tell Overture*. Again the playing was well received. It seemed that we could do no wrong. At the end of the concert we were given a standing ovation and after giving a couple of encores we walked off that bandstand proud as punch. We had done it! We had stood in for a top section band and done ourselves proud.

Afterwards, David Green said, "How about that then? It just goes to show that we can do it when we really try."

Bert Rawlins let out such a laugh, "Aye, and if we had them ten borrowed players playing with us regularly, it'd make a few more people I know sit up and listen."

He was, of course, referring to the ten very good players we had borrowed from other bands who were being paid to play for us just for this afternoon's concert.

We suddenly stopped gloating. Why did Bert have to put the 'Kibosh' on things? Just when we were beginning to feel good. We knew at the back of our minds that having players of the calibre of the ten borrowed players would make any band sound good, even ours.

When everything had been packed away and we were finished for the day, we decided to have a meeting of the 'boozing committee'. It was decided that we would not go back with the rest of the band. A night out in Oldham, that would be it. We had Jack Nuttall's car and Jim Tubbs' old truck available so we were all right for transport then, armed with our hymn and march books, we set off for the flesh pots of Oldham.

Jack Nuttall had made arrangements over the phone before we set off. It seems that he had a friend who ran a pub in Oldham and Jack had asked him to put a few sandwiches on while we were on our way. This he had agreed to do. Afterwards we thought that doing a bit of busking around some selected spots in the town centre could not only bring in some beer money but might open up other doors in pubs of the bawdy kind necessary for our late night boozing. The name of the pub was The Bridge Inn and it was just off the town centre.

Jack had told us that for a small fee the landlord of the 'Bridge' had put on some sandwiches. This was great news, not just because of the food, we were always ready for some good grub, but because we would be having it during closing time. There was always something about drinking during closing time that seemed to add spice to the proceedings. Cards, darts, Dominoes, a pint of good ale and a bit of food, who could want for more? I was going to miss all this. Never mind, let us get to it while the night's still young. Maybe we would not have time for games later on.

We arrived at The Bridge Inn at about five thirty, and after Jack had announced himself at the back door of the pub, we were allowed inside. Jack then introduced us all to the landlord, Bert Thompson and his wife Lilly. It was Lilly who ushered us into the tap-room where the sandwiches were laid out on one of the tables and told us to get stuck in. Very soon the ale was flowing and we had started what promised to be a very enjoyable evening.

We had paid Lilly for the sandwiches as soon as we had arrived and so we owed nothing in that direction. The main thing was to keep our eyes on the small amount of cash we had between us and then hopefully the rest of the evening would sort itself out. We did intend to augment our small amount of cash by playing a few tunes for the pub customers during the evening, in which case cash or beer would be acceptable, it did not matter which. In the meantime Bert Rawlins had got a dominoes game going while some of the others had started a card school.

Then a funny thing happened. Jack Nuttall slipped a ten bob note to Ernie Benson with the instructions that the landlord, Bert Thompson, was to be kept busy winning at either the cards or dominoes. Then he disappeared for about an hour. It was not until later in the evening that we managed to extract the truth from him.

It seems that when Jack had phoned the Bridge Inn to make arrangements for the sandwiches for us, it was not the landlord who answered the phone, it was his wife Lilly and during his talk with her about the food he had made some suggestions to Lilly which certainly did not include her husband, so when Jack had disappeared whilst we were playing dominoes he had been upstairs in the bedroom entertaining Lilly. The cheek of the over-sexed sod, fettling the landlord's wife just a few feet away and leaving us to keep her husband busy. He had not told us everything in case we accidentally let the cat out of the bag. If Bert had been given just an inkling about what was going on behind his back, and in his own pub, he would have murdered Jack and scattered the rest of us all around Oldham. He was certainly big enough. As it turned out, it was just as well that we did not know anything, we would have had kittens.

After the pub had officially opened and it started to fill up with the regulars, we retired to the singing room for a while. We had told Bert that we would be leaving at about nine o'clock in order to sample the delights of Oldham's night life. In our case this meant any pub that would allow us to busk and pick up a collection for the rest of our evening's drinking.

It was just before nine when we left the 'Bridge' having completed our full repertoire of marches and a few well chosen hymns. One of the regulars took this opportunity to start playing the piano. We decided that this was some sort of a hint that it was time to leave. We had been well fed and had partaken of quite a few pints, all of them free. We were also pleasantly surprised to find that one of the patrons had passed a pint glass round the room whilst we had been playing, the contents of which were thrust into Ernie Benson's hands. It was all in coppers but every little helped and so we left the pub, very well oiled, our pockets jingling and ready for a good night ahead.

A short time later, after parking the vehicles somewhere they would be easy to get at should the need arise, well, you never know who you may upset, we pushed through the front doors of the Robin Hood, a rather dour looking pub near the centre of Oldham. Once inside we ordered our drinks and at the same time asked the landlord if it would be all right to use the piano in the singing room.

The landlord turned out to be not only a sour-faced individual but bad tempered with it.

"What's ta want tuh be makin' all that noise fer? Carn't tha just sit down an sup like most on 'em in 'ere?"

We took this as a definite 'No' and sat down with our beer. We had no sooner sat down than he then up and asked us why we were not playing and singing like he had said we could.

"You've just told us you didn't want us to play," Ernie said.

"No, I meant you're damned brass instruments, I can't stand them bloody things."

If it had not been for the fact that we had only just got our drinks I think that we would have left there and then. We should have realised straight away that this was not our sort of pub, just a stopping shop before the evening's entertainment. We mumbled something about him making his mind up and then moved into the singing room. Ernie sat down at the piano and we were away, from then on it did not take us much time before we were all singing.

Slowly the singing room started to fill up as people from outside heard the piano and came in to see what was going on. It seems that the landlord was well known for his bad temper and they were wondering what had made him let anyone play his piano. In next to no time the pub was heaving. It looked like the night had started off quite well, at least for us. If we managed to take a collection in here now we would be all right for the rest of the week. The gleeful anticipation of a cash collection was a non starter. As we finished singing a song we heard Ernie's voice above the noise.

"Hey lads come-on I'm suppin' bout. Never mind, who's payin'? Get 'em in again."

This brought a laugh from the good humoured crowd and soon the landlord was pushing his way through the crowd blocking the doorway with a tray of drinks. Meanwhile, Ernie had returned to his playing and, as he did so, his empty beer glass, which he had rested on the piano top, started to dance towards the edge, quite unknown to us or Ernie and when it reached the edge it fell off smashing on the floor. The sound of the glass breaking reduced the noise in the room down to a quiet roar but when they realised it was only a beer glass they took no further interest in it.

Unfortunately, the landlord did.

"That'll cost you two bob," he said to Ernie. "Them glasses cost money tha knows." And he held his hand out for the cash. For once in his life Ernie was speechless.

"Nay landlord," Jim Tubbs said. "Surely tha doesn't mean it,'e's bin singin' an playin' an' he's filled tha bloody pub fer they, thy 'art bein' a bit tight chargin' a bloke fer a bloody broken glass when the lad's brought thee more custom than tha must of had in the last month."

The landlord stood his ground defiantly. "Two bob," he said again putting his tray down on the table. If I lets thee off, everybody else that breaks a glass'll want lettin' off so, come on, two bob."

There was a deathly hush in the room as the landlord stood there holding his hand out to Ernie, then an angry mutter started and calls of scrooge and mean old bugger were heard, and a voice from the crowd:

"Tha mean owd fart. Tha'rt tighter than a duck's arse, an' that's water tight."

The landlord looked round for the owner of the voice but all he could see were angry faces and not just a few titters coming from the bar outside the room. The landlord was adamant, "Two bob fer't glass, an' ten bob fer't th'ale."

Bert Rawlins moved towards him angrily and I thought for a minute that there was going to be a punch-up but Jim Tubbs grabbed him by the arm and said, "Reight lads, sup up. That's enough fer me. I've never met anybody as tight as this bugger, I'm off to find a decent pub." With that he turned to the landlord, still stood holding his hand out. " 'ere thy'rt," he said slapping a two shilling piece down on the table, "that's fer't glass."

"What about the ale?" The now red-faced landlord asked, pointing at the tray full of beer. "Ten pints. I can't put it back in't barrels."

"Tha should a thought about that afore tha showed us just how far tha'd go fer a copper. Tha probably gets the bloody glasses free from't bloody brewery." He turned towards the door, with the rest of us right behind him, and stalked out of the pub.

As we put space between us and the Robin Hood we could still hear the landlord ranting and raving.

"Serves him bloody well right," Jim Tubbs said. "The tight

arsed sod. We'll find somewhere else tuh sup. We certainly don't need a tight sod like that. I hope the pub's empty for the rest of the bloody week. All that fer a soddin' beer glass."

I glanced back up the street to make sure that the landlord was not following us. That was all we needed, an irate landlord chasing us around Oldham. When I glanced back, I was amazed to see that quite a lot of the people from the Robin Hood following us. For a second I thought that they were after us for the broken glass, but when I heard them shouting for us to wait, I realised that they were not chasing us, they wanted to come with us.

"Owd on lads," one of the blokes said, breathlessly as he caught up to us, "where are tha off to now?"

"We don't know yet," Bert said, scratching his head. "It were just that if I'd a stayed in theer a minute longer, I'd a belted the tight pillock." He looked at the bloke who had caught us up. "Tha lives around 'ere doesn't tha? Tha could point us in the reight direction. Where's there a good pub?"

"Aye, I do," the bloke said with a smile. "Come on with us, there's a pub just down the next side street, by't canal. It looks a bit scruffy on th' out side but Jimmy Baker'll make thee welcome I'm sure, an' th' ales better'n the Robin Hood's. I were just on my way there when I heard the piano goin', so I stopped for a pint an'a listen. I'd never heard a piano goin' in that pub before. In fact, I've never heard music of any kind goin' in theer before. Mind you, it's got the right bloody name, Robin Hood, the only difference is that bugger'd rob the poor as well."

This drew the required laugh and, with our new friend leading the way we turned down the side street and entered the portals of the Waterside Inn.

As our new friend said, it did look scruffy on the outside, but the inside was entirely different. A low ceilinged room crossed with large oak beams. On the beams were fastened dozens of horse brasses of various shapes and sizes and all gleaming, it must have taken some time to clean that lot.

The room was small but then we were only in the bar. There were other rooms leading off from it, the tap-room, singing room and a nice looking snug. On closer examination we found the bar to be made of oak and judging from the many indentations, it had been there for years. I would not mind betting that if it could talk there would be some tales to be told. In perfect keeping with the aged bar top was the floor. It was stone flagged. Not only that but it had a light covering of sawdust.

I had heard my grandfather talk about pubs in the olden days and this had been the way in most public houses, the sawdust soaked up ale, blood, spit and anything else that got spilt on the floor. All that had to be done every night was to sweep up the sawdust and put some clean down, simple. I had heard about it but never for a minute did I think that in this day and age I would come in a pub where it was still done. It was like being transported back in time, about a hundred years I should think. It was obvious at a glance that nothing much had changed in this pub since the year dot, the only exceptions, of course, being the landlord and his wife.

It was the landlady who was facing us across the bar. She was a very plump lady, about five foot two inches tall with greying hair and a great big smile which seemed to light up the whole of her face.

"Now gents, what'll it be?" Her question and smile made us feel right at home as she got straight to work providing us with pints of golden nectar.

"There y'are lads straight from't wood."

At the first sip we realised the difference between here and the Robin Hood, that and the fact that there were no pumps because the beer was pulled straight from the barrels, the taste was perfect. We were home. This was the best ale I had ever tasted, mind you that's not saying much, me being only eighteen, but I could stay here forever. Not that we had any thoughts of going, I had the feeling that we would not leave this pub until we were forced to.

After a few minutes of drinking and and voicing our opinion of this excellent ale, we were introduced to the bar-maid by the man who had brought us to this hidden oasis.

"By the way, I'm Jack Bardsley and this lady behind the bar is the landlady, Anne Barker. Anne serves the best pint anywhere in town. Don't let those rosy cheeks and that quick smile fool you though, she's thrown more men out of here, who thought that they were tough, than you've had hot dinners. Any rough stuff, shout for Anne, and if they know her they'll run like hell."

He gave a big laugh and continued.

"Come 'ere lads and I'll tell you a true story about yon lass."

We gathered round him conspiratorially and he went on to tell a story about a fight that had broken out in the pub some years ago.

It seems that at that time Anne and Jimmy Barker had been celebrating a wedding anniversary or something. Later that evening, with everyone having a good time, a very large man had entered the pub. It was obvious straight away that he was a foreigner. After a bit of me-moing between himself and Anne she realised that he wanted a drink and after more hand signals she pulled a pint and put it down in front of him. He paid her and he tried to hold onto her hand. It was only after another agitated exchange of words that Anne realised that he was only trying to thank her. She had been the only one that night to have the patience to try to understand him.

At the beginning of the war there were a lot of Poles who had come to England trying to enlist in the forces, their own country being threatened with the Germans, and of course most of them could not speak any English at all. Demitre, as he was called, had arrived at that time from Poland to look for his brother, and with only a smattering of English he found it very hard to get anyone to understand him, well, Anne had been the first to try and he was very grateful. The point is that he became a regular at the Waterside Inn. He was a quiet man but if anyone started any trouble in the pub Demitre just picked them up and threw them out.

You did not have to be a brain of Britain to see that soon he had taken a shine to Anne, and this did not go unnoticed by Jimmy Barker, and they all had a good laugh at Jimmy's expense.

One Saturday night a group of young men arrived, already in good spirits and ready for some fun. Later in the evening, after a bit more drink, they started poking some fun at Demitre but he, not understanding much of what they said, just laughed with them. Anne could understand though and warned them to cool it, if Demitre got wind of what they were really saying there could be a separate war in this bar.

Later on that night they started again, bating the large Pole. They must have been mad. He was well over six feet tall and he had shoulders on him like a bull. Just as they were getting going Jimmy stepped into the room. "That's it," he said. "Out you go, I'm not having you lot playing silly buggers in my pub." With that he started pushing them towards the door. Well, there were five of these blokes and only one of Jimmy, so they suddenly turned on him trying to shove him back into the bar. Although he could not understand what was going on, Demitre saw them pushing Jimmy and giving a shout jumped into the middle of them knocking them left right and centre. One or two of the customers joined in and in no time at all the fight got out of control and it was a free for all.

It was during the battling that someone opened the door and Demitre started to throw them out into the road. Unfortunately, by now Demitre was fighting mad and he was not watching just who he was throwing out. He turned round, and without looking he grabbed Jimmy, quite forgetting that Jimmy was the landlord, and pitched him straight through the door where he landed on top of a pile of squirming bodies. Anne, seeing this, decided that it was time that she took a hand. She was not having her Jimmy thrown out of his own pub. She dashed round the bar and grabbing Demitre by his family jewels, head down like a goat she rushed poor Demitre through the door and out into the street with all the others. Demitre did not know what to say, in his mind he had only been trying to help and now he was out on his ear. The incident quietened them all down. The sight of a little stout woman throwing out the biggest bloke in the pub amazed them all. If she could do it to him what could she do to the rest of them? She did not stop there either, she grabbed Jimmy and dragged him inside and cleared out the rest of the customers in two minutes flat.

No one could quite explain how she did it and she was not sure herself but once she had her Jimmy inside and the pub empty, she shot the bolts on the closed door at the same time shouting, "Don't none of yer come back, or I'll have yer tripes out."

The thing is that they never saw Demitre again. They think that he could not face anyone after being thrown out by a woman, and only a little one at that.

At this point in his tale, Jack Bardsley paused to have a drink and with a big smile crinkling his face at the memory, said, "Mind you that was some years ago." Anne made a grab at him over the bar, simulating a right hook and as Jack moved out of distance he finished off, "An' I'm too old now to find out if she can still do it."

The laughter spread round the bar and Anne blushed furiously at the re-telling of this obviously well aired tale.

"Get on with you Jack Bardsley," she said. "You know it isn't true, the man wasn't born who could throw my Jimmy out of his own pub." She looked across the bar at her husband who just winked and they both burst out laughing but still not admitting that the story was true or false. Jack, however, swore that the story was true because he had got it from a personal friend of his who had been in the bar that night. He did admit though that the tale may have gained some in the constant retelling, but it had happened. I was on the side of Anne, but seeing the twinkle in her eyes I was not entirely convinced.

It was Anne herself who changed the subject by asking us if we would give them a tune. This was more in our line so, once again we got out our march books and played a few rousing tunes, the favourite of which was *The Wearing Of The Green* which some of the audience knew the words to. At the finish of each tune our audience showed their appreciation by clapping and cheering. An added bonus would be the heart gladdening shout of, "Come on Anne, get these lads some ale in. They're suppin' bout."

Who paid for all these drinks we never asked, then again we were not the sort to care, as long as we were not the ones to pay.

Any time we stopped for a drink, our new friend would carry on by playing his mouth-organ, to the delight of the packed pub. We eventually finished off the evening with a drinking contest, mainly to get rid of all the ale bought for us. Farewells were said and we left with a promise to come back again sometime.

Another pub name was added to our list of watering holes. Whether we would be made welcome during closing time I was not sure but I felt sure that someone would have broached the subject some time during the evening, anyway we would know during the coming weeks.

It was not until we were nearly home that Bert Rawlins announced joyfully, "D'you realise that since we left the Robin Hood we haven't paid for a drink?"

I think that he must have been a bit sozzled. I said, "Who paid for the first pint then?"

Ernie Benson, who we thought had fallen asleep, suddenly piped up, "It were Jack Bardsley, he gave me the money to get the ale in and we got one free from Jimmy and Anne and the rest from our wonderful public." Then with a sigh he went back to sleep.

This was much better than we thought. Any pub that gave us free drinks went straight to the top of our list.

The following week Jack Nuttall arrived at the band-room with some bad news. Bert Thompson, the landlord of the Bridge Inn in Oldham was on his own now because his wife Lilly had left him. She had emptied the till and taken all the cigarettes and gone leaving poor Bert high and dry. He was well in the soup now because the pub was in Lilly's name and it would have to close down until everything had been sorted out.

This was bad news for Bert but even worse for us. We had lost one of our best watering holes. This was a very sad time and as Jack said at the time, "The wearing of a black armband for this week would not be out of order." It was worse than being on the dole.

After band practice that night, we had a few jars at the Duke of Wellington, but the bad news that Jack had brought was just too much for us and there were long faces all round. So much so, that we all went home reasonably early, it was not even midnight. As we walked home we could only console one another over this disastrous event.

The next time we saw Alf Worthington he told us that the takings at the 'Duke,' had been the worst since the band had moved into his pub and if it kept on like this he might have to move us out to make way for some paying customers, though who would want that musty room I could not begin to think. I think it was just his way of telling us why we got the room so cheap in the first place. We told him of our sad loss but he said that it was not his loss and he did not want to be the one to pay for it. What a rat bag, the sooner we got back into our own band-room the better.

It was Wednesday night after band-practice that I said a last farewell to the lads in the band. It would be two years before I took my place regularly amongst them again but with a bit of luck I might get to play with a band in the army.

Later that week when I met some of the lads in town they said that my farewell night was unforgettable; unfortunately, I can't remember much about it, I was plied with so much ale. Much more than was good for me. I'm told by my mother, who was totally disgusted, that I was carried back home from the 'Duke' by some of the lads because I was really plastered. They did try to explain that they had been giving me a good send-off but one look at my mother's face had stopped them in their tracks so, without another word, they had dumped me on the couch in the living-room before my mother had unceremoniously chucked them all out with a few curses about 'them and their damn band', something she always came out with at the mention of Burston Band, having spent a lifetime as a brass band widow, first with my father and now it was happening all over again with her son. She had fought against it for so long, but as she wrung her hands in exasperation she realised that the cause was lost, so she just threw a blanket over me and went to bed leaving me to sleep it off.

I was roused next morning at about six o'clock by my father, who, seeing me snoring away, just tipped the couch up and ditched me in a tangled heap onto the floor. When I got my senses back and pulled myself together I got a strange feeling that everything was not well with me and my dad. I tried to think. Had I been sick or something? I could not remember, nor could I understand why he was so grumpy. Had he forgot that today I was to become a young warrior who was going away to fight for King and country? What a way to treat a probable hero. In a few hours I would be reporting at Catterick Camp in Yorkshire. Was it not enough that I had to go into enemy country to be trained and that from midday today I would be in the Royal Signals for two years. 'Certo Ceto'. I was told it meant 'Swift and Sure' though a friend of mine already in the forces said it was better known as 'S--T or Bust'. I must remember not to say it out loud when I got to Catterick.

I relaxed on the couch, still part asleep wondering what the next two years would bring. My mind drinking in all those dreams of travel to foreign places. Dusky maidens waiting on me hand and foot. Door to door sunshine. I imagined myself defending the fort against the oncoming hordes. I was shaken out of my reverie by another shout from my father. At least I would not have to be ordered about so much. Just imagine, two whole years of being my own boss. If only I had known!

20

Certo Ceto

This was it. I was on my way. What was that saying, 'The world is your oyster', well, it was all up to me now, so, watch out Royal Signals. 'Certo Ceto, Swift and Sure' I'll show 'em.

My slow steam train pulled into Victoria station Manchester in plenty of time and after a few words with the ticket collector I moved my case onto the bus for Piccadilly Station, which was on the other side of Manchester. Trust me though to get on the wrong bus which threw me out in Piccadilly itself, where the bus station was. I asked a young lady in a very short skirt, the way to the station. She proved to be so friendly that she said that she would take me to the station the short way for a couple of quid. I had heard of these girls but I thought that they only plied their trade at nights and anyway I did not have a couple of quid to spare. Still, she was a cracker and when I explained that I was short of cash, she pointed out that it was only about two hundred yards away.

Two hundred yards does not seem far when you say it quick but when you're lugging a case like mine, which had everything in it but the kitchen sink, it might as well have been a mile. Still, a strong lad like me out to take on the world, what was a couple of hundred yards?

The War Office had said in their letter that we only need take the absolute necessities because when we had been kitted out we would be sending the rest of our clothes home. Well, I needed all my stuff, I might want to go for a night out in Richmond.

m

At last I arrived at Piccadilly Station to find that there seemed to be hundreds of young blokes like myself crowding the station, not all of which were going to Catterick, it seemed that there were other training camps elsewhere in England just waiting for the opportunity to train young men to be killers.

The station café was packed. Everybody stacking up with grub. Good thing I remembered to shove that bag of meat pies into my case, I fancy that ten should see me through, but if they did not they would have a canteen at the camp and I felt sure that they would have laid on a good meal for us. (Like a lamb to the slaughter.)

The train pulled out of the station amid weeping mothers and with fathers trying to appear nonchalant about the whole thing but, with the train gathering momentum and everyone trying sheepishly to settle down and hide behind a newspaper or magazine, slowly we started to get to know one another and I realised, from some of the talk, that I might have been able to get to Catterick by a much shorter route.

When we got chatting I found that some of the lads came from the same part of the country as myself and that when they had enquired why they should have to get to Catterick by going through Manchester when they could have gone more easily from Rochdale, they had been told not to question the army way but to follow the instructions in their letter. I kept my mouth shut. I did not even know that it was shorter from Rochdale.

When all the introductions were over we settled down to a game of cards. As one of the lads put it, 'just to pass the time'. The result was that within a short space of time I found that my resources were being stretched to the limit as one of the lads seemed to be having such good luck that he was winning every time. It was not until another bloke grabbed him by the collar and threatened him that I found out why he was so lucky. He was only eighteen but it soon became obvious that he was very clever, and country bumkins like some of us were his bread and butter.

The cards were his own and when they were examined they were found to be marked. The big bloke gave his first name as Melvin, and with a name like that you had to be good with your fist. The thing is he had spotted the cheating going on and as some of the money was his, he wanted it back. It was only after the cheat had been threatened with being thrown out of the window that he admitted his error in trying to do us out of our cash and we got all our money back, mainly through Melvin turning him upside down and emptying his pockets. I think that he was very lucky to come out of it with his head on the right way round, and for the rest of our journey he had to keep right out of Melvin's reach.

It was some time later that the train pulled into Richmond station and that is where the fun started. Everything was chaotic as the train emptied and amid shouted orders we were herded out of the station and into waiting trucks, some with wooden seats and others with only the floor to sit on.

In charge of each of these trucks were what we were later to come to know as NCOs. They were young men like us, but they were in uniform. On their sleeves were stripes, what I suppose my grandfather referred to when he said they had 'chicken-shit' on their sleeves. It did not take us long to realise that these one stripers were Lance-Corporals and that the one striper was the nearest thing to God. After a short while we found out that when he said jump to it, our only thought was 'how high'?

The squad I was about to join did not look at all smart. Some were scruffy and dirty whilst others were in what was obviously their best suits, this was my group. Some of the accents were a bit weird but we managed to understand most of what they said.

All this ceased to matter when at last the trucks pulled into the brilliantly white painted gates of the barracks. A soldier with his rifle stood on guard at the gates which had a neatly painted hut at the side and as we approached he lifted a bar which was painted red and white like a barber's pole, to allow us to go straight through.

As we looked out of the back of the truck all we could see was a massive square bordered by stones painted white. Across the square were Nissen huts which, we were told, were where we were going to live for the next four or five weeks.

Our day-dreaming came to an abrupt halt as the trucks pulled up outside one of the Nissen huts and the first thirty of us were detailed, in no uncertain tones, to get inside, find a bed and stand by it till someone told us different. Each command was said in a screech which seemed to do the particular owner no good at all because he went red in the face and looked as though he was going to burst a blood vessel, and at the end of which was followed by 'at the double'.

I suppose we would soon get to know these little sayings as time went on. The point is we went along with him. It made life so much easier. Soon we found ourselves sat on a single iron bed with diamond shaped springs and a rolled up mattress. I thought that it was a bit spartan even for the army still, I supposed someone would come and explain everything to us shortly.

If we could have known just what this day was going to bring I feel that some of us would have stayed at home. Firstly we were rudely awakened out of our reverie by one of those Godly one stripers entering the room and screaming for us to get outside and form three ranks. Well, he did not have to shout. He could have asked. After much screaming from the unpaid and unwanted Lance-Corporal we stumbled outside and soon he had pulled and pushed us into something resembling three lines.

Here we were still in civilian clothes and he was treating us as if we were idiots. Left turn. Right turn. What the hell did he want us to do? I wish he would make his mind up. At last, with a very distressed look on his face, he told us that we were going to the squad office to get our 'AB 64 Part One' which, he then explained slowly as though to small children, was our pay book and also our identification while in the army.

Later on we would be given a lecture on why it was one of the most important documents we would have to know about and one that we should carry on our persons at all times. Ah well, anything to keep him happy. In the meantime we were to go and get our kit.

In no time at all we were lined up outside the quartermaster's stores ready to enter and collect our kit. This has to be seen to be believed, the bewildering speed at which we were kitted out.

On entering the store we started at one end of a long counter behind which were a number of uniformed men, each of which were responsible for a certain piece of equipment. As we moved past them we were supplied with each piece and as it was handed to us the name of it was shouted out, so you can imagine the ensuing debacle as we shuffled down the line.

"Eating irons. Knife, fork, spoon, set for the use of, one."

"Housewife, one, for the use of." (Cotton needle etc.)

"Greatcoat, one, for the use of."

"Helmet, one, for the use of."

This went on until we had reached the far end of the counter, by which time we were piled up with everything needed in the immediate future for our stay in the army. Piled high with all our kit we were then taken, if this is the right word because we could not march, we had to keep stopping to pick up dropped kit, back to our hut and there we just dropped everything on our beds as the raucous voice once more bellowed for us to get outside, once again we were on the move.

The next stop was to be the camp barber's. That should not take me very long. Only yesterday I had had my hair cut in Burston and paid extra to have it blocked at the back so that it would look decent and neat and though I do say it myself, he had made a very good job of it. A nice even straight line just above my shirt collar with my side-boards trimmed to be even at both sides.

One by one we were told to enter the barber's. When my turn came I wondered why no one had come out of the barber's by our door. I soon found out.

I entered and the barber told me to come and sit in the chair which I did. I explained that I had had my hair cut only yesterday. He smiled. Much like Sweeney Todd must have done.

"How would you like it trimmed son?" he asked.

This was OK, I suppose he had to trim us all to suit the army way so I told him and he started to cut.

"Hey, take it easy," I shouted, as the shears cut a great swathe across the top of my head.

"Quiet!" barked the NCO. "Regulations state that the hair shall be worn short on both back and sides. Carry on barber."

I watched horrified through the mirror as the shears made a complete mess of my special hair-do. Hair flew to the left and right of me as the barber's hand never deviated from the task in hand. Within a very short space of time I was nearly hairless except for a tuft which the barber had so generously left me at the front of my head. The sight took me back to the days when I was a small boy and my grandfather cut it by putting a pudding bowl on my head and using horse shears cut round the pudding bowl leaving a nearly straight line round my head. Then, it did not matter very much, but now, oh God, what a mess.

I did not have much time to dwell on the matter though, as the barber whipped the towel from round my shoulders and shouted for the next one. I took one last look through the mirror and realised that he had finished. The short haired mess he had left me with would have to stay with me until it grew. I stumbled out of the door indicated still in shock.

Once outside I waited for the laughter and when none came I turned to look at them all. He had done it to all of them. That bloody barber was a masochist. One thing was for certain, he was not a barber. We stood there self-consciously, berating the masochistic tendencies and the vague ancestry of that man who called himself a barber, as one after another the rest of my group stumbled out of the hut, some of them in tears as their special hair cuts were decimated.

At last the horror of the barber's shop was over, at least for now, and we were marched to the hut with a red cross painted on the door. The next part of our indoctrination was about to begin. Another medical? No, just inoculations. Line up with left hand on left hip and so it went on until we were all done, that is except for the one who had fainted at the sight of the needle, why, I do not know, they just did. Some of them just could not stand the sight of it.

After the Medical Officer had finished jabbing us with blunt needles, with the exception of one or two who had not come out of the faint yet, we were marched back to our hut, wounded and aching. The fact that we had just had our jabs, as they were called, did not deter the Lance-Corporal from venting his fury as he screamed again and again for us to swing those arms shoulder high, the idiot! Did he not realise that our arms were bruised and aching. I felt that we would need at least twenty-four hours to get over this day. Either that or sick leave.

We had no sooner flung our aching bodies down on our beds than the by now hated Lance-Corporal or Lance Jack as they were known (Jack as in Jack-ass), arrived in the doorway screaming for us to get outside once again. Oh God, what now. We heaved ourselves off the beds as the hated voice screamed, "Outside with your eating irons and mess-tins. At the double!"

We pushed and shoved to get outside, because every time he shouted it seemed to be a matter of life or death.

"Come on now, jildy, jildy you bloody morons, if I don't get you to the cookhouse quick, some of you lilly-whites'll be writing to your MPs and we cannot have that, can we?"

Feeling very self conscious in our civilian clothing we were

270

marched down towards a larger building which turned out to be the cookhouse, I know because it said so in letters a foot high over the top of the door. We were stopped outside and allowed to walk inside in single file.

So, this was an army cookhouse. Row upon row of wooden tables filled most of the place. On the left hand side as we walked in was a very long, steel topped counter behind which were various cooks in their off-white jackets and hats. The trousers were in a small blue checked material. We stood there waiting for God knows what when a bellow interrupted our reverie.

"Come on you bloody 'Nig Nogs' what'er you waitin' for? Get a bloody move on, or shall I come down there and serve you my bloody self. This isn't the bloody 'Ritz', get yer bloody mess tins at the bloody ready, we 'aven't got all bleedin' day." This maniacal intrusion into our thoughts came from a very fat cook at the far end of this massive counter. Any reply that we might have thought of was cut short at the sight of the three stripes on his sleeves, obviously in the cookhouse, he was master.

With our steel mess-tins at the ready we slowly moved down the line towards the large containers on the counter. After one or two of the first ones in line had asked what we were getting and been told in no uncertain tones to shut up and move along, we just held out our mess-tins and, as we passed each container, it was suggested that we might want to partake in some of the unsightly gunge he was serving out. Fortunately we did have a choice. We could either say yes or say no and, after one daft lad pulled his mess-tin away at the last minute letting the gunge fall onto the floor, we decided to let them know in good time whether we wanted any or not.

The lad who pulled his mess-tin away was obviously in trouble because before the gunge had hit the floor the bull had bellowed once again.

"Stand still that dozy man."

The poor lad stood as if frozen stiff, still in the act of trying to reach down and pick the mashed potatoes from off the floor. The room quieted down as the fat sergeant waddled down the room, coming to an abrupt halt in front of the unfortunate lad.

"You dozy little pillock," he reiterated, still at the top of his voice. "You haven't been here ten bloody minutes and you have the nerve to slop good food on my clean floor. You horrible little man. That food is wasted now, and it is an offence to waste good food."

He glared round at the rest of us lined up against his shining steel-topped counter. "Who's in charge of this shower of shit?" He suddenly yelled. The Lance-Corporal suddenly appeared coming to a stud-screeching halt in front of the sergeant.

"I am sergeant. They're the new intake." The sergeant fair bristled at him.

"I might of known. Lance-Corporal bloody Perkins. Unpaid, un-bloody wanted and totally bloody useless. You couldn't control a bloody light switch. Take this man's name and tell him to report to me at eighteen hundred hours in the cookhouse." His face nearly purple the sergeant turned about and strode back to his place at the head of the now even longer queue. Why he could not have told the lad himself I will never know, when the lad had been stood petrified in front of him.

The Corporal pulled himself together, after getting a rollicking in front of the nearly full cookhouse he felt stupid. He had to do something so, bending down with his mouth close to the lad's ear, he shouted:

"Did you hear that you useless little turd. Step out of the line and go and get a mop. Move!"

The last word was screeched and seemed to galvanise the lad into action. He stepped out of the grub line and turned to go out of the cookhouse.

"Where the hell do you think you are going?" The Lance-Corporal shouted.

The lad stopped in his tracks and stuttered, "To get a mop Corporal."

"And where the bloody hell do you think that the mops for the cookhouse are kept?"

"I don't know Corporal."

"That's the bloody trouble, you dozy man, you don't know nothing but after tonight you will. Go down to the sergeant at the end of this counter and ask him nicely, perhaps he'll help you."

The lad's face turned red as he looked at the sergeant who had just rollocked him then, setting his face, he ran towards the sergeant who was watching him. Another bellow.

"Don't run in my cookhouse!"

He stopped running and walked the rest of the way with the

beady eyes of the sergeant watching his every move. He stopped in front of him.

"Sergeant, could you please find me a cloth to clean the floor with?"

The sergeant glared at him for a second and then turning to a cook standing beside him dishing out the butter he growled. "Get this bloody 'Nig Nog' a shovel brush and a cloth." He then turned back to watch the rest of us, completely ignoring the poor lad still standing stiffly beside him.

The cook reappeared a minute later and handed the implements to the now thoroughly demoralised lad who came slowly back to the scene and started to clean up the blob of mash. When he had completed the task the corporal told him to take it outside and round the back to the dustbins and then to come back to get his meal. As it happened the lad did not return at all, it seemed it was too much for him to face us again after being shown up like he was. It was a lesson to us all.

The slop being served up to us was soon a soggy mess which even a good dousing with salt could not make tasteful. The sweet was not much better either. Plum duff without sweetness, we found out later that when we had a sweet like plum duff you always grabbed a table spoonful of jam and mixed it in. We had a lot to learn, but learn we did, and quickly too.

While we were eating we were visited by what is called the 'Orderly Officer' who was about our age. He was accompanied by the 'Orderly Sergeant', who wore a red sash across his shoulders. We watched with a certain amount of trepidation as he passed down the lines of tables, stopping now and then to taste at some food. "Yes, very good," he said after one taste. Put lead in your pencil that will. Then he turned away with what I thought was a forced smile, I hoped they taught him more than that at University. How could he say it was very good, it had no taste. He walked on to another table and stopped, surely he was not going to taste again. Not this time.

"Right chaps, any complaints?"

"No sir." Came back the chorus, seeing the the dead-eye glint of the 'Orderly Sergeant' daring them to say yes.

He stopped at our table and asked the same question. We gave him the same reply. Before we complained about anything we had found that it was better to see how the land lay and what would happen if we did complain. I had wanted to say that the tea tasted funny but maybe it was just a different tea that they used.

When I had got my food I had noticed that at the end of the counter was a large tray full of cheese. I was a lover of cheese but this sort was what we used at home for cooking. When I asked the corporal what it was there for he said we could have as much as we wanted so I picked out some of the better pieces and wrapped them in some grease-proof paper on the counter. If the lad who had spilt the mash potato was hungry he could have it and if he did not then I would eat it myself.

At the end of our first meal at Catterick Camp we were bundled outside and doubled back to our hut where we were told to get into our uniforms. This was the laugh of all laughs. When we had been collecting our uniforms in the quartermaster's stores they had looked at our height and threw a uniform at us saying that if it did not fit properly there was a camp tailor where we could get them fitted. They had not told us that we would have to pay for these alterations.

So, the fitting of uniforms started and with a lot of swopping about we managed to get most of us fitted fairly decently, leaving only five with unfitting uniforms. These were allowed to return to the stores where they were returned with uniforms reasonably correct. They had been lucky. Normally uniforms were not returnable to the stores, they were told to get them fitted by the camp tailor, quite an unfair order.

Any alterations done would not have to be done immediately because we were told that our daily dress would be 'Denims', like an army overall. These 'Denims' would come to be known as 'fatigues uniform' even though they were 'denims', mainly, I suppose, because they were always worn when doing 'fatigue duty'. This was any duty usually done as a punishment, like peeling mountains of 'spuds' in the cookhouse under the beady eye of cook Sergeant Tomkins. The denims were designed like our best battle-dress and were the work clothes all other ranks wore in camp. Other ranks being below Lance-Corporals.

Once the fitting of our uniforms was completed we had to wrap all our civilian clothes in 'brown paper for the use of' provided, and address them to our homes. It did not seem two minutes since we were getting off the train at Richmond and here we were severing all connections with civilian life. What a day, and what

274

was still to come? This was to be a change of civilisation as we knew it. From now on life would be regulated to army standards, the rules of which we had already started to learn.

I was now a number, 22864040, Signalman Clayton J, and would answer with that name and number, any time I was challenged, it was a number which was to become emblazoned on my mind.

When we got back to our hut we were allowed to rest amid various items of kit which we had just dropped on our beds. We were shattered and bewildered. No wonder we won the last war, equipped at the speed and dexterity that we had been today.

My first day had started back in good old Burston and in a few short hours we had been initiated and inoculated, head shaved and kitted out as soldiers, now all we had to do for today was to sort out our kit as per the army manual, a printed drawing of a bed layout to be found on the notice board fastened to the wall, just inside the door of our room.

Each set of kit had to be set up exactly like the next one in such a manner that the drill sergeant could stand at one end of the line and see that all kit was lined up from the top of the room to the bottom on our fresh made beds, and woe-betide anyone not having his kit in line. Anything that was not shown on the board had to be packed into a large box by the side of your bed-head and even this was inspected once a week.

First of all try to get some sort of order. What were these, drawers cellular, three? These were our underpants. One pair on, one in the wash and one clean. Four blankets, three to be wrapped up every morning inside the other one in a regulation manner. Sheets cotton four, one pillow case, bayonet scabbard, three vests red, three pairs of socks, two pairs of boots with the regulation number of studs, one pair to be worn, and one on show. Three shirts khaki (it should have said hair-suit they were so coarse). Webbing, packs, ammunition pouches, kit-bag, oh God had I signed for all of this? Yes, there it was on my inventory. What was this? I had not got a rifle but I had signed for one, and so it went on, I felt that I could never remember all this.

I despaired at the amount of things that I had signed for and could not find and we were still at it when 'lights out' was sounded at ten o'clock. The only thing we could do was to just push everything into the box and get into bed. This day had been an eye opener. We had not stopped, from coming in through those gates, getting mattresses and kit; and we had not even sorted much of it out and they had turned out the lights. Ah well, let us see what tomorrow brings, surely it could not be worse than this. Could it?

My restless sleep, through being cold, was rudely awakened by the sound of reveille and the door of our hut being thrown wide open. A gust of icy April wind that had been scourging the great Yorkshire moors blew in to the shouts of our own Lance-Corporal Perkins. What was wrong with him, could he not sleep?

A gasp cut through the noisey chatter, "Bloody hell, it's only five-thirty."

The voice of our master raised above the noise.

"Come on you dozy lot, hands off cocks, on socks. Do you want to sleep all bloody day? Out of yer pits and stand by yer beds. Move it now we have not much time and we have a lot to do today."

We stood there shivering in the early morning cold as he moved to one bed that was still full of a bulky figure.

"Hello young fella," he said in an unnaturally dulcet voice. "Don't you want to get up yet?" He gave the figure a prod. The figure moved but did not get up, so the corporal with one heave upended the bed throwing the figure onto the floor.

"What the bloody!" The figure started to say and then seeing the corporal stood there and the rest of us lined up at the end of our beds, spluttered to a standing position. The corporal pushed his face close to our miscreant threateningly.

"I told you to stand by your bed and you disobeyed me." His voice starting to rise. I think that he must have stood in front of a mirror for hours trying to get this pose off. "D'you know soldier I could have you run down to the guardhouse and charged with mutiny for disobeying my orders, but I will not because I am nice, I look after my new recruits and because it is your first morning I will overlook it." He was looking into the lad's eyes from about two inches away.

"Thank you corporal," he managed to splutter, before the corporal carried on.

"But, just so that you don't think that I'm a soft touch I want you outside in your pumps and three times round the square. At the double. Move it!" The last part came out as a screech. We all stood to what we thought was attention at the foot of our beds as our friend scattered outside. The corporal turned to us. "Right, I'm going to call the roll. As I call your name you will answer 'Here Corporal' and then I'll know that you haven't left to join the 'Foreign Legion' during the night."

He called the roll and by the time he had finished we were beginning to feel our legs ache at the unaccustomed standing stiff. The frost on the windows did not help much either. He kept us there in the freezing cold as he enlightened us on what we were about to do outside and how we had to react. Just as he finished the door opened and a sergeant walked in. No, I am wrong. He did not walk in, he entered, his presence stilling the room. Brass buttons gleaming in the barrack-room lights, back straight as a ram-rod. Under his arm he carried a sort of stick. We were to get to know this stick intimately, it was called various names, a yard stick, a pace stick, mainly because its main function was to measure the correct stride length.

The room was deathly quiet and he stood without saying a word, his eyes flitting from one to another as we stood there. The corporal spoke.

"Squad one this is your drill sergeant, Sergeant Williams."

No one spoke and even the corporal stood stiff as a board. The sergeant spoke.

"Stand at ease, stand easy." We relaxed as he walked down the centre of the room, his figure and the stiffness of his back posed a very intimidating presence as he glanced at each bed as he passed by. It was obvious that he was not pleased by what he saw. He stopped at the far end and turned then he started giving us the rules we were to live by for the next two years. They seemed to go on forever until suddenly there was a shout of, "Everybody outside."

The Sergeant looked at us and screamed, "Well, you dozy lot, what are you waiting for? Outside!"

The rush for the door nearly brought the Nissen hut tumbling down but at last we were lined up outside. All other squads were out lining the huge square in the centre of which stood a small man with a stiff nebbed hat.

He stood to attention and waited, he was the Sergeant Major, the last person you would wish to speak to any time any where. He was the senior Warrant Officer, the nearest thing to an officer that there was and, unlike a mere Second Lieutenant, he was the most feared man on the camp, even the Colonel called him Mister.

When all the recruits had gone silent the stiff little figure opened his mouth and screamed out.

"Get on parade!"

My God! How could such a small figure have such a loud voice? They must have heard him in Richmond.

The voice immediately penetrated every brain cell and there was a mad rush as everyone tried to get to their designated place on the parade ground. After a lot of shuffling about silence descended on the assembly and we were attended by about a dozen men in white vests and running trousers elasticated at the ankle. One of them, obviously the boss, stood on a platform at the front and started to shout out the exercises and then proceeded to do them, the rest of them wandered amongst us correcting any wrong stances and screaming in our ears when we did something wrong etc. They were called Physical Training Instructors, or PTIs for short.

The exercising went on for about half an hour and we were then dismissed for breakfast. This meant doubling back for our mess-tins and dashing off to the cookhouse. The sooner we got our breakfast the more time we would have before the main parade at nine o'clock, when we would be inspected by the Colonel of our Regiment, Colonel Smithson. He wasn't a full colonel really he was only a Lieutenant-Colonel but like Lance-Corporals were addressed as 'Corporal'; Lieutenant-Colonels were addresses as 'Colonel'. What a crazy world we live in.

Breakfast was much the same as the meal we had yesterday. All queuing up along the long counter getting as much in our mess-tins as we could. Sausage, bacon, eggs, fried bread, toast butter and the funny tasting tea. By the time we had got our food and found a table the eggs, bacon and sausage had congealed on our plate and was nearly cold, but we had learned something since we had arrived, and that was to accept everything to eat, you could always swop it for something you liked.

Breakfast was gobbled down quickly. Had it only been yesterday that we had arrived? It seemed like years. Before I had finished my breakfast I found out why the tea tasted like it did, it seems that the army, in all its wisdom did not want over-sexed

278

soldiers wandering around so they added something called 'Bromide' to the tea and this was to enable young men to lose that feeling or urge to want sex. It did not work though, as the squeak of the bedsprings at night proved, but we still had to put up with the stuff in our tea. After a week or so we got used to it and after that it did not bother us any more.

Once back in the barrack room we were indoctrinated into the art of 'Bull-shit'. All webbing had to be covered in 'Blanco' to make it look smart. All brasses had to be cleaned till they positively shone. The hardest part was bulling your boots. With hints from the room corporal we sat up and by candlelight and we pressed the pimples out of the black calf leather of the boots. Once the pimples had been boned down to a smooth level then black boot polish was applied with abandon and burned into the leather with a hot spoon. Once that had been done then it was pure 'elbow grease'.

Round and round with small circles we covered the leather until after about five nights of this the boots, especially the hard toes were highly polished, in fact, the most highly polished of the two pairs of boots were hardly ever worn as they were kept under covers to be laid out on our bed every day for inspection with the rest of our kit. I must admit though, that at the end of that time I was very pleased with the high polish I had attained on them, and they did look smart laid out with my other kit.

In the centre of the room was a black enamelled stove with attachments, small shovel and poker. This stove was never lit while I was there, it was just highly polished by different signalmen from the room each week, who were detailed to clean and polish everything in the room before it was examined by our squad commander Lieutenant Johnson while we were outside on parade. Should there be any dust found anywhere in the room then the two signalmen detailed to clean the room were on a charge, and that meant certain 'jankers'.

'Jankers' was any extra duty that anyone above the rank of 'Signalman' could find that you were able to do. Mainly, two hours in the cookhouse after tea. At the end of that first week with the hell of those first few days now past we settled into the routine of eat sleep march drill, occasionally the routine being broken by a bout on fatigues. Just having to sit in the cookhouse peeling spuds was a break, though the way some of them peeled would have brought a sharp crack round the ear from my mother. It was a quick six strokes and a small square of potato was thrown in the pot.

The days quickly went by to the monotonous eat, sleep, clean, polish, drill. Scream, shout, bawl. Could we do nothing right? We did have some thought for those poor lads who just could not march or drill. For some unknown reason their arms and legs would not synchronise. Left turns, right turns and about turns were quite foreign to their nature and no matter how loud the NCO in charge shouted, it seemed to make no difference, they just could not do it. To see a soldier walking with the left arm going in the same direction as the left leg was so awkward, even to watch, and it took many hours of the NCOs spare time to correct the bad habit, but correct it they finally did.

It was in those first four weeks training that I lost any faith I might have had in 'bull-shit'. As usual my kit was laid out for the morning inspection and, as basic 'bull-shit' was really only keeping yourself clean and smart, once your kit had been brought up to standard, it was only a matter of giving it the once-over each morning as you laid it out and everything would be ready. This particular morning I had laid my kit out as usual and checked that everything was in order, polished brasses and spoons gleamed, the rest of my kit was clean and lined up with the other beds, but one thing I must have overlooked, and the Sergeant found it.

A small particle of dust in the welt of my boot and the beady eye of Drill Sergeant Williams lit on it. He picked up the offending boot and showed me the particle of dust by thrusting it under my nose.

"What's this, you dirty man. Filth! You've let the whole room down with your lackadaisical attitude. You're a dirty, scruffy soldier, what are you?"

"A dirty, scruffy soldier Sergeant," I croaked out, wishing that I could become invisible. He turned and with one heave turned my bed completely over, scattering all my well cleaned kit over the floor, knowing full well that they would all have to be cleaned again, and then with a flick of his hand he threw my highly polished boots through the window. I heard a sickening clang as they hit something on the way out, then silence.

"Corporal!" He screeched at the top of his voice. The clatter of boots echoed loud in the room as the NCO doubled down the room to the Sergeant's side.

"Yes Sergeant."

"Take this man's name and number. He will do four hours in the cookhouse starting at eighteen hundred hours tonight. I will inspect his kit after parade in the morning and if there is the smallest thing wrong with it he will be on a charge. See to it!"

The Corporal pulled out his notebook and, standing directly in front of me said, "Name and number."

"22864040 Clayton J. Corporal."

"Report to the cookhouse at eighteen hundred hours in your fatigue dress, and report back to me at twenty-two hundred hours when you have finished. You will then take all your kit into the ablutions room (washroom, where the lights were on all night) and scrub them clean, I will check them directly after reveille tomorrow. Do you understand?"

"Yes Corporal."

The inspection over, I just had time to go outside and find my boots. As I lifted them from the grass I found that one of them must have landed on one of the supporting bars of the Nissen hut we were in, it had starred it just as though it was glass. My pride and joy ruined. I nearly cried. The hours spent getting that glass-like polish and all for nothing, and they had to be made right again before morning or I would be on a charge.

At half past four we were back in our hut getting ready for tea. No tea for me tonight though, I had to use this time trying to get my boots up to scratch. It was like trying to patch a broken window. There was no chance that I could remove the polish that I had so painstakingly applied in my first week here. All I could do was to fill in the cracks with polish and bull them in the hope that they would pass inspection.

What with my 'jankers' in the cookhouse and then scrubbing and cleaning my kit in the 'ablutions room' where the smell of the 'latrines' did not help, I felt very dejected. I had the feeling that if things were not right in the morning I could find myself scraping the piss-stones with a razor-blade and that would be the end. What a degrading thing to have to scrape the smelly urinals, with everyone coming in and splashing all over you. God, that would be the pits!

At last I finished my cleaning and 'blancoing' and stumbled into the room sometime early in the morning, I didn't even get into bed I just put a blanket on the floor with my pillow and slept. My head had no sooner touched the pillow when 'reveille' was sounded. I just replaced my blanket and pillow and returned to the 'ablutions room' where my kit had been left to dry, if I did not get it before the rush for a wash, they would be covered in soap spots. I set my packs out on the bed in regulation fashion. It looked OK, but those boots stuck out like a sore thumb. They were clean all right, but nothing I could do would remove that starring of the toe.

The morning passed off with the sergeant giving my layout only a cursory glance as he passed. At least he could have looked at them after all the work I had done on them. He did not even apologise for damaging my boots. Ah well, roll on demob.

We were now getting to the end of our basic training, having done all the leg weary marches and drills, though as yet not to the satisfaction of our sadistic drill sergeant. I think that he must have loved the power he had over us, being able to give us 'jankers' for the slightest infringement. Nothing was missed by the eagle eyes of drill Sergeant Williams and I am sure that he must have had some misgivings about taking us on our final visit to the rifle range.

We had been allowed to go to the rifle range on two occasions, but only to mark the targets. Mainly, I think it was to get us used to the bullets flying overhead and of course the noise.

A great deal of time had been spent on pulling the 'Bren Gun' to bits and then putting it together again, stripping your rifle down and cleaning it, even though it had not been used. Pistols, Sten guns. Well today it was our turn to get some shooting in and God help the bloke who showed his head over the parapet down at the targets.

We were marched up to the 'butts' in squads and taught how to lay down with feet apart, rifle pulled well into the shoulder, sights set at two hundred and fifty yards, breath in, hold it, squeeze the trigger, do not jerk it. What a nice sight to look down at the targets and see a white inner.

After the shooting we had to boil out the rifles and clean them to perfection. They were all inspected, and woe-betide the man who had not cleaned it right. I did not mind cleaning, at least now I knew that I had a rifle of my own, and the same one that I had signed for. After the guns had been inspected and were passed as

OK, we were marched down to the armoury where the rifles were once more installed and locked up. Not much chance of leaving them under the care of 'Nig Nogs' like us. Who knows, we might have shot the sergeant!

The next day we were again up on the rifle range but this time it was with the 'Sten gun'. This nearly proved a great mistake. The rule was that no matter what happened, you always kept the 'Sten' pointed down the range. It had been drummed into us till we were sick of hearing it. Today we were to find out why they continued to drum it into our thick heads.

Earlier I said that one or two of our squad had trouble in marching correctly. This had been put down to lack of coordination. It should have been branded on all the drill NCOs brains that if they were uncoordinated on one thing then perhaps there might be other things which might be wrong. They found out the hard way.

With 'Sten guns' we stood up facing down the range and on the command fire it was just a matter of blasting away. If we hit anything then it was pure luck. These 'Stens' had been used by thousands of young soldiers and were prone to jamming. When this happened you kept the 'Sten' pointing down the range and shouted that the gun had jammed. The armourer on duty then ran up and taking the gun, unloaded it, released the jammed bullet and checked that there were no more bullets up the spout, adjusted it and you started all over again.

Simple? Not so. That was what was supposed to happen. What really did happen was that unfortunately the gun that jammed was in the hands of one of our uncoordinated soldiers and to give him his due he did shout that the gun was jammed and kept it pointing down the range. Unfortunately he continued to try to free the jamming and the sergeant seeing this shouted at him to stop.

Well, he must not have heard him correctly because on hearing the sergeant's voice he turned his whole body round in the direction of the sergeant, turning the gun as well. The sergeant had only time to shout for us to get down when the jammed part suddenly released and before he could take his finger off the trigger, the gun went off spraying bullets all over the place. It seemed to go on forever but in fact it was all over in seconds as the gun emptied.

The poor lad was terrified as he stood there holding the now

283

empty 'Sten gun'. Everywhere there was quiet as the noise of the gun stopped. The sergeant leapt to his feet, and for a moment I thought he was going to clobber the poor lad, but he did not, he just grabbed the 'Sten gun' from the shaking lad and handed it to the armourer. Inquiries were going on all round as to if anybody had been hurt but apart from a few facefuls of dirt everyone was OK. By now the sergeant had recovered his composure and had the hapless lad marched off, more for his own safety than anything else.

This was one for the book. Nearly getting shot by one of your own side just was not on and I felt sure that the poor lad's days were numbered. A charge was the least he could expect and what would come of that we were never to know because we never saw him again. I think that he was drummed out of the service, not that it was his fault completely. It was known that he was a dope and they still allowed him to fire a loaded gun on the firing range. It only went to prove the mentality of men with stripes.

That was the last bit of excitement we were to have during our basic training because the next week was our passing out parade. We were considered competent at cleaning out the latrines, cleaning our kit and the smartness of our turnout, all we had to do now was to win the best squad at the parade and our sergeant would be over the moon. Nice!

The night before our passing out parade was spent on bulling everything in sight. We cleaned and polished till well into the night. Anything missing from our kit was 'Acquired'. Yes, we'd learned. What was pinched from you had to be acquired back, one way or another.

The morning arrived and after PT (physical training) we had breakfast and then it was last minute cleaning and polishing and then into our best BDs (battle dress), specially pressed with soaped seams to give a knife edged crease after which the corporals went round removing the weights which some of the craftier recruits had in their trousers, just above the 'puttees', in order to weight down the turnovers and make the trousers hang down in a smart way. Unfortunately they were not allowed.

We then had to collect our rifles and with bayonets gleaming in there scabbards (known as frogs), we went round one another adjusting here and there. The nerves were creeping in. We had just heard that the competition for top soldier had been won by another squad so, that was that. Our man had come in third. Useless prat.

At nine thirty we were lined up outside while the sergeant inspected us minutely. At last, with one or two adjustments he adjudged that we were ready and at nine forty-five precisely we were marched out onto the square and into position one. We were to lead the parade, not because we were the best (although we thought we were), but because we were the first squad.

At the far end of the square the Royal Signals Band was lined up. This was the band I had hoped to get into, unfortunately I had been turned down. They would be playing all the time we were marching and I knew that this would put a spring into everyone's step. After various shufflings and checking of the lines we were made to stand easy.

It must have been exactly ten o'clock when we were called to stand at ease and the group of officers collected round the raised dias stiffened themselves. The RSM (Regimental Sergeant Major) gave his screamed command and about seven hundred pairs of boots crashed as of one to attention. No sooner had we come to attention than the RSM was again bellowing for us to give the general salute 'Present Arms'. Another wait as our commanding officer escorted two officers with gold braid and red epaulettes up onto the dias. This must have been the Northern Command Brigadier that was said to be taking the salute.

The Brigadier stood to attention as the band struck up with the national anthem after which he then commenced to inspect the troops. All this time we were stood to attention but eventually he finished and returned to the dias where he sat down while the RSM bellowed out his orders and then the sergeants started bellowing, you would not have been far wrong if you had thought that they were trying to outdo one another, then we were off.

The band did us proud with the regimental march *Begone Dull Care* (we thought it should have been 'Beyond All Care') as we marched round and round the square doing every drill we had been taught. It was exhilarating. We had managed to do everything without making pillocks of ourselves. At last it was all over and the Brigadier made a speech about how we would soon be going to be trained as linemen, wireless operators and the thousand and one jobs that go to make up a signals unit. There was a lot of waffle about smartness and 'bullshit' and then he named the top squad.

It was us. We gave a cheer and nearly got shot on the spot as the sergeant screamed for quiet. He then marched smartly to the front where he was presented with the cup for best squad. That was the last thing we saw of that cup and later when he decided to come and see us for the last time he was a different smiling sergeant, saying how he was proud of us and good luck on our different courses. We said our good-bye's and then all the NCOs made themselves scarce before we got the bit between our teeth. It had been known in the past for the drill NCOs to get scragged, after what we had put up with from them, so they were not taking any chances.

Well, school was out and we were now free to go into town and have a few beers. Our flashes, which we had been allowed to put on the arms and shoulders of our tunics were looking new and smart and we were ready to howl at the moon. A photographer arrived and photos were taken in different poses, all to be sent home to mothers and sweethearts to show them that we were real soldiers.

Real soldiers! We looked around at one another and I am sure some of them must have been thinking the same as me. God help England. The next morning we all received our postings. These were the appointments of where we would be going in order to learn a 'trade'. I looked at the list, because of my 'hammer toes', which excused me from any further form of walking, I was to go and train as a wireless operator with one or two of my own squad at a unit about half a mile away, so I was not going to travel very far. Why I had not been excused drills etc. during my basic training I do not know, but that was all done with now so why argue? The army had its own way of interpreting things. Ah well, dit dit dit, dah dah dah, dit dit dit, only another seven hundred days to do and I can get back to the band. Bugger this for a game of soldiers.